THE MERCERS' SERIES

Oil Paintings in Public Ownership in
Greater Manchester Vol. III

The *Oil Paintings in Public Ownership* series of catalogues is an extraordinary work in progress. Published by The Public Catalogue Foundation, it is the result of the determined efforts of a small team of administrative staff, researchers and photographers spread across the United Kingdom.

Our national collection of oil paintings in public ownership is probably one of the finest anywhere in the world. It is held not just by our museums and galleries but is also to be found in hospitals, universities and other civic buildings throughout the United Kingdom. A large proportion of these paintings are not on display and many have never before been reproduced.

This series of books for the first time allows the public to see an entire photographic record of these works – a collection likely to number some 200,000 in total. In doing so, these volumes provide a unique insight into our nation's artistic and cultural history.

As Patron of The Public Catalogue Foundation, my visits to collections across the country have highlighted to me not only the desire of curators to publicise their paintings, but also the limited resources at their disposal. The Foundation's work goes a long way towards helping to create access to these collections, while at the same time giving the British public the opportunity to see and enjoy *all* the paintings that they own.

I wish The Public Catalogue Foundation every success in its continuing endeavours.

Camilla

Oil Paintings in Public Ownership

in

Greater Manchester Vol. III

Funding Patron
The Mercers' Company

Coordinator: Pam Walker
Photographer: Gordon MacGregor

The Public Catalogue Foundation

Patron
HRH The Duchess of Cornwall

Contents

Facing page: Harvey, Harold C., 1874–1941, *My Kitchen*, 1923, Gallery Oldham, (p. 21)
Image opposite HRH The Duchess of Cornwall's statement: La Thangue, Henry Herbert, 1859–1929,
The Festa, Rochdale Arts & Heritage Service (p. 115)
Image opposite title page: Collier, John, 1850–1934, *The Death of Cleopatra*, 1890, Gallery Oldham (p. 9)

Foreword

Manchester can be most confusing. On my first visit to the Manchester City Art Galllery, a pilgrimage to one of this country's finest public collections, I had not done my research and arrived at its entrance only to find that the gallery was completely closed for a major refurbishment. Not a single painting was available to be seen.

My next visit was more successful. The gallery had been gloriously restored. The paintings were even finer than I had expected. The gallery was spacious and uncrowded. The hang was well considered and the experience hugely enjoyable.

Only one aspect of my visit jarred. Surely, closing the gallery and removing all the paintings into store was a God-given opportunity to photograph and catalogue the collection? Apparently not, for the only hint at a catalogue was a slight pamphlet, covering a few paintings and other items ranging from a Marshmallow Love seat to an early Egyptian funeral jar, which I reluctantly acquired and which I appear now to have lost. It contained the reproduction of a painting, *Summer in Cumberland*, by the late Edwardian artist James Durden. It is a glorious post-Edwardian painting in golden hues: the artist's wife and two children are enjoying a 'high tea', (certainly not the meal they are enjoying), and is a splendid and evocative period piece. More startling was the accompanying comment however that this painting was the Gallery's most popular work, "although it has been seldom exhibited". Which begs a big Why?

I chuckled to myself over that contradiction and used the tale to illustrate to those who needed to understand, how bad the situation had become and how much help even the great galleries now needed, if only to change their hangs more frequently and show the best of their paintings to a public that manifestly wished to see and enjoy them. I little understood in that just-pre-Foundation moment, that this was less a self-inflicted wound by the gallery than a comment on the situation throughout the national collection as a whole, as it was steadily deprived of funds, and focus. A situation that continues to this day (although I understand that the painting in question has since been on view).

Predictably, I suppose, Manchester has required compensation for my hubris. That moment came when the two planned volumes covering Greater Manchester had been laid out and were ready to go to the printers. Whilst establishing the size of the print run, our sales team found themselves talking to a collection that they could not find in the index of either volume. Further investigation showed that it and several other collections amounting in sum to another whole volume, had not been included. The responsibility did not lie with our sainted editor, Sophie, although the remedy did: and that required her to create a third volume and lay out all three of them afresh. Manchester's revenge. But, none of that is begrudged as the three volumes constitute an enduring monument to the magnificence of the collections in the region, and we are proud to be publishing them, whatever the cost.

Particular thanks go to Pam Walker, coordinator and Gordon MacGregor, photographer. In addition, all of us have cause to be grateful to the Mercers' Company, whose generosity has allowed these volumes to be printed.

Fred Hohler, Founder

Catalogue Scope and Organisation

Medium and Support

The principal focus of this series is oil paintings. However, tempera and acrylic are also included as well as mixed media, where oil is the predominant constituent. Paintings on all forms of support (e.g. canvas, panel, etc.) are included as long as the support is portable. The principal exclusions are miniatures, hatchments or other purely heraldic paintings and wall paintings *in situ*.

Public Ownership

Public ownership has been taken to mean any paintings that are directly owned by the public purse, made accessible to the public by means of public subsidy or generally perceived to be in public ownership. The term 'public' refers to both central government and local government. Paintings held by national museums, local authority museums, English Heritage and independent museums, where there is at least some form of public subsidy, are included. Paintings held in civic buildings such as local government offices, town halls, guildhalls, public libraries, universities, hospitals, crematoria, fire stations and police stations are also included.

Geographical Boundaries of Catalogues

The geographical boundary of each county is the 'ceremonial county' boundary. This county definition includes all unitary authorities. Counties that have a particularly large number of paintings are divided between two or more catalogues on a geographical basis.

Criteria for Inclusion

As long as paintings meet the requirements above, all paintings are included irrespective of their condition and perceived quality. However, painting reproductions can only be included with the agreement of the participating collections and, where appropriate, the relevant copyright owner. It is rare that a collection forbids the inclusion of its paintings. Where this is the case and it is possible to obtain a list of paintings, this list is given in the Paintings Without Reproductions section. Where copyright consent is refused, the paintings are also listed in the Paintings Without Reproductions section. All paintings in collections' stacks and stores are included, as well as those on display. Paintings which have been lent to other institutions, whether for short-term exhibition or long-term loan, are listed under the owner collection. In addition, paintings on long-term loan are also included under the borrowing institution when they are likely to remain there for at least another five years from the date of publication of this catalogue. Information relating to owners and borrowers is listed in the Further Information section.

Layout

Collections are grouped together under their home town. These locations are listed in alphabetical order. In some cases collections that are spread over a number of locations are included under a single owner collection. A number of collections, principally the larger ones, are preceded by curatorial forewords. Within each collection paintings are listed in order of artist surname. Where there is more than one painting by the same artist, the paintings are listed chronologically, according to their execution date.

The few paintings that are not accompanied by photographs are listed in the Paintings Without Reproductions section.

There is additional reference material in the Further Information section at the back of the catalogue. This gives the full names of artists, titles and media if it has not been possible to include these in full in the main section. It also provides acquisition credit lines and information about loans in and out, as well as copyright and photographic credits for each painting. Finally, there is an index of artists' surnames.

Key to Painting Information

Almost all paintings are reproduced in the catalogue. Where this is not the case they are listed in the Paintings Without Reproductions section. Where paintings are missing or have been stolen, the best possible photograph on record has been reproduced. In some cases this may be black and white. Paintings that have been stolen are highlighted with a red border. Some paintings are shown with conservation tissue attached to parts of the painting surface.

Adam, Patrick William 1854–1929
Interior, Rutland Lodge: Vista through Open Doors 1920
oil on canvas 67.3 × 45.7
LEEAG.PA.1925.0671.LACF 🐝

Artist name This is shown with the surname first. Where the artist is listed on the Getty Union List of Artist Names (ULAN), ULAN's preferred presentation of the name is given. In a number of cases the name may not be a firm attribution and this is made clear. Where the artist name is not known, a school may be given instead. Where the school is not known, the painter name is listed as *unknown artist*. If the artist name is too long for the space, as much of the name is given as possible followed by (…). This indicates the full name is given at the rear of the catalogue in the Further Information section.

Painting title A painting title followed by *(?)* indicates that the title is in doubt. Where the alternative title to the painting is considered to be better known than the original, the alternative title is given in parentheses. Where the collection has not given a painting a title, the publisher does so instead and marks this with an asterisk. If the title is too long for the space, as much of the title is given as possible followed by *(…)* and the full title is given in the Further Information section.

Execution date In some cases the precise year of execution may not be known for certain. Instead an approximate date will be given or no date at all.

Artist dates Where known, the years of birth and death of the artist are given. In some cases one or both dates may not be known with certainty, and this is marked. No date indicates that even an approximate date is not known. Where only the period in which the artist was active is known, these dates are given and preceded with the word *active*.

Medium and support Where the precise material used in the support is known, this is given.

Dimensions All measurements refer to the unframed painting and are given in cm with up to one decimal point. In all cases the height is shown before the width. An (E) indicates where a painting has not been measured and its size has been calculated by sight only. If the painting is circular, the single dimension is the diameter. If the painting is oval, the dimensions are height and width.

Collection inventory number In the case of paintings owned by museums, this number will always be the accession number. In all other cases it will be a unique inventory number of the owner institution. (P) indicates that a painting is a private loan. Details can be found in the Further Information section. Accession numbers preceded by 'PCF' indicate that the collection did not have an accession number at the time of catalogue production and therefore the number given has been temporarily allocated by The Public Catalogue Foundation. The   symbol indicates that the reproduction is based on a Bridgeman Art Library tran🐝rency (go to www.bridgemanart.com) or that Bridgeman administers the copyright for that artist.

Facing page: Phillips, Peter, b.1939, *Gravy for the Navy* (detail), 1963, Gallery Oldham (p. 41)

THE PAINTINGS

Gallery Oldham

Oldham Library and Art Gallery opened in 1883. The majority of the fine art collection was built up from the late 1800s to the 1930s, with an emphasis on British painting. Of particular interest is the Charles Lees collection of Victorian works, presented in 1888, which includes oil paintings and watercolours by J. M. W. Turner, John Constable, John Everett Millais and William Holman Hunt. Additions were made by Charles Lees in the 1890s and by his daughter, Marjorie Lees, in 1952 and 1970.

Since the 1930s, the Collection has benefited from gifts from the Contemporary Art Society as well as from numerous purchases and donations.

The Collection consists of over 550 oil paintings, ranging from works of the Pre-Raphaelite era, British Realism and late Victorian genre to post-war paintings, including Pop and abstract art.

Gallery Oldham, a new gallery designed by Pringle, Richards and Sharatt, opened in 2002 and not only houses the borough's collections of fine and decorative art but also displays one of the best collections of natural history in the North West, and holds extensive social history collections.

A key work from the collection of Victorian paintings is John William Waterhouse's *Circe*. Waterhouse is famous for his paintings of female figures from classical mythology. His image of the goddess Circe offering a poisoned drink to Odysseus is one of his most accomplished works. In a similar vein, John Collier's *The Death of Cleopatra* has captured our visitors' attention since it was first displayed here in 1891. Ernest Normand's sensual depiction of *Vashti Deposed*, whose story is told in the Old Testament, is another important and popular painting.

Two Lancashire artists' work also appears in the Collection. The group of paintings by William Stott of Oldham is outstanding and works by Edward William Stott of Rochdale are also represented.

From the late nineteenth century through to the 1930s, Oldham began to acquire major paintings from the Royal Academy and the New English Art Club and the Gallery became a significant patron of modern art. John Keating's fascinating *Night's Candles Are Burnt Out*, painted from 1928 to 1929, illustrates the building of an hydroelectric power station in Ireland. It also uses the huge public investment by the new Irish Free State as an allegory to chart the birth of an independent nation. From the same date, David Bomberg's *Toledo, Spain*, is a much more personally expressive work. Bomberg uses dynamic, energetic brushstrokes and raw unblended colours to give a powerfully physical sense of the landscape. This is an outstanding painting and like many of the more adventurous works in Oldham's collection was given by the Contemporary Art Society.

As you might expect, Gallery Oldham has a fine collection of work by Northern artists, including a painting by L. S. Lowry bought for just £16 in 1934. Titled *The Procession*, it shows a typical Whit Walk scene – a most appropriate and evocative image for Oldham. More recently the Gallery has acquired paintings by the popular Oldham artist Helen Bradley and Lowry's contemporary Theodore Major.

At the core of Oldham's fine art collection are a number of paintings of the Newlyn and St Ives Schools. These include Stanhope Alexander Forbes' *The Drinking Place*, an idyllic image of a scene in the Lamorna valley, Cornwall; Albert Julius Olsson's seascapes as well as *A Theatre Dressing Room* by Laura Knight, and other important British Impressionist works by Alfred James Munnings and William Orpen.

In the 1950s, Oldham acquired works through the Contemporary Art Society by Carel Victor Morlais Weight, Stanley Spencer and John Craxton. For a brief time during the 1960s the Gallery was able to make some very adventurous acquisitions of more avant-garde art. These included the large scale Pop Art painting *Gravy for the Navy* by Peter Phillips, abstract works by Sandra Blow, Patrick Heron and Howard Hodgkin, and sculpture by F. E. McWilliam, Jacob Epstein and Elisabeth Frink.

Since the 1980s, Oldham has again begun to collect modern art, adding important paintings, mixed media and photographic work by Estelle Thompson, Susan Hiller, Andy Goldsworthy, Laura Ford and Yasumasa Morimura. We have also explored ways of reflecting the ethnic diversity of the borough through exhibitions and acquisitions. There has been an increased focus on photography, mainly by young British artists, and a large number of paintings and sculpture from contemporary Bangladeshi artists has been acquired, creating one of the largest such collections in Britain.

While most of the more significant contemporary works have been acquired through the Contemporary Art Society, the Museums, Libraries and Archives Council/Victoria and Albert Museum Purchase Grant Fund and The Art Fund have also allowed us to fill important gaps in the permanent collection. We are also extending our collection of twentieth-century studio ceramics with funding from the Heritage Lottery Fund. Gallery Oldham has benefitted from many gifts from individual artists and donors, to whom we extend our thanks. They have all helped to build our distinctive museum and gallery collections.

Stephen Whittle, Museum Manager

Adam, Patrick William 1854–1929
Interior, Morning
oil on canvas 67.5 x 42.5
2.12

Adams, William Dacres 1864–1951
Southwark Cathedral, London c.1920
oil on canvas 56 x 38
1.22

Aikman, George W. 1831–1905
Weighing the Anchor
oil on canvas 59.5 x 98.5
4.93

Allinson, Adrian Paul 1890–1959
Somerset Farm
oil on canvas 55.8 x 78.7
5.5 🐝

Anne, Atia Islam b.1962
Cancer c.2001
acrylic on canvas 181.5 x 91.4
2006.51

Anne, Atia Islam b.1962
Insulin c.2002
acrylic on canvas 182.5 x 90.8
2006.5

Anrooy, Anton Abraham van 1870–1949
No.182 Ebury Street, London
oil on canvas 71 x 57
2.26

Anthony, Henry Mark 1817–1886
Huge Oak that O'ershadows the Mill
oil on canvas 160 x 180
3.83/31

Appleton, John H. active 19th C
William Noton, Mayor of Oldham (1892–1893) c.1892
oil on canvas 67 x 54.5
4.98

Ashton, Andrew 1811–1883
William Johnson Fox (1786–1864), MP c.1860
oil on canvas 61 x 50.8
11.29

Ashton, Andrew 1811–1883
James Mellodew, JP, Mayor of Oldham (1874–1875) 1875
oil on canvas 137 x 107.8
5.82

Auerbach, Frank Helmuth b.1931
E. O. W. on Her Blue Eiderdown 1963
oil on canvas 47 x 54
PCF23

Baker, Christopher b.1956
Arena 1982
acrylic on cotton duck 82 x 110
G775

Banner, Delmar Harmond 1896–1983
Coniston Fell, Lancashire, from Harter Fell, Cumberland 1947
oil on canvas 63.5 x 76.2
6.48

Barnes, Archibald George 1887–1972
The Red Lacquer Cabinet
oil on canvas 76.2 x 62.2
2.23

Bartlett, William Henry 1858–1932
Unloading Kelp Weed
oil on canvas 44.5 x 70
8.52

Bates, John Stanley b.1871
Albion Street, Oldham, Lancashire, 1910 1911
oil on canvas 68 x 50
G765

Baxter, Charles 1809–1879
Portrait Study (Rose)
oil on canvas 57 x 47
1.18/6

Bayes, Walter 1869–1956
A boire
oil on canvas 134.5 x 182
5.2

Bayliss, Wyke 1835–1906
The Basilica of St Mark's, Venice, Interior
oil on canvas 79.5 x 123.5
2.92

Beattie-Brown, William 1831–1909
The River Dochert, at Killin, Perthshire
oil on canvas 85 x 122
3.19

Beeton, Alan 1880–1942
Girl in a Wood
oil on canvas 152.5 x 100
1.26

Bhattacharjee, Shishir b.1960
Untitled 2002
acrylic on canvas 200 x 150
2008.106

Birch, Samuel John Lamorna 1869–1955
*The Serpentine Quarry, near Mullion,
Cornwall* c.1920
oil on canvas 90 x 120.5
5.21

Blow, Sandra 1925–2006
Number Seventeen 1961
oil on board 122 x 112
12.62

Boddington, Henry John 1811–1865
Morning on the Usk 1861
oil on canvas 76.2 x 137
3.67/1

Bold, John 1895–1979
A North Country Landscape
oil on canvas 51.4 x 66
8.61

Bold, John 1895–1979
Blackstone Edge
oil on canvas 75 x 100
3.83/17

Bomberg, David 1890–1957
Toledo, Spain 1929
oil on canvas 58.4 x 76.2
10.44

Booth, Samuel Lawson 1836–1928
Tŷ Croes, near Holyhead, Anglesey 1901
oil on canvas 103 x 152
1.44

Bottomley, Edwin 1865–1929
The Saddleworth Viaduct, Oldham,
Lancashire 1885
oil on canvas 86 x 117
G807

Bottomley, Eric b.1948
Oldham, Lancashire, Clegg Street Station,
1953 1987
oil on canvas 39 x 49
G934

Bottomley, Richard Oastler 1843–1886
On the Greta, County Durham 1883
oil on canvas 61 x 91.5
3.35

Bottomley, Richard Oastler 1843–1886
Chadderton Park, Oldham, Lancashire (Road
through Nordens)
oil on canvas 49.5 x 67
5.89

Bowie, Janis b.1956
Spinning Mules 3 and 4 2005
acrylic on canvas 80 x 100
2006.7

Bradley, Basil 1842–1904
Hard Times 1898
oil on canvas 115 x 195.5
2.01

Bradley, Helen 1900–1979
A Special Treat 1967
oil on board 62 x 45
2005.23

Bradley, Helen 1900–1979
'It was early spring...' (Fire on Union Street)
1969
oil on canvas 86.4 x 132
7.7

Bradley, Helen 1900–1979
'Buckley & Proctor' c.1970
oil on board 36 x 54
2.75/37

Bratby, John Randall 1928–1992
Sewing Machine, Wife and Baby c.1960
oil on board 89.5 x 118
10.66 🐝

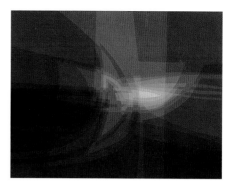

Brooker, William 1918–1983
Orange Label 1965
oil on canvas 76.2 x 91.4
3.66/1

Buckley, John
Yellow Scape
oil on board 44 x 59
1.75/23

Budd, Herbert Ashwin 1881–1950
The Bird Shop c.1920
oil on canvas 101.5 x 127
7.27

Bundy, Edgar 1862–1922
The Puritans
oil on canvas 87.5 x 166.5
3.98

Burn, Rodney Joseph 1899–1984
St Brelade's Bay, Jersey
oil on canvas 45 x 55.5
G867

Carse, James Howe 1819–1900
Oldham, Lancashire, from Glodwick Fields
1831
oil on canvas 43 x 60
3.16/3

Carse, James Howe 1819–1900
Uppermill from Dobcross, Oldham,
Lancashire 1858
oil on canvas 80 x 132
12.27

Carse, James Howe 1819–1900
Opening Game of the Oldham Subscription
Bowling Green, Frankhill, 1860 after 1860
oil on canvas 49 x 65
10.3

Carse, James Howe 1819–1900
Medlock Vale in 1866, Oldham, Lancashire 1866
oil on canvas 29 x 24
11.07/2

Carse, James Howe 1819–1900
Nordens, Oldham, Lancashire 1866
oil on canvas 76 x 64
71.33/2

Carse, James Howe 1819–1900
Sheepwashes Brook
oil on canvas 42 x 32
3.16/2

Chakma, Kanak Chanpa b.1963
In the Red
acrylic on canvas 60 x 60
2006.21

Charles, James 1851–1906
Hide and Seek
oil on canvas 47 x 37.5
12.24

Charles, James 1851–1906
Companions
oil on canvas 39 x 30
4.08/4

Charles, James 1851–1906
Joshua Walmsley Radcliffe, Mayor of Oldham (1884–1887) c.1884–1887
oil on canvas 125.5 x 100
8.88

Chevska, Maria b.1948
Tantamount (diptych, left panel) 1990
oil on linen 107 x 76
G896A

Chevska, Maria b.1948
Tantamount (diptych, right panel) 1990
oil on linen 107 x 229
G896B

Chuhan, J. b.1955
Cha
oil on canvas 149 x 117
G679

Clausen, George 1852–1944
Phyllis 1880
oil on canvas 65 x 30
3.55/3

Codrington, Isabel 1874–1943
Old Tramp
oil on canvas 150.5 x 100
9.28

Collier, John 1850–1934
The Death of Cleopatra 1890
oil on canvas 395 x 315
3.91 ✣

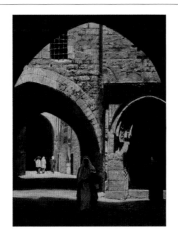

Collier, John 1850–1934
A Street in Jerusalem
oil on canvas 63.5 x 53.5
5.27

Collier, John 1850–1934
*Samuel Radcliffe Platt, Mayor of Oldham
(1887–1889)*
oil on canvas 141 x 110.5
5.93

Colman, Samuel 1780–1845
Belshazzar's Feast c.1833
oil on canvas 136 x 197.5
1.95 ✣

Connard, Philip 1875–1958
A Chelsea Interior
oil on canvas 100.5 x 75
1.14 ✣

Connard, Philip 1875–1958
Merry England
oil on canvas 246 x 121
62.37

Cooper, Thomas Sidney 1803–1902
Cattle
oil on panel 40 x 33.5
1.18/4

Cope, Charles West 1811–1890
George Herbert and His Mother 1872
oil on canvas 74 x 61
1.1 🐝

Cotman, Frederick George 1850–1920
Her Ladyship's First Lesson
oil on canvas 92 x 182
3.9

Craxton, John 1922–2009
Beach Scene 1949
oil on canvas 99 x 75.5
27.56

Crossley, Terence active 1975–1981
And the Blind Eye Creates
oil on canvas 128 x 70
8.81/103

Crossley, Terence active 1975–1981
Man Sitting in a Pub
oil on canvas 39.5 x 29.5
6.75/14

Crozier, George 1846–1914
Reverend R. M. Davies
oil on canvas 125.5 x 93.5
3.08

Cundall, Charles Ernest 1890–1971
Early Morning, Josselin, France
oil on canvas 50 x 62
8.28 🐝

Cundall, Charles Ernest 1890–1971
La passerelle
oil on panel 48 x 60
18.35 🐝

Facing page: Gertler, Mark, 1891–1939, *The Bokhara Coat*, 1920, Rochdale Arts & Heritage Service, (p. 101)

Darien, Henri Gaston 1864–1926
Quai Malaquais, Paris, Twilight
oil on canvas 106.5 x 202.5
3.92

Davey, Derek active 1980–2002
Remembrance Day 1980
oil on canvas 70.5 x 103
G930

Davidson, T.
Girl with Red Hair
oil on canvas 74 x 62
G648

Davies, James Hey 1844–1930
Scared
oil on canvas 70 x 126
4.88

Davies, John R. 1899–1985
Sisteron, France
oil on canvas 49 x 60
20.51

Delmard, M.
Goatherd 1874
oil on canvas 55 x 76
5.86

Dicksee, Margaret Isabel 1859–1903
The Children of Charles I
oil on canvas 105.5 x 85
1.96

Dicksee, Thomas Francis 1819–1895
Little Florist
oil on canvas 76 x 63
11.69/1

Dobson, William Charles Thomas
1817–1898
Wild Flowers 1864
oil on canvas 49.5 x 60
1.18/5

Downing, Charles Palmer c.1848–1902
William Jones, First Mayor of Oldham
oil on canvas 90 x 70
2.98

Downing, Charles Palmer c.1848–1902
William Jones, First Mayor of Oldham
oil on canvas 75 x 61
14.6

Dunlop, Ronald Ossory 1894–1973
Chrysanthemums
oil on canvas 90 x 54
6.5

Dunlop, Ronald Ossory 1894–1973
Faith
oil on canvas 76.5 x 47.5
66.33

Durnini, F.
La Madonna della sedia (copy after Raphael)
oil on canvas 45
3.67/4

Dvorak, Franz 1862–1927
*Saint Laurence Distributing the Treasures of
the Church to the Poor*
oil on canvas 253 x 127
1.99

Easby, Steve b.1958
Suspension
acrylic on canvas 144 x 144
2.81/110

East, Alfred 1844–1913
Autumn in the Valley of the Ouse, Sussex
oil on canvas 120.5 x 151
8.07

Ellis, William 1747–1810
Cader Idris, Gwynedd
oil on canvas 51 x 76
11.78/15

Emsley, Walter 1860–1938
*George Hanson, Mayor of Oldham
(1902–1903)*
oil on canvas 125 x 79
1.11

Etty, William 1787–1849
Female Nude
oil on canvas 49 x 36.7
2.66

Eurich, Richard Ernst 1903–1992
The Donkey Boy 1951
oil on canvas 24.2 x 19.5
2.53 🐝

Fantin-Latour, Henri 1836–1904
Roses II 1879
oil on canvas 39 x 31.5
3.55/4

Fidler, Harry 1856–1935
Work
oil on canvas 136 x 183
9.29

Fish, G. W. active 1893–c.1900
*Winston L. S. Churchill (1874–1965), MP for
Oldham (1900–1905)* c.1900
oil on canvas 90 x 70
7.02

Fisher, Mark 1841–1923
The Manor Farm
oil on canvas 58.5 x 76
7.07 🐝

Fisher, Samuel Melton 1859–1939
Dreams, E dolce dormire
oil on canvas 143 x 107.5
1.02 🐝

Fitton, Harvey
Press Conference
oil on canvas 42 x 55
17.49

Fitton, James 1899–1982
Doll on a Chair
oil on canvas 45 x 45
G651

Fitton, James 1899–1982
Tavern Brawl
oil on canvas 87.5 x 80
53.33

Fletcher, Geoffrey Scowcroft 1923–2004
A Summer Afternoon 1948–1949
oil on canvas 40 x 50
9.49

Fletcher, William Teulon Blandford
1858–1936
'O yez, o yez!'
oil on canvas 101 x 151
5.9

Foottet, Frederick Francis 1850–1935
The Orchard
oil on canvas 75 x 90
35.35

Forbes, Stanhope Alexander 1857–1947
The Drinking Place 1900
oil on canvas 174 x 152.5
1.01 🐝

Foweraker, Albert Moulton 1873–1942
*Bridge of St Bénézet at the Palace of the Popes,
Avignon, France*
oil on canvas 108 x 150
5.09

France, Ada active 1900–1906
Red Setter
oil on canvas 50.5 x 91
12.77/2

Frost, Terry 1915–2003
59/60 1959/1960
oil on canvas 120 x 118
10.62/2

Gabain, Ethel Leontine 1883–1950
Adelaide Stanley as Kate in 'The Two Bouquets' (from the play by Herbert Farjeon)
oil on canvas 74.5 x 62
40.37

Gertler, Mark 1891–1939
Tulips and Mimosa
oil on canvas 75 x 82
19.35

Gibbs, Thomas Binney 1870–1947
Samuel Buckley, Mayor of Oldham (1883–1884 & 1889–1891)
oil on canvas 125 x 85.5
2.07

Gibson, William Alfred 1866–1931
Near Savona, Italy
oil on canvas 101.5 x 126
4.13

Gledhill, James active 1884–1891
Farm Scene
oil on canvas 49 x 74.5
13.39

Gledhill, James active 1884–1891
Landscape
oil on canvas 24 x 34
11.78/4A

Gledhill, James active 1884–1891
Landscape with Cattle
oil on canvas 40 x 35
19.37

Gledhill, James active 1884–1891
Turnip Field
oil on canvas 40 x 61
11.78/4C

Gledhill, James active 1884–1891
Welsh Peasants Crossing the Conway, High Spring Tide
oil on canvas 24 x 35
63.37/1

Glendening, Alfred Augustus 1840–1921
On the Thames 1875
oil on canvas 45.5 x 36
11.78/19

Glendening, Alfred Augustus 1840–1921
View near Kenmore, Loch Tay, Perthshire
oil on canvas 76 x 121.8
20.39/1

Gordon, Cora Josephine 1879–1950
Flatford Pool, Suffolk
oil on canvas 31 x 40
55.37

Gosse, Laura Sylvia 1881–1968
Dieppe, France
oil on canvas 59.5 x 49.5
12.33 🐝

Gow, Andrew Carrick 1848–1920
Napoleon on the Sands at Boulogne, France
oil on canvas 65.5 x 125.5
8.98

Grassel, Franz 1861–1948
Weiße Enten in Wasser
oil on canvas 68.5 x 99
11.12

Greuze, Jean-Baptiste (attributed to)
1725–1805
Portrait of a Woman
oil on canvas 48 x 40
2.84

Grice, Albert active 1973–1974
Platting Road, Oldham, Lancashire 1973
oil on canvas 23.5 x 39.5
5.74/23

Grice, Albert active 1973–1974
Hawthorns
oil on canvas 39 x 60
5.74/22

Grice, Albert active 1973–1974
L. S. Lowry (1887–1796)
oil on board 30 x 23
6.75/19

Griffith, Thomas
View on Yorkshire Street, Oldham, Lancashire
1949
oil on canvas 43.2 x 53.4
10.49

Grosvenor, Thomas active 1909
Houghton Mill on the Ouse
oil on canvas 145.5 x 176.5
4.09

Gwynne-Jones, Allan 1892–1982
The Soldier's Daughter 1930
oil on canvas 43.2 x 40.6
6.32 ✳

Hacker, Arthur 1858–1919
A Difficulty
oil on canvas 90 x 126
9.08 ✳

Hague, John Haughton 1842–1934
*Keeper's Cottage, Chadderton Park, Oldham,
Lancashire* 1872
oil on canvas 61 x 91.5
4.33

Hague, John Haughton 1842–1934
Oldham Street Sweepers, Lancashire 1873
oil on canvas 71 x 91.4
67.33

Hague, John Haughton 1842–1934
The Chadderton Taxidermist 1875
oil on canvas 90 x 60
3.83/33

Hague, John Haughton 1842–1934
*The Old Bridge, Chadderton Fold, Oldham,
Lancashire* 1877
oil on canvas 60 x 90
3.83/29

Facing page: Barber, Charles Burton, 1845–1894, *A Special Pleader*, 1893, Rochdale Arts & Heritage Service, (p. 79)

Hague, John Haughton 1842–1934
*Washing Day, Bishop Lakes House,
Chadderton, Oldham, Lancashire* 1878
oil on canvas 61 x 92
1.35

Hague, John Haughton 1842–1934
Weaver and a Magpie 1880
oil on canvas 119.5 x 75
4.84

Hague, John Haughton 1842–1934
*Chadderton Fold, Oldham, Lancashire,
1881* 1881–1887
oil on canvas 65 x 95
7.26

Hague, John Haughton 1842–1934
Riversdale, Bardsley, Lancashire 1896
oil on canvas 75 x 50
46.37

Hague, John Haughton 1842–1934
*John Dodd, President of Oldham Lyceum
(1898–1899)* 1898–1899
oil on canvas 60 x 50
8.81/102

Hague, John Haughton 1842–1934
Strawberry Gardens c.1890
oil on canvas 60 x 90
6.75/18

Hall, H. R. active 1895–1902
Denizen of the Highlands
oil on canvas 62 x 52
11.78/16

Hall, H. R. active 1895–1902
Highland Cattle
oil on canvas 50 x 75
11.78/17

Hampson, Mark b.1968
*A Brief History of Romance: The Romance of
History* 1994
oil on canvas 182 x 236
2008.104

Hardy, Frederick Daniel 1827–1911
Paid Off 1890
oil on canvas 15 x 19.5
1.18/14

Hardy, Frederick Daniel 1827–1911
The Wedding Dress
oil on panel 25.5 x 38
1.18/15

Hare, Julius 1859–1932
Day Fades
oil on canvas 94.5 x 151
6.88

Harvey, Harold C. 1874–1941
My Kitchen 1923
oil on canvas 100.5 x 77.5
6.24 🐝

Hayter, George 1792–1871
John Fielden (1784–1849)
oil on board 34 x 29
24.37

Hearne, Edward active 1934
Chamber Hall Barn
oil on canvas 74 x 62.1
20.34

Hearne, Edward active 1934
*The Demolition of Copster Mill, Oldham,
Lancashire*
oil on canvas 70 x 80 (E)
2010.117

Helcke, Arnold c.1843–1912
Squally Weather, Coast of Guernsey
oil on canvas 129.5 x 221
4.9

Hemy, Charles Napier 1841–1917
Boat Adrift
oil on canvas 92 x 136.5
2.9

Henderson, William Samuel P. 1816–1876
A Hard Word 1838
oil on board 29.5 x 39.5
3.65

Herkomer, Hubert von 1849–1914
Toreador of Valencia
oil on canvas 100.5 x 66
9.13

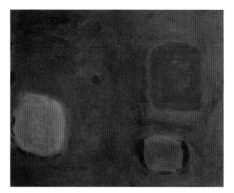

Heron, Patrick 1920–1999
Scarlet and Green in Brown, November, 1961 1961
oil on canvas 74 x 100
10.62/1

Heywood, Thomas 1846–1919
Dead Game
oil on canvas 64 x 45
6.41

Heywood, Thomas 1846–1919
Landscape, North Wales (Harvest)
oil on canvas 21.5 x 35.5
3.19a

Heywood, Thomas 1846–1919
Spaniel and Rabbit
oil on canvas 30.5 x 41
7.3

Hill, Adrian Keith Graham 1895–1977
Farm at Singleton, Lancashire
oil on canvas 48.5 x 58.5
6.4

Hillier, Tristram Paul 1905–1983
Trujillo, Spain 1965
oil on canvas 59 x 79
3.66/2

Hodgkin, Howard b.1932
Husband and Wife 1963
oil on panel 46 x 64
7.68

Hoggatt, William 1879–1961
In the Lezayre Valley, Isle of Man
oil on canvas 122 x 151
4.28

Holland, John 1830–1886
*Crompton from Tandle Hills, Royton,
Lancashire* 1870
oil on canvas 86 x 150
3.83/36

Holt, S. F.
Sheep in a Stable
oil on canvas 32 x 43
11.78/10

Hook, James Clarke 1819–1907
The Mackerel Take 1865
oil on canvas 76 x 114
5.23

Hornel, Edward Atkinson 1864–1933
A Summer Idyll 1908
oil on canvas 126 x 151
7.1

Horsley, John Callcott 1817–1903
*Josiah Radcliffe, Mayor of Oldham (1856–
1858)*
oil on canvas 108 x 70
1.84

Houston, George 1869–1947
An Ayrshire Glen
oil on canvas 99 x 150
4.11

Hoyland, John b.1934
Untitled 1978
acrylic on paper 76 x 56.5
5.83/38

Hutchinson, Michael
*Delph Donkey at the Measurements Factory,
Oldham, Lancashire* 1975
oil on canvas 59 x 49.2
3.83/4

Hutchison, Robert Gemmell 1855–1936
The Young Laird
oil on canvas 127 x 159
4.19

Ibbotson, Karen
Memory I
oil on canvas 154 x 122
PCF30

Ince, Charles Percy 1875–1952
Monuments, Men's Movement, Time's Conquest
oil on canvas 99 x 74
1.23

Jackson
Moses Mills (the last Head Constable of Oldham prior to the incorporation of the borough)
oil on canvas 90 x 60
2.48

Jackson, Frederick William 1859–1918
In Summer Time 1888
oil on canvas 100 x 126
13.60/5

Jackson, Frederick William 1859–1918
Runswick Bay, North Yorkshire
oil on canvas 71.5 x 110
44.37

Jackson, Frederick William 1859–1918
Abraham Crompton, Mayor of Oldham (1871–1872)
oil on canvas 125.5 x 100.5
6.02

Jackson, Frederick William 1859–1918
Alfred Waddington, Mayor of Oldham (1897–1898)
oil on canvas 126 x 100
4.99

Jackson, Frederick William 1859–1918
Drinking Trough
oil on canvas 27 x 37
26.38

Jackson, Frederick William 1859–1918
Henry Lees Hollingsworth
oil on canvas 130 x 90
4.55

Jackson, Frederick William 1859–1918
Herbert Wilde, Mayor of Oldham (1913–1914)
oil on canvas 110 x 90
1.15

Jackson, Frederick William 1859–1918
Jackson Brierley, Mayor of Oldham (1898–1899)
oil on canvas 126.5 x 100.5
4.01

Jackson, Frederick William 1859–1918
James Yates, Mayor of Oldham (1880–1882 & 1904–1905)
oil on canvas 125.5 x 87.5
3.06

Jackson, Frederick William 1859–1918
John Armitage, Headmaster of Oldham Technical School
oil on canvas 75 x 59.5
2.11

Jackson, Frederick William 1859–1918
Robert Jackson, Organist of St Peter's Church
oil on canvas 75 x 62
12.07

Jackson, Frederick William 1859–1918
Robin Hood's Bay, North Yorkshire
oil on canvas 107 x 86
13.60/4

Jackson, Frederick William 1859–1918
Scene in Capri, Italy
oil on canvas 121 x 88
G700

Jackson, Frederick William 1859–1918
The Green Tub
oil on canvas 50 x 60.4
7.2

Jackson, Frederick William 1859–1918
The Harvest of the Sea
oil on canvas 131 x 221
2.89

Jackson, Frederick William 1859–1918
Thomas Bolton, Mayor of Oldham (1908–1909)
oil on canvas 125 x 100
8.1

Jackson, Thomas Graham 1835–1924
View near Morecambe, Lancashire
oil on canvas 40 x 55.5
1.55/2

Jackson, William
Railway Scene
oil on canvas 34.5 x 44
3.83/3

Jamieson, Alexander 1873–1937
The Frozen Meadow, Winter 1929
oil on canvas 92.5 x 113
7.31

Jamieson, Robert Kirkland 1881–1950
Approach to a Cotswold Village
oil on canvas 100 x 126
41.37

Jenkins, Paul b.1923
Phenomena, If Is for Why
acrylic on canvas 82 x 117
9.65

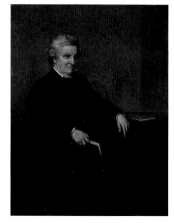

Johnston, W. Herbert active 1882–1892
William Wrigley, Mayor of Oldham (1872–1873)
oil on canvas 140.5 x 110
3.82

Jones, Phyllis active 1983
Dancers on a Chequered Floor
oil on canvas 106 x 240
3.83/28B

Jones, Phyllis active 1983
Model in a Room
oil on canvas 102 x 89
3.83/28A

Jones, Wil b.1960
Eric Sykes (b.1923) 2007
acrylic on canvas 182.9 x 213.4
2008.147

Joy, George William 1844–1925
A Dinner of Herbs
oil on canvas 124.5 x 123
2.05

Keating, John 1889–1977
Night's Candles Are Burnt Out 1928–1929
oil on canvas 103 x 127
6.31 🐝

Kehoe
Sir George William Needham (1843–1928)
oil on canvas 121 x 92.5
G927

Kelly, Gerald Festus 1879–1972
The Burmese Dancer IV 1919–1920
oil on canvas 117 x 81
3.22

Kemm, Robert 1830–1895
Missing
oil on canvas 70 x 89
1.89

Kershaw, Joseph Franklin 1885–1917
Portrait of a South Kensington Model 1908
oil on canvas 59.5 x 49.5
9.2

Kershaw, Joseph Franklin 1885–1917
The Meeting of Spring and Winter
oil on canvas 101.6 x 76.2
17.53/2

Kershaw, Joseph Franklin 1885–1917
Washing Day
oil on canvas 76 x 76
17.53/1

King, Henry John Yeend 1855–1924
Girls Herding Geese
oil on canvas 65 x 49
7.51/1

King, Henry John Yeend 1855–1924
The Mill Stream
oil on canvas 64 x 49
7.51/2

Knight, John William Buxton 1843–1908
Portsmouth Harbour, Hampshire
oil on canvas 80 x 79.5
2.08

Knight, Joseph 1837–1909
Meadow Scene
oil on canvas 38 x 40
3.67/26

Knight, Joseph 1837–1909
Snowdonia
oil on canvas 130 x 150
5.88

Knight, Joseph 1837–1909
*Wood with a Woman, Sheep and a Boy
(Meadow Scene)*
oil on canvas 59 x 39
3.67/2

Knight, Laura 1877–1970
A Theatre Dressing Room
oil on canvas 75 x 62.5
13.56

Knight, Patrick active 19th C
John Platt, MP for Oldham (1865–1872) (after
James Sant)
oil on canvas 206.5 x 128
14.98

Facing page: Clausen, George, 1852–1944, *The Golden Barn*, Rochdale Arts & Heritage Service, (p. 87)

Knowles, George Sheridan 1863–1931
Seeking Sanctuary
oil on canvas 87.5 x 151
2.96

La Thangue, Henry Herbert 1859–1929
The Last Furrow 1895
oil on canvas 201.5 x 214.5
3.96

La Thangue, Henry Herbert 1859–1929
Packing Stocks 1920
oil on canvas 63 x 72
5.42

La Thangue, Henry Herbert 1859–1929
The Appian Way c.1920
oil on canvas 72 x 82.5
1.42/1

La Thangue, Henry Herbert 1859–1929
A Provençal Morning
oil on canvas 56.5 x 49.2
1.42/3

La Thangue, Henry Herbert 1859–1929
Trellised Vines
oil on canvas 66.2 x 73.3
1.42/2

Ladbrooke, John Berney 1803–1879
Summer Landscape
oil on canvas 80 x 67
10.27/2

Langley, Walter 1852–1922
'The tender grace of a day that is dead will never come back to me' 1909
oil on canvas 115.5 x 105.5
3.1

Latter, Ruth 1869–1949
Flowers
oil on canvas 60.5 x 49.5
2.25

Lawson, Kenneth 1920–2008
Moon and Sea 1942
oil on board 65 x 80
2010.118

Leader, Benjamin Williams 1831–1923
Manchester Ship Canal: The Making of Eastham Dock 1891
oil on canvas 112 x 184
13.27/1

Leader, Stanley
On the Lledr
oil on canvas 41 x 61
11.78/14

Leader, Stanley
The Falls at Turnbrill, Perthshire
oil on canvas 42 x 62
11.78/13

Lee, Terry b.1932
Near Thing, 1937 1963
oil on canvas 213 x 181
G696

Lee-Hankey, William 1869–1952
First Steps c.1927
oil on canvas 59 x 44
6.27

Lees, Derwent 1885–1931
Landscape with a Figure
oil on canvas 23.5 x 32
9.46

Lewis, Charles James 1830–1892
Our Holiday
oil on canvas 41 x 98
2.95

Lewis, Neville 1895–1972
Gipsy Boy
oil on canvas 49.5 x 39.5
4.23

Livens, Horace Mann 1862–1936
Black and White 1916
oil on canvas 56 x 46
7.24

Long, Edwin 1829–1891
Head
oil on board 33.5 x 24
12.44/3

Long, Edwin 1829–1891
Spanish Beggars
oil on canvas 72.5 x 59.5
4.08/2

Lord, Francis
The Battery, New Brighton, Wirral
oil on canvas 65 x 102
26.39

Loudan, William Mouat 1868–1925
The Crystal Gazer
oil on canvas 183 x 152.5
18.32

Lowry, Laurence Stephen 1887–1976
The Procession
oil on canvas 35.5 x 54.5
3.34

MacAndrew, E. H. active 1924
Spanish Lace
oil on canvas 110.5 x 85
8.24

MacDougall, William Brown 1869–1936
Castle and Priory
oil on canvas 75 x 100 (E)
PCF26

MacKenzie, Alexander 1923–2001
Flint: White 1962
oil on board 18.5 x 55
2.63a

MacKenzie, Alexander 1923–2001
Shore 1962
oil on board 26.5 x 55
2.63c

Majid, Aneela b.1963
Portrait of Two Sisters
oil on canvas 153 x 114.4
2008.348

Major, Theodore 1908–1999
Wigan Landscape 1960s
oil on board 74.5 x 94.3
2009.1

Major, Theodore 1908–1999
Red Farm
oil on canvas 76 x 94
2009.2

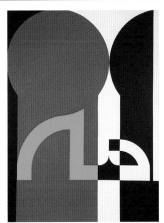

Makhoul, Bashir b.1963
Intifada (diptych, left panel)
acrylic on canvas 201 x 150.5
2008.105.1

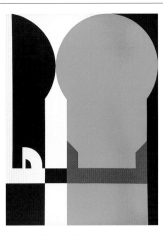

Makhoul, Bashir b.1963
Intifada (diptych, right panel)
acrylic on canvas 201 x 150.5
2008.105.2

Massani, Pompeo 1850–1920
The Old Musician
oil on canvas 30 x 21.5
1.18/7

Mayor, Patti 1872–1962
Mill Girl with a Shawl
oil on canvas 70 x 46
2.82/26

McBey, James 1883–1959
Saada 1936
oil on canvas 79.2 x 63.5
42.37

McCombs, John b.1943
Gateshead Farm, Delph, Lancashire 1990
oil on board 31.2 x 42.2
G886

Mellor, John active 1976
Moorland Man, the Shadow of the Man
oil on canvas 59 x 44
9.76/34

Meninsky, Bernard 1891–1950
Toddler c.1938
oil on canvas 99.5 x 74.4
24.38 ※

Messenger, A. J.
Cathedral 1957
oil on canvas 118 x 120
10.59

Millais, John Everett 1829–1896
The Departure of the Crusaders 1857–1858
oil on canvas 51.5 x 64
6.70/1

Millais, John Everett 1829–1896
John Joseph Jones (1830–1888)
oil on canvas 147 x 112
8.82/34 (P)

Millais, John Everett 1829–1896
Thomas Oldham Barlow
oil on canvas 100.5 x 117
13.88

Millais, John Everett (attributed to)
1829–1896
Boys Rabbiting
oil on canvas 81.5 x 74.7
10.27/1

Mills, Frank
Portrait of a Spirit Guide
oil on board 40 x 29
2005.55.1

Mills, Frank
Portrait of a Spirit Guide
oil on board 25 x 20
2005.55.3

Mills, J. W. active 1939
Pheasants and a Plover
oil on canvas 76 x 51
28.39

Mitchell, Arthur Croft 1872–1956
Interior of a Religious House
oil on canvas 86.5 x 59.5
2.1 🐝

Mitchell, Pamela
Mick Jagger (b.1943) 1968
acrylic on canvas 76 x 61
12.79/2

Mogford, John 1821–1885
Cliffs at Barlow
oil on canvas 29.5 x 47
7.48/4

Mole, John Henry 1814–1886
Near Tarbert, Loch Fyne, Argyll
oil on canvas 59 x 90
3.67/3

Montague, Alfred 1832–1883
A Breezy Day on the Meuse
oil on canvas 60 x 50
2.56

Moore, Henry 1831–1895
Westward
oil on canvas 105.5 x 181.5
3.93

Morley, Robert 1857–1941
The Press Gang
oil on canvas 138 x 183.5
3.44 🐝

Morris, Cedric Lockwood 1889–1982
Harding Down, Llangynwyd, Bridgend 1928
oil on canvas 61 x 75
16.31

Morris, Philip Richard 1836–1902
Crowd Scene
oil on canvas 118 x 116
1.62

Morris, Philip Richard 1836–1902
The Last Load
oil on canvas 38.5 x 74
1.18/11

Mostyn, Thomas Edwin 1864–1930
A Fisherman's Daughter
oil on canvas 89 x 70.5
10.07/1

Mostyn, Thomas Edwin 1864–1930
Morning, Burnham Beeches, Buckinghamshire
oil on canvas 69.5 x 89.5
10.07/2

Muckley, William Jabez 1829–1905
Peonies 1885
oil on canvas 62 x 52
2.67/8

Muckley, William Jabez 1829–1905
Apple Blossom
oil on canvas 60 x 49.5
4.85

Muckley, William Jabez 1829–1905
Oranges
oil on canvas 55 x 66
1.85

Muckley, William Jabez 1829–1905
Water Lilies
oil on canvas 39 x 49.5
2.85

Facing page: Keating, Séan, 1889–1977, *Night's Candles Are Burnt Out*, 1928–1929, Gallery Oldham, (p. 27)

Muirhead, David 1867–1930
The End of Autumn
oil on canvas 49.5 x 75
1.34

Munnings, Alfred James 1878–1959
A White Slave
oil on canvas 99 x 150
4.07

Murphy, Cliff b.1944
The Beautiful Game 2003
acrylic on board 122 x 247
2005.18

Murray, David 1849–1933
Silvery Summer, Kennet and Avon Canal,
Berkshire
oil on canvas 121 x 182
23.39

Murray, David 1849–1933
Twixt Croft and Creel
oil on canvas 101.5 x 152.5
1.86/1

Musgrave, E. active c.1900–1985
Dame Sarah Lees (1842–1935) c.1900
oil on board 34 x 24
G706

Nasmyth, Alexander 1758–1840
Landscape
oil on canvas 62 x 85
3.83/26

Normand, Ernest 1857–1923
Vashti Deposed
oil on canvas 161 x 244.5
4.96

Ogden, Geoff b.1929
Cottage Interior
oil on hardboard 28.5 x 33
10.77/34

Olsson, Albert Julius 1864–1942
Rising Moon, St Ives Bay, Cornwall
oil on canvas 115.5 x 151
4.08/3

Olsson, Albert Julius 1864–1942
Rum from Eigg, Inner Hebrides
oil on canvas 44.5 x 61
10.29

Oppenheimer, Charles 1875–1961
Artist's Garden
oil on canvas 112 x 102
8.31

Orpen, William 1878–1931
Behind the Scenes 1910
oil on canvas 92 x 72
6.1

Orpen, William 1878–1931
In the Dublin Mountains
oil on canvas 115 x 97.5
4.2

Padwick, Philip Hugh 1876–1958
Rye, East Sussex 1931
oil on canvas 35.5 x 51
5.31

Park, John Anthony 1880–1962
May Pageantry
oil on canvas 59.5 x 49
43.37

Parker, Frederick H. A. d.1904
James Collinge, Mayor of Oldham (1850–1852)
oil on canvas 65 x 49.5
5.97

Parr, Edward active before 1910
Edwin Butterworth (1812–1848), Historian of Oldham
oil on canvas 115 x 98
1.03

Parsons, Alfred William 1847–1920
Meadows by the Avon
oil on canvas 89 x 151
1.86/2

Parsons, Alfred William 1847–1920
On the Cotswolds
oil on canvas 120.5 x 183
1.97

Partington, John Herbert Evelyn 1843–1899
Charles Potter as Amiens in 'As You Like It' at a Calvert Shakespearian Revival
oil on canvas 58.5 x 49
2.34

Partington, Richard Lantry 1868–1928
Edwin Waugh Winter
oil on canvas 129 x 102
19.50/2

Paterson, James 1854–1932
An East Lothian Village 1906
oil on canvas 118.5 x 97.5
6.08

Pears, Charles 1873–1958
The Needles, Isle of Wight
oil on canvas 38 x 59.5
6.20/1

Pegg, John Christopher b.1949
Street in Oldham, Lancashire 2007
oil on canvas 29 x 32.5
2010.119

Pelham, Thomas Kent c.1831–1907
Spanish Woman and Child
oil on canvas 98 x 78
12.44/4

Penn, William Charles 1877–1968
Dr Thomas Fawsitt
oil on canvas 110 x 100.5
4.22

Percy, William 1820–1893
William Bodden, Mayor of Oldham (1877–1878)
oil on canvas 141 x 110.5
4.82

Pettie, John 1839–1893
Charles E. Lees c.1880
oil on canvas 170 x 80
6.70/3

Phillip, John 1817–1867
Ellen Barlow, Wife of Thomas Oldham Barlow 1857
oil on canvas 52 x 38
4.36

Phillip, John 1817–1867
Return from a Shooting Party in Scotland
oil on panel 17.8 x 37.5
G980

Phillips, Peter b.1939
Gravy for the Navy 1963
oil & gloss paint on canvas & hardboard
240 x 159
8.64

Philpot, Glyn Warren 1884–1937
Lilacs
oil on canvas 112 x 85
15.35

Pickering, James Langsdale 1845–1912
At Rest
oil on canvas 94 x 164
3.07

Pitt, William c.1818–c.1900
The Village at the Head of the Creek, Helford, Cornwall
oil on canvas 40 x 75
9.45

Platt, Stella b.1913
Flowers (recto)
oil on canvas 52 x 42
3.83/8a

Platt, Stella b.1913
Houses in the Valley (verso)
oil on canvas 45 x 35
3.83/8b

Potter, Charles 1832–1907
A Christmas Dawn
oil on canvas 89 x 136
11.88

Potter, Charles 1832–1907
A Quiet Pool
oil on canvas 40 x 70
7.4

Potter, Charles 1832–1907
A Winter's Tale
oil on canvas 90 x 145
2.82

Prinsep, Valentine Cameron 1838–1904
At the First Touch of Winter, Summer Fades Away 1897
oil on canvas 189 x 136
9.98

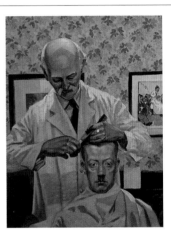

Purdy, James 1900–1972
Haircut c.1930
oil on canvas 90 x 70
2.78/1

Purdy, James 1900–1972
Millbottom (2) 1935
oil on canvas 55 x 34
36.36

Purdy, James 1900–1972
Carnival
oil on canvas 39 x 29
2.78/10

Purdy, James 1900–1972
Fisherman
oil on paper 56 x 38
2008.164

Purdy, James 1900–1972
John Edmunds Purdy
oil on canvas 59 x 50
G800

Purdy, James 1900–1972
Landscape with Sheep
oil on canvas 39 x 49
2.78/8

Purdy, James 1900–1972
Moorland Cloud
oil on canvas 49.5 x 74.5
2.78/2

Purdy, James 1900–1972
Moorland Road
oil on canvas 31 x 47
2.78/9

Purdy, James 1900–1972
Mr Waring, Principal of Oldham Technical College
oil on canvas 80 x 63
8.81/99

Purdy, James 1900–1972
Oldham Wakes, Lancashire
oil on canvas 29 x 44.5
2.78/11

Purdy, James 1900–1972
Pennine View
oil on canvas 50 x 60
2.78/6

Purdy, James 1900–1972
Reflections
oil on canvas 24.5 x 34
2.78/13

Purdy, James 1900–1972
Rocky Stream
oil on canvas 44 x 60
2.78/3

Purdy, James 1900–1972
Self Portrait
oil on paper 56 x 38
2008.159

Purdy, James 1900–1972
Sky Scene
oil on canvas 23 x 31.5
2.78/15

Purdy, James 1900–1972
Snow on the Hills
oil on canvas 26.5 x 37
2.78/12

Purdy, James 1900–1972
The Studio
oil on canvas 47 x 57
2.78/4

Purdy, James 1900–1972
*Unveiling of the War Memorial, Oldham,
Lancashire, 28 April 1923*
oil on canvas 101.5 x 122
10.24

Purdy, James 1900–1972
Wooded Stream
oil on canvas 24 x 34
2.78/14

Purdy, James 1900–1972
Woodland Glade
oil on canvas 52 x 40
2.78/7

Purdy, James 1900–1972
Woodland Pool
oil on canvas 22.5 x 27
2.78/16

Radcliffe, Paul active 1956
Helen
oil on board 118.5 x 76
42.56/1

Ramsey, David
Portrait of a Young Girl with a Head Sash
oil on canvas 61 x 45
2.6

Ranken, William Bruce Ellis 1881–1941
The Baker's Roundsman, Madeira
oil on canvas 68 x 48
11.46/1

Rankle, Alan b.1952
Fairlight from the Water Meadows 2009
oil on canvas 50 x 50
2009.3

Rathans, W.
Landscape
oil on canvas 26 x 32
12.71/3

Reynolds, Daphne 1918–2002
Ding Dong Mine 1967
oil on canvas 130 x 195
4.69/2

Reynolds, Daphne 1918–2002
Standing in Tunnels
oil on canvas 70 x 91
4.69/3

Richards, Paul b.1949
Green Apple 1994
oil on canvas 45 x 45
2007.54

Richardson, A. E.
Failsworth Pole, Oldham, Lancashire 1975
oil on canvas 44 x 61
PCF10

Richter, Herbert Davis 1874–1955
Summertime, 1930
oil on canvas 100 x 76
7.32

Riley, Harold b.1934
Boating Lake, Alexandra Park, Oldham, Lancashire
oil on paper 74 x 100
4.69/4

Riviere, Hugh Goldwin 1869–1956
Dame Sarah Lees (1842–1935) c.1910
oil on canvas 350 x 145 (E)
16.12

Roach, J. active 19th C
William Johnson Fox, MP for Oldham (1847–1856 & 1857–1862)
oil on canvas 35.5 x 29
4.06

Roberts, Lancelot Percival 1883–1950
Two More Minutes to Go
oil on canvas 61 x 42
8.32

Ronaldson, Thomas Martine 1881–1942
Ann Todd
oil on canvas 112 x 85.5
11.44

Rothenstein, William 1872–1945
A Corner of the Talmud School 1907
oil on canvas 90 x 70.5
5.08 ✦

Royle, Stanley 1888–1961
A Derbyshire Landscape
oil on canvas 63.5 x 76
4.27 ✦

Russell, Walter Westley 1867–1949
Tying Her Shoe c.1910
oil on canvas 93 x 73.5
6.12 ✦

Russell, Walter Westley 1867–1949
On the Sands
oil on canvas 110.5 x 141
8.13/1

Facing page: Bomberg, David, 1890–1957, *Toledo, Spain*, 1929, Gallery Oldham, (p. 5)

Rutherford, Harry 1903–1985
Yorkshire Street, Oldham, Lancashire c.1935
oil on canvas 91.4 x 61
1.49

Rutherford, Harry 1903–1985
Ammon Wrigley (1861–1946) 1938
oil on canvas 76.2 x 61
8.42

Salisbury, Frank O. 1874–1962
Sir Frank Platt (1890–1955)
oil on canvas 111 x 79
8.81/100

Samsu, S. M.
A Rickshaw Workshop 2005
oil on card 42 x 55
2006.18

Sandby, Paul 1731–1809
A Woody Landscape
oil on canvas 32 x 45
1.05/1

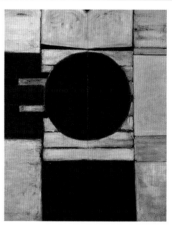

Sandle, Michael b.1936
Untitled
oil on canvas 181 x 151
8.62

Sant, James 1820–1916
John Platt
oil on canvas 125 x 94
G801

Sant, James 1820–1916
Alice Platt
oil on canvas 121 x 90
3.83/19

Sephton, George Harcourt 1860–1923
E. Lyneph Stanley, MP for Oldham (1880–1885)
oil on canvas 75.5 x 60.5
6.98

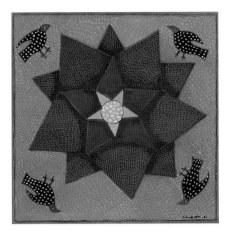

Shah, Abdus Shakoor b.1946
Tradition 2001
oil on canvas 91 x 91
2006.19

Shah, Abdus Shakoor b.1946
She and Chandrabaty 2002
oil on canvas 100 x 60
2006.34

Shah, Abdus Shakoor b.1946
The Story of Mahua 2002
oil on canvas 100 x 60
2006.33

Shannon, James Jebusa 1862–1923
Robert Whittaker
oil on canvas 143.5 x 106.5
10.98

Shannon, James Jebusa 1862–1923
Sir J. T. Hibbert
oil on canvas 139.5 x 92.5
1.98

Sharp, Dorothea 1874–1955
Paddlers
oil on canvas 84 x 87
54.37

Shayer, William 1788–1879
Old Farmyard Scene c.1840
oil on canvas 72.5 x 98.5
3.60/2

Shayer, William 1788–1879
Coast Scene with Figures
oil on canvas 49.5 x 90
3.87

Sheringham, George 1884–1937
The Water Forces Raged against Siegfried
oil on canvas 96.5 x 151
5.43/1

Sheringham, George 1884–1937
The Earth Forces Raged against Siegfried
oil on canvas 96.5 x 151
5.43/2

Sickert, Walter Richard 1860–1942
Barnet Fair, Hertfordshire 1930
oil on canvas 73.5 x 61
31.36

Simcock, Jack b.1929
Cottage on a Hillside 1963
oil on board 80 x 130
G667

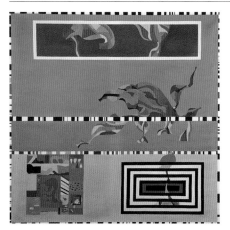

Smith, Jack 1928–2011
Floating Number 2 1964
oil on canvas 183 x 183
1.66

Solomon, Abraham 1824–1862
A Lesson in the Use of the Fan
oil on canvas 48 x 75
1.18/17

Solomon, Solomon Joseph 1860–1927
Joseph Smith, Mayor of Oldham (1893–1894)
oil on canvas 137 x 103
11.98

Somerville, Howard 1873–1952
*Alderman Charles Hardman, Mayor of
Oldham (1919–1920)*
oil on canvas 152.5 x 101.5
3.21

Somerville, Howard 1873–1952
Miss Nora Baring
oil on canvas 125 x 99
6.55

Somerville, Howard 1873–1952
The Red Burnous
oil on canvas 126 x 102
1.25

Somerville, Howard 1873–1952
Zulu with a Black Eye
oil on canvas 59 x 49
6.20/2

Southall, Joseph Edward 1861–1944
Along the Shore 1914
tempera on silk 53.3 x 36.8
3.48/1

Southall, Joseph Edward 1861–1944
The Food Queue
tempera on panel 25.5 x 54
3.48/2

Spencelayh, Charles 1865–1958
A Lover of Dickens 1947
oil on canvas 59 x 49.5
17.51

Spencer, Stanley 1891–1959
Landscape, near Halifax, West Yorkshire
oil on canvas 50 x 60
19.54/1

Stanaway, Peter b.1943
Now the Mill Has Gone 2005
oil on canvas 48.3 x 50.8
2006.2

Stanaway, Peter b.1943
Helen Bradley's House, Spring Lane, Lees,
Lancashire 2006
oil on board 33 x 25.5
2006.68

Stanaway, Peter b.1943
The House of L. S. Lowry, Mottram,
Longdendale, Greater Manchester
oil on board 33 x 25.5
2006.69

Steele, Jeffrey b.1931
Scala
oil on canvas 152 x 101
G697

Stott, Edward William 1859–1918
The Ferry
oil on canvas 68 x 119
3.89

Stott, Samuel Taylor 1845–1913
Valley of the Lauterbrunnen, Switzerland
1882
oil on canvas 100.5 x 152.5
4.04

Stott, William 1857–1900
Wild Flower 1881
oil on canvas 80 x 46
8.2

Stott, William 1857–1900
My Father and Mother 1884
oil on canvas 102 x 160
34.38

Stott, William 1857–1900
Hollyhocks (A Fairy Tale) 1886
oil on canvas 120 x 80
10.25

Stott, William 1857–1900
Venus Born of the Sea Foam 1887
oil on canvas 183
8.3

Stott, William 1857–1900
Hide and Seek in the Garden of Epicurus,
Leontium and Ternissa
oil on canvas 175 x 127
4.03

Stott, William 1857–1900
Pastoral
oil on canvas 63 x 103.5
18.53/2

Stott, William 1857–1900
The White Mountain
oil on canvas 94.6 x 145
5.03

Strang, William 1859–1921
The Feather Fan
oil on canvas 99 x 75
2.21/3

Stuart, Elsie
Oldham Church from Goldbourne, Lancashire
oil on canvas 49 x 75
3.83/18

Stubbs, Frederick J.
Old Oldham Church, Lancashire
oil on canvas 38.5 x 46
3.56

Swanwick, Joseph Harold 1866–1929
Ducks
oil on canvas 59.5 x 80
4.05

Swynnerton, Annie Louisa 1844–1933
Cupid and Psyche 1890
oil on canvas 147 x 91
4.92

Talmage, Algernon Mayow 1871–1939
The Ford
oil on canvas 98 x 151
4.08/1

Tarbet, John A. Henderson 1865–1938
Highland Landscape
oil on canvas 115 x 140
15.39

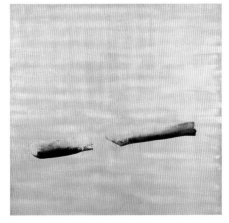

Thompson, Estelle b.1960
Spirit
oil on linen 152 x 152
G898

Titcomb, William Holt Yates 1858–1930
Jubilee Day, St Ives, Cornwall (Good News from the Front) c.1897
oil on canvas 113 x 151
30.35

Topham, Francis Williams 1808–1877
Lady of Quality
oil on canvas 137 x 91.5
3.60/1

Townsend, Ernest 1885–1944
F. G. Isherwood, Mayor of Oldham (1911–1912) c.1911
oil on canvas 142 x 112
1.13

Turner, Alice acive 1981
Nicker Brow, Oldham, Lancashire
oil on canvas 37 x 48
8.81/90

Tuttle, J. R. active 1897 or earlier
James Mackensie Maclean, MP for Oldham (1885–1892)
oil on canvas 75 x 62
6.97

Uhlman, Fred 1901–1985
Two Welsh Cottages
oil on canvas 39 x 50
G84 🐝

unknown artist
Thomas Henshaw, Founder of the Bluecoat School, Oldham c.1810
oil on canvas 75 x 62
5.02

unknown artist early 19th C
Old Oldham Church, Lancashire
oil on canvas 54 x 66
3.47

unknown artist
Abstract
oil on canvas 91 x 91
PCF29

unknown artist
Abstract
oil on board 125 x 108
PCF35

Facing page: Craxton, John, 1922–2009, *Beach Scene*, 1949, Gallery Oldham, (p. 11)

unknown artist
Creg-Ny-Baa, Isle of Man
oil on canvas 28 x 42
12.80/8

unknown artist
Dorothy and Marjory Lees
oil on canvas 49 x 59.5
PCF16

unknown artist
Edmund Hartley, Mayor of Oldham (1869–1870)
oil on canvas 74.5 x 62
5.98

unknown artist
Eli Lees
oil on canvas 89 x 69.5
3.83/15

unknown artist
Mrs Eli Lees
oil on canvas 90 x 69.5
3.83/16

unknown artist
James Buckley of Holleyville
oil on canvas 39 x 32
G802

unknown artist
James Wolfenden
oil on canvas 71.5 x 59.5
34.36

unknown artist
John Buckley
oil on canvas 89 x 69.5
3.83/25

unknown artist
Mrs J. Buckley
oil on canvas 89 x 69.5
3.83/14

unknown artist
John Jones (1755–1821)
oil on canvas 76 x 68.5
6.82/18 (P)

unknown artist
John Rowntree the elder
oil on canvas 60 x 50
31.51/2

unknown artist
John Rowntree the younger
oil on canvas 67 x 56
31.51/3

unknown artist
Joseph Jones (1756–1845)
oil on canvas 101.5 x 89
6.82/20 (P)

unknown artist
Joseph Jones (1782–1858)
oil on canvas 168 x 145
6.82/19 (P)

unknown artist
Mountain Stream in Flood
oil on canvas 60 x 90
11.78/12

unknown artist
Pitbank House, Oldham, Lancashire
oil on canvas 52 x 75
G895

unknown artist
Portrait of a Stockport Worthy
oil on canvas 90 x 70
9.56

unknown artist
Portrait of an Unknown Lady
oil on canvas 54 x 44
3.83/20

unknown artist
Portrait of an Unknown Man
oil on canvas 90 x 75
3.18/13

unknown artist
Portrait of an Unknown Man
oil on canvas 127 x 102
3.87/24

unknown artist
Portrait of an Unknown Man
oil on canvas 54 x 44
PCF18

unknown artist
Portrait of an Unknown Man
oil on canvas 91 x 70
PCF19

unknown artist
Portrait of an Unknown Man
oil on canvas 91 x 71
PCF20

unknown artist
Reverend J. F. Walker, Former Incumbent of St James's, Oldham
oil on canvas 90 x 70
2.86

unknown artist
Reverend William Winter, Former Incumbent of St Peter's, Oldham (1796–1838)
oil on canvas 92.5 x 70
3.86

unknown artist
Samuel Lees
oil on canvas 70 x 62
3.83/23

unknown artist
Mrs Samuel Lees
oil on canvas 70 x 62
3.83/22

unknown artist
Samuel Radcliffe
oil on canvas 110.5 x 85
15.98

unknown artist
Trees
oil on canvas 65 x 106
PCF31

unknown artist
William Cobbett
oil on canvas 61 x 50
28.38

unknown artist
William Jones (1759–1833)
oil on canvas 76 x 68.5
6.87/17 (P)

Verboeckhoven, Eugène Joseph 1799–1881
Sheep
oil on canvas 13.5 x 18.5
1.18/2

Wadsworth, Edward Alexander 1889–1949
Imaginary Harbour II 1934
tempera & linen canvas on hardboard
59.9 x 85.1
4.67

Wagner, Cornelius 1870–1956
Low Tide Work c.1910
oil on canvas 104 x 148.5
10.11/1

Walker, Ray 1945–1984
Self Portrait (recto) 1985
oil on canvas 152 x 111
G821

Walker, Ray 1945–1984
Untitled (verso)
oil on canvas 141 x 100
PCF48

Waterhouse, John William 1849–1917
Circe 1891
oil on canvas 148 x 92
3.55/9 🐝

Watson, Harry 1871–1936
Morning in a Wood
oil on canvas 120.5 x 160
2.21/2

Watson, Robert H. active 1894–1920
Evening in the Highlands
oil on canvas 38.5 x 57.5
11.38/1

Watson, Robert H. active 1894–1920
In the Trossachs, Stirling
oil on canvas 39.3 x 59.3
11.38/2

Watson, Thomas J. 1847–1912
The Brook
oil on canvas 75 x 60
3.67/5

Watts, George Frederick 1817–1904
Aurora c.1842
oil on canvas 82 x 88
6.70/2

Watts, James Thomas 1853–1930
Autumn's Bravery
oil on canvas 53 x 74
3.67/6

Webb, James 1825–1895
Italian Landscape 1868–1869
oil on canvas 63 x 109.5
3.67/7

Webster, Thomas George 1800–1886
Beating for Recruits (Rocking the Cradle)
oil on canvas 15 x 13
G990

Webster, Walter Ernest 1877–1959
Rhapsody
oil on canvas 94 x 78
4.3

Weight, Carel Victor Morlais 1908–1997
As I wend to the shores I know not, As I list to the dirge, the voices of men and women wreck'd' (from 'Leaves of Grass' (...) 1951
oil on panel 120 x 260
PCF21

Weir, Linda Mary b.1951
Still Life with Flying Fish
oil on canvas 80 x 73
G797

Wells, William Page Atkinson 1872–1923
Home across the Sand
oil on canvas 49.5 x 75.5
3.09

Westcott, Philip 1815–1878
John Summerscales, First Town Clerk of Oldham (1849–1862)
oil on canvas 122 x 96.5
15.12

Wetherbee, George Faulkner 1851–1920
Dawn at the Gate
oil on canvas 65 x 151
7.08

Wheelwright, Rowland 1870–1955
Don Quixote and Maritornes at the Inn (from the novel by Cervantes)
oil on canvas 150 x 99
3.05

Whitehead, Richard Henry 1855–1889
Rhododendrons
oil on canvas 43 x 34
13.29

Whitehead, Richard Henry 1855–1889
The Musician
oil on canvas 101 x 127
5.47

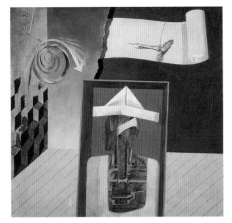

Wilkes, Paul
The Clockwork Admiral
oil on canvas 121 x 127
5.65

Willaert, Ferdinand 1861–1938
Béguinage flamand
oil on canvas 94 x 127
5.07

Williams, Terrick John 1860–1936
Cassis, France c.1929
oil on canvas 76 x 94
3.3

Wimpenny, George Henry 1857–1939
The Old Fish Market, Oldham, Lancashire
1883
oil on canvas 53 x 42.5
58.37

Wimpenny, George Henry 1857–1939
Chew Valley, Greenfield, Lancashire 1897
oil on canvas 29 x 19
12.29

Wimpenny, George Henry 1857–1939
Italian Grandmother 1897
oil on canvas 44.5 x 34.5
1.07/1

Wimpenny, George Henry 1857–1939
*Henry Lister Hargraves (d.1914), Oldham's
Leading Quaker* 1904
oil on canvas 110.5 x 85
1.07/2

Wimpenny, George Henry 1857–1939
Memories 1908
oil on canvas 77.5 x 58.5
8.08

Wimpenny, George Henry 1857–1939
The Terrace, Haddon Hall, Derbyshire 1909
oil on canvas 76 x 128
12.32

Wimpenny, George Henry 1857–1939
Sam Fitton (1868–1923) 1911
oil on canvas 45 x 30
12.78/11

Wimpenny, George Henry 1857–1939
Finishing Touches c.1920
oil on canvas 102 x 65
43.56

Wimpenny, George Henry 1857–1939
The Naturalist 1920s
oil on canvas 100 x 70
43.38

Wimpenny, George Henry 1857–1939
The Woods, Betws-y-Coed, Conwy 1929
oil on canvas 59.7 x 89.3
4.72/1

Wimpenny, George Henry 1857–1939
A Patchwork Quilt
oil on canvas 75 x 62
4.08/5

Wimpenny, George Henry 1857–1939
Annie Maycock
oil on canvas 50 x 40
4.72/2

Wimpenny, George Henry 1857–1939
Chester Cathedral from the Shropshire Canal
oil on board 23 x 33
15.44/5

Wimpenny, George Henry 1857–1939
Chetham's Hospital, Manchester
oil on canvas 52.7 x 76.8
28.54/1

Wimpenny, George Henry 1857–1939
Farmyard Scene
oil on canvas 18.5 x 28.5
G705

Wimpenny, George Henry 1857–1939
James Dronsfield (Jerry Lichenmoss)
oil on canvas 59 x 49
10.21

Wimpenny, George Henry 1857–1939
Summer Garden
oil on canvas 34 x 24
3.83/7

Winder, David 1824–1912
*James Ashworth (1815–1889), First Chairman
of the Royton Local Board (1863)* 1883
oil on canvas 112 x 85
PCF9

Workman, Harold 1897–1975
A Lancashire Town 1938
oil on canvas 49 x 60
50.38

Workman, Harold 1897–1975
Barge Corner
oil on canvas 75 x 62
45.38

Workman, Harold 1897–1975
Borough Market, Southwark, London
oil on canvas 56 x 66
44.38

Workman, Harold 1897–1975
Bridge Street, Christchurch, Hampshire
oil on canvas 35 x 44.5
4.78/12

Workman, Harold 1897–1975
Tower Bridge, London
oil on canvas 65.2 x 96.2
12.39

Wright, Ethel 1866–1939
Bonjour, Pierrot!
oil on canvas 160 x 109
1.93

Facing page: Pickersgill, Frederick Richard, 1820–1900, *Ferdinand and Miranda*, 1863,
Rochdale Arts & Heritage Service, (p. 127)

Wyllie, William Lionel 1851–1931
The Pool of London
oil on canvas 100.5 x 151
1.94

Yale, Brian 1936–2009
A Door and a Window in Acre, Israel 1980
acrylic on canvas 61 x 76
8.81/98

Yarnold, Joseph c.1817–1852
Woodland Scene with a Waterfall
oil on canvas 52 x 43
11.78/9

Zeba, Fareha b.1961
Child with Stars and Stripes 2 2002
oil & newspaper on board 72 x 72
2006.35

Pennine Acute Hospitals NHS Trust

Aston, S. & Prestwich Creative Living Centre
View of the Sea 2007
oil on board 39 x 39
PCF14

Corbett, Angela & Prestwich Creative Living Centre
City 2007
oil on board 29 x 39
PCF1

Corbett, Angela & Prestwich Creative Living Centre
Firework 2007
oil on board 19 x 39 (E)
PCF7

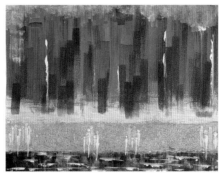

Corbett, Angela & Prestwich Creative Living Centre
Landscape 2007
oil on board 29 x 39
PCF12

Corbett, Angela & Prestwich Creative Living Centre
Stormy Sea 2007
oil on board 39 x 49
PCF15

Corbett, Angela & Prestwich Creative Living Centre
Stormy Sea 2007
oil on board 49 x 39
PCF2

Coverdale, Mark
Still Life with Chair
acrylic on paper 58 x 41
PCF44

Cymel & Prestwich Creative Living Centre
Abstract 2007
oil on board 29 x 29
PCF5

Cymel & **Prestwich Creative Living Centre**
Houses by the Sea 2007
oil on board 19 x 49
PCF9

E., Judy & **Prestwich Creative Living Centre**
Flowers 2007
oil on board 29 x 29
PCF10

E., Judy & **Prestwich Creative Living Centre**
Pink Flowers 2007
oil on board 29 x 39
PCF8

Hepworth, Louise
Still Life with Apples
acrylic on paper 60 x 42
PCF47

Johnson, Pat
Stampede c.1989
enamel on steel or copper 180 x 65.5
PCF35

Johnson, Pat
Stampede c.1989
enamel on steel or copper 180 x 65.5
PCF36

Johnson, Pat
Stampede c.1989
enamel on steel or copper 180 x 87
PCF37

Johnson, Pat
Stampede c.1989
enamel on steel or copper 180 x 87
PCF38

Johnson, Pat
Stampede c.1989
enamel on steel or copper 180 x 87
PCF39

Johnson, Pat
Stampede c.1989
enamel on steel or copper 180 x 65.5
PCF40

Johnson, Pat
Stampede c.1989
enamel on steel or copper 180 x 65.5
PCF41

Johnson, Pat
Stampede c.1989
enamel on steel or copper 180 x 65.5
PCF42

Lamb, Nick
Papier-mâché
acrylic on paper 50 x 36
PCF46

Prestwich Creative Living Centre
Castle 2007
oil on board 29 x 39
PCF13

Prestwich Creative Living Centre
White Cliffs 2007
oil on board 29 x 39
PCF11

Prestwich Creative Living Centre & **Riley**
White Cliffs 2007
oil on board 29 x 29
PCF3

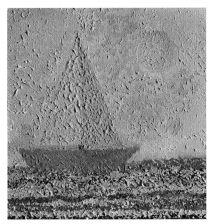

Prestwich Creative Living Centre &
unknown artist
Boat at Sea 2007
oil on board 29 x 29
PCF4

Prestwich Creative Living Centre & **V., Roma**
Blue Sea 2007
oil on board 19 x 49
PCF6

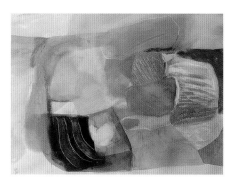

R., J.
Abstract
acrylic & mixed media on paper 55 x 74
PCF20

Spencer, Liam David b.1964
Crumpsall Hospital
oil on board 41 x 244
PCF21

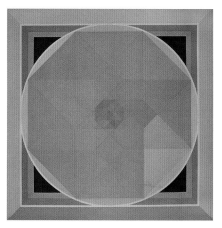

unknown artist
Abstract
acrylic on canvas 152 x 152
PCF16

unknown artist
Abstract
acrylic on board 140 x 87
PCF33

unknown artist
Abstract
acrylic on fabric 90 x 90
PCF34

unknown artist
Abstract Landscape
acrylic on canvas 183 x 183
PCF18

unknown artist
Abstract Spots
acrylic on canvas 169 x 190
PCF19

unknown artist
Batik Figures
acrylic on fabric 142 x 98
PCF17

unknown artist
Cows in a Lane
acrylic on paper 31 x 25.5
PCF30

unknown artist
Doves
acrylic on canvas 152 x 107
PCF43

unknown artist
Ducks in Reeds
acrylic on board 122 x 90
PCF31

unknown artist
Ducks in Reeds
acrylic on board 117 x 90
PCF32

unknown artist
Flowers
acrylic on paper 57 x 80
PCF22

unknown artist
Garden
acrylic on paper 58 x 81
PCF49

unknown artist
Garden with Trees and a Pond
acrylic on paper 81 x 58
PCF50

unknown artist
Garden with Waterlilies
acrylic on paper 76 x 56
PCF48

unknown artist
Snow Scene
acrylic on paper 40 x 56
PCF52

unknown artist
Tardis in a Field
acrylic on paper 41 x 57
PCF24

unknown artist
Tree
acrylic on paper 56 x 38
PCF28

unknown artist
Trees
acrylic on paper 40 x 56
PCF51

unknown artist
Water Lilies
acrylic on paper 39 x 58
PCF23

unknown artist
Woodland
acrylic on paper 39 x 56.5
PCF25

unknown artist
Woodland
acrylic on paper 56 x 39.5
PCF26

unknown artist
Woodland
acrylic on paper 44.5 x 51
PCF27

unknown artist
Woodland Waterfall
acrylic on paper 56 x 41
PCF29

unknown artist
Yellow Flowers
acrylic on paper 107 x 85
PCF55

Greater
Manchester Fire
Service Museum

Airey, Lilian
Manchester Blitz (Piccadilly), 1940 1971
oil on board 43 x 90
P94

Banks, Brian
Horse-Drawn Fire Escape
oil on board 57.5 x 150
P190

Above: Flint, William Russell, 1880–1969, *Maruja the Strong*, Rochdale Arts & Heritage Service, (p. 100)

Above: Jacopo di Cione, c.1320–1400, *Madonna and Child with Angels*, 1350–1400,
Tameside Museums and Galleries Service: The Astley Cheetham Art Collection, (p. 205)

Rochdale Arts & Heritage Service

Rochdale Art Gallery, now known as Touchstones Rochdale, was founded in 1903 when the original 1884 Carnegie Library building was extended to house a museum on the ground floor and two gallery spaces on the first floor. A further two galleries and an art store were constructed in 1912. *The Daily Mail* commented on the official opening of the new art gallery extension on 8th February 1913 saying, 'with the extensions which were opened yesterday the Rochdale Municipal Art Gallery is now the most important in Lancashire outside Manchester and Liverpool'.

The Arts & Heritage Service continued in this way until the Museum moved to another site in the town in 1975 and the library relocated to another building in 1993. In 2002 the building was re-launched as Touchstones Rochdale following a refurbishment, funded by the Heritage Lottery Fund. The building now includes four art gallery spaces, a museum, heritage gallery, local studies centre, tourist information centre, café and an education space. The Service has a second accredited site in the Arts & Heritage Resource Centre where many of the collections are stored. Since 2007 the Service has been part of Link4Life, the Rochdale Boroughwide Cultural Trust, caring for the collections on behalf of Rochdale Borough Council.

The Art Gallery collections comprise over 1,500 works, primarily paintings, prints and drawings, with some sculpture, photography and contemporary craft. When the Gallery opened in 1903, it did so with 164 donated works, a substantial number of which came from local textile industrialist Robert Taylor Heape (1847–1917). Over the period of 1901 to 1913, Heape's donations came to total 103 and he remains the Gallery's most significant benefactor. As with many public collections in the North West, donations from wealthy industrialists, particularly associated with the textile industry, formed the backbone of the Collection and there was a great deal of kudos and civic pride associated with giving to the local Collection.

Alongside donations, in the early years of the Gallery paintings were sent from art dealers in London for potential purchase. Town councillors, with the help of a local art expert, discussed and decided on which they would purchase, negotiating the price and trying to obtain copyright as part of the deal. This arrangement developed into a committee which worked alongside the post of chief librarian and curator, although it seems this post was always held by a librarian and it was not until the 1970s that a professional art curator was appointed. Purchases were also made from the annual spring exhibition held at the Gallery during the first half of the century, as well as from the Royal Academy summer exhibition, using bequest funds. Three major bequests came from James Ogden, James Handley and Mrs Bright and these funds continue to help purchase works for the Collection today. Other important contributors in more recent times are the Contemporary Art Society, the Art Fund, the Victoria and Albert Museum Purchase Grant Fund and the Friends of Rochdale Art Gallery, established in 1974.

In terms of oil paintings, the scope of the Collection ranges from a panel painting dating from 1423–1426 by the Italian artist Giovanni di Paolo depicting *The Crucifixion*, to the 2009 work *Untitled Painting I (Calder Heights)* by the artist Alan Rankle, who trained at Rochdale College of Art in the 1960s. The Giovanni di Paolo is part of a small group of Renaissance and Baroque paintings predominantly by Dutch, French and Italian artists collected by a pharmacist called Thomas Kay (1841–1914) who was born in Heywood. In 1904 Kay offered to present an art gallery and museum to his native town. This was realised in 1912 with the opening of Heywood Municipal Art Gallery and Museum within Heywood Technical School. The collection, known as the Kay Bequest, became part of Rochdale Art Gallery's collection following local government re-organisation in 1974. At this point collections from Middleton also became part of the Gallery's holdings. These included a number of paintings by Middleton-born British Impressionist Frederick William Jackson who worked *en plein air* at Staithes and taught Laura Knight, whose work also features in the Collection.

So-called British Impressionists who were associated with artists' colonies at Staithes, Newlyn and St Ives in the late nineteenth and early twentieth centuries are a feature of the Collection. There are works by Rochdale-born Edward William Stott, Harold Knight, George Clausen, William Stott (of Oldham), Samuel John Lamorna Birch, Henry Herbert La Thangue and Dorothea Sharp.

Traditional Victorian artists form a significant part of the Collection, including Rochdale's well-known painting *A Special Pleader* by Charles Burton Barber. This is a typically sentimental work which was widely reproduced in the 1980s during a resurgence of interest in narrative painting. Other Victorian artists featured include David Roberts, Frederick Goodall, Alice Havers, Joseph Farquharson, Frank Holl, Philip Edward Burne-Jones and John William Waterhouse.

Post-Victorian holdings from the first half of the twentieth century include both the traditional and the more avant-garde. William Russell Flint's *Maruja the Strong* and a typical Gerald Festus Kelly Burmese portrait represent the more traditional, whilst Augustus Edwin John, Mark Gertler, David Bomberg, John Piper and Stanley Spencer are amongst highlights of more progressive work.

The Collection also holds a number of significant works from the 1970s, with paintings by Frank Helmuth Auerbach, Gillian Ayres, Adrian Berg, John Wonnacott and Tess Jaray as well as a large number of prints. There is also a Lucian Freud portrait dating from 1963 which the Gallery acquired in 1983. The disparity between the execution and acquisition dates reflects the fact that the 1960s was not a strong time for collecting in Rochdale.

Other significant holdings include works by the eighteenth-century dialect poet and artist John Collier, known as Tim Bobbin, who lived in Milnrow near Rochdale. His satirical prints and paintings have a Hogarth-esque quality about them, capturing the rogues and scandals of society at that time. Some of these fall into a group of paintings in need of conservation unfortunately caused by poor storage in the years before professional curatorial staff were appointed. The Gallery hopes to remedy this situation over time and has a regular programme of conservation work.

Whilst conserving existing works in the Collection, the Gallery continues to acquire new pieces and is particularly looking to increase the diversity of artists represented in the Collection working across a range of media.

Yvonne Hardman, Art Gallery Officer, Rochdale Arts & Heritage Service

Adams, Norman 1927–2005
The Great Garden 1974
oil on canvas 139 x 185
986

Addison, Alfred Henry
Landscape
oil on hardboard 40.5 x 50
586

Aelst, Willem van (circle of)
1627–after 1687
Dead Game
oil on panel 39 x 50
1236

Ainscow, George Frederick b.1913
Celebration 1986
acrylic on paper 46.4 x 34.3
1432

Ainscow, George Frederick b.1913
*The Garden of the Villa Cipressi, Varenna,
Lake Como, Italy* 1991
oil on board 18.5 x 24.1
1435

Airy, Anna 1882–1964
July Piece c.1935
oil on canvas 126.5 x 76
594

Allinson, Adrian Paul 1890–1959
The Cornish April
oil on canvas 108 x 161.4
630a

Allori, Alessandro 1535–1607
Isabella Medices Ursina (1542–1576)
oil on canvas 67 x 52.7
1223

Anderson, Paul G.
Middleton Library, Rochdale, Lancashire 1993
oil on canvas 59.2 x 75
1421

Ansdell, Richard 1815–1885
Dog and a Dead Partridge 1850
oil on board 32.5 x 46
46

Ansdell, Richard 1815–1885
Ronda, Spanish Travellers 1864
oil on canvas 106.7 x 149.2
181

Appleyard, Frederick 1874–1963
A Child's Grief, Called away from School 1906
oil on canvas 65 x 132
93

Archer, Frank Joseph 1912–1995
Piano Concerto
oil on hardboard 83.7 x 120
810

Auerbach, Frank Helmuth b.1931
St Pancras Steps, Station 1978/1979
oil on canvas 168.2 x 137.5
1269

Aumonier, James 1832–1911
*An Easter Holiday, the Children of Bloomsbury
Parochial School in a Wood at Watford* 1874
oil on canvas 63 x 103.5
200

Ayres, Gillian b.1930
Mons Graupius 1979/1980
oil on canvas 272.8 x 254.5
1272

Bagshaw, Olive
Dorothy Heap 1965
oil on canvas 59.1 x 49.5
1445

Bancroft, Elias 1846–1924
Rothenburg ob der Tauber, Bavaria, Germany
1903
oil on canvas 54.6 x 39
92

Barber, Charles Burton 1845–1894
A Special Pleader 1893
oil on canvas 97 x 127.6
201 🐝

Barlow, Bohuslav b.1947
Skull and Birds c.1973
oil on canvas 82 x 68.5
973

Barlow, John Noble 1861–1917
Early Spring 1904
oil on canvas 77 x 101.2
94

Baron, Geoffrey
John Entwistle
oil on board 10 x 8.5
PCF11

Bartholme, G. L.
Swallow Falls, Betws-y-Coed, Conwy c.1880
oil on canvas 69.5 x 54.5
438

Bartlett, William Henry 1858–1932
Fishing off Chioggia, Venice 1883
oil on canvas 56.5 x 89.5
182

Bartlett, William Henry 1858–1932
Off Greenwich, London 1897
oil on canvas 52 x 77
256

Beaumont, Edward active 1885–1903
Oakenrod Hall, Rochdale, Lancashire 1885
oil on card 28 x 40.6
1466

Beaumont, Edward active 1885–1903
Ashworth Church, Rochdale, Lancashire 1891
oil on card 14 x 19.7
1050

Beaumont, Edward active 1885–1903
Ashworth Chapel and Inn, Rochdale,
Lancashire 1893
oil on card 21.7 x 30.5
1051

Beaumont, Edward active 1885–1903
St John's Church, Smallbridge, Rochdale,
Lancashire 1903
oil on board 21.5 x 29
1061

Beavis, Richard 1824–1896
Hauling up a Fishing Boat, The
Netherlands 1870
oil on canvas 30 x 60
202

Beggs, Guy b.1947
The Summer House 1973
acrylic on canvas 155.5 x 155.5
912

Bell, Vanessa 1879–1961
Interior
oil on canvas 36.5 x 44
1273

Berchem, Nicolaes (attributed to)
1620–1683
Cattle, Figures and Landscape
oil on canvas 49.5 x 65
1230

Berg, Adrian b.1929
Gloucester Gate, Regent's Park, London,
Summer, Autumn, Winter, Spring 1977/1979
oil on canvas 177 x 177
1268

Biddle, Lawrence 1888–1968
Chinese Bowl and Pansy 1925
oil on panel 23.5 x 30.8
539

Biddle, Lawrence 1888–1968
Wallflowers and Bluebells in a Bowl 1928
oil on panel 28 x 35.5
816

Facing page: Knight, Laura, 1877–1970, *A Theatre Dressing Room*, Gallery Oldham, (p. 29)

Birch, Samuel John Lamorna 1869–1955
*The Stream at Lamorna, Penzance,
Cornwall* c.1914
oil on canvas 76.9 x 102.3
295

Bishop, Henry 1868–1939
Bedouins Outside a Town
oil on canvas 51 x 61
628

Bock, Théophile de 1851–1904
Autumn
oil on canvas 45 x 36.5
495

Bomberg, David 1890–1957
Underground Bomb Store 1942
oil on paper 56.5 x 67.5
1271

Booth, James William 1867–1953
*A Country Horse Fair at Hinderwell, North
Yorkshire* c.1897
oil on canvas 101.7 x 152.5
1029

Booth, James William (attributed to)
1867–1953
Weir, Rhodes Wood
oil on board 16.5 x 26
1316

Bowen, Owen 1873–1967
*The Village on the Hill, Appletreewick, North
Yorkshire* 1945
oil on canvas 72 x 92
681

Brangwyn, Frank 1867–1956
All Hands Shorten Sail 1889
oil on canvas 183 x 152.5
203

Bratby, John Randall 1928–1992
Elm Park Gardens, I c.1959
oil on hardboard 122 x 122
795

Bratby, John Randall 1928–1992
Irises and Tulips c.1967
oil on canvas 114.9 x 86.5
868

Briscoe, Arthur John Trevor 1873–1943
The Bowsprit 1930
oil on canvas 66.5 x 102
571

British (English) School
Portrait of a Nobleman 1556
oil on board 33 x 26
1221

British (English) School
*Richard Assheton of Middleton's Son whilst a
Child* c.1604
oil on panel 48.3 x 29.2
1191

British (English) School
*Darcy Lever (1760–1839), with His Son John
and Daughters Frances and Emelia
Charlotte* c.1820
oil on canvas 61 x 74.4
1167

British (English) School
Robert Turner, JP c.1890
oil on canvas 117.5 x 88
1188

British (English) School 19th C
Napoleon Bonaparte (1769–1821)
oil on wood 29.5 x 24.2
699

British School
John Stock, Donor of Stock's Charity c.1700
oil on canvas 66.7 x 59.7
1187

British School
Sir Darcy Lever (1703–1742) c.1730
oil on canvas 69.9 x 61
1184

British School
Reverend William Ashton c.1740
oil on canvas 73.6 x 53.4
1190

British School
J. Lonsdale c.1830
oil on canvas 97 x 76
1174

British School
Middleton, Rochdale, Lancashire, in 1835 c.1835
oil on canvas 54 x 74.3
1322

British School
John Roby (1793–1850) c.1840–1876
oil on canvas 91.5 x 71
9

British School
Robert Taylor Heape (1848–1917) c.1880
oil on canvas 152 x 122
1193

British School
Interior of the Town Hall, Rochdale, Lancashire c.1890
oil on canvas 59.7 x 49.5
1172

British School 19th C
Seventeenth-Century Half-Timber Building (formerly standing in Yorkshire Street, Rochdale, Lancashire)
oil on canvas 74 x 64
1197

British School
Alderman James Booth c.1900
oil on canvas 91.5 x 71
1058

Brouwer, Adriaen (after) 1605/1606–1638
A Dutch Tavern Scene early 17th C
oil on panel 38 x 28
1363

Brown, John Alfred Arnesby 1866–1955
A Fellside Cumberland Village c.1939
oil on canvas 64 x 76
624

Brown, Taylor 1869–1924
Ayrshire Pastoral c.1910
oil on canvas 71 x 91
192

Buhler, Robert A. 1916–1989
Still Life
oil on canvas 28.5 x 22
742 🐝

Bundy, Edgar 1862–1922
The Coffee House Orator c.1880
oil on panel 33.5 x 51
232 🐝

Burgess, John Bagnold 1830–1897
An Irritable Appeal 1877
oil on canvas 81.4 x 102
204

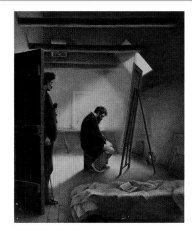

Burne-Jones, Philip Edward 1861–1926
An Unfinished Masterpiece
oil on canvas 61 x 51
47 🐝

Burr, Alexander Hohenlohe 1835–1898
The Mask c.1880
oil on canvas 35 x 47
25

Cadell, Francis Campbell Boileau
1883–1937
Ben More in the Isle of Mull, Inner Hebrides
c.1932
oil on canvas 102 x 127
579 🐝

Cameron, David Young 1865–1945
Head of Loch Ness
oil on canvas 45 x 49
497

Cameron, David Young 1865–1945
The Sanctuary
oil on canvas 77 x 121
559

Carolus, Jean 1814–1897
The Introduction 1865
oil on canvas 96.5 x 112
183

Carpenter, Henry Barrett 1861–1930
James Ogden 1910
oil on canvas 91.6 x 71.5
191

Carter, Samuel John 1835–1892
Deer and a Fawn 1871
oil on canvas 108 x 140
205

Carvell, Graham b.1945
The Mule Spinner 1975
oil on canvas 60 x 90
E512.1

Charles, James 1851–1906
A Glade
oil on canvas 41 x 29.5
500

Charlton, Alan Bengall 1913–1981
Landscape
oil on canvas & board 30.7 x 45.7
589

Charlton, John 1849–1917
James Griffith Dearden, Lord of the Manor of Rochdale 1897
oil on canvas 127 x 110.5
293

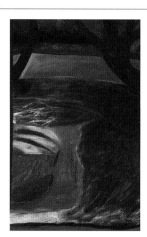

Clarkson, Pamela b.1946
Common Day 1981/1982
acrylic on canvas 183 x 117
1275

Claus, Emile 1849–1924
Poultry in a Wood c.1890
oil on canvas 58.5 x 71.5
208

Clausen, George 1852–1944
The Golden Barn
oil on canvas 68.5 x 56
560 🐝

Clays, Paul Jean 1819–1900
On the Scheldt
oil on panel 59 x 48.5
498

Clouet, François (circle of) c.1515–1572
*Hercule François de Valois-Angoulême, Duc
d'Alençon et d'Anjou (1555–1584)* 16th C
oil on panel 24.1 x 18.8
1241

Coker, Peter 1926–2004
Low Tide, Seascale, Cumbria c.1969
oil on board 120 x 120
881

Cole, George 1810–1883
The Closing Day, Scene in Sussex 1872
oil on canvas 84 x 120
206

Cole, George Vicat 1833–1893
A Surrey Cornfield 1864
oil on canvas 30.5 x 44.5
436

Cole, George Vicat 1833–1893
Surrey Hills 1875
oil on canvas 36.2 x 53.4
257

Collier, Edwaert (follower of) c.1640–c.1707
Memento mori c.1670
oil on canvas 67.4 x 58.5
1239

Collier, John 1708–1786
Self Portrait c.1750
oil on canvas 61 x 45.7
1066

Collier, John 1708–1786
Man with a Broken Pipe 1750–1759
oil on canvas 44.9 x 33.7 (E)
2

Collier, John 1708–1786
Man with a Broken Pipe 1750–1760
oil on panel 13.5 x 16.1
244

Collier, John 1708–1786
Human Passions (Two Drunkards, a Glass, a Bottle and a Pipe) 1766
oil on canvas 66.8 x 95.1
1045

Collier, John 1708–1786
Human Passions (Five Heads) 1770s
oil on card & board 56 x 44.1
36

Collier, John 1708–1786
Human Passions (Three Drunkards and a Bottle) 1770s
oil on canvas 66.5 x 102
1047

Collier, John 1708–1786
Human Passions (Tooth Pulling) 1770s
oil on canvas 64.5 x 88
1049

Collier, John 1708–1786
Human Passions (Two Figures, a Lord and a Moneylender) 1770s
oil on canvas 65 x 100.5
1048

Collier, John 1708–1786
Human Passions (The Parson and the Devil) 1773–1780
oil on canvas 67.5 x 105
1046

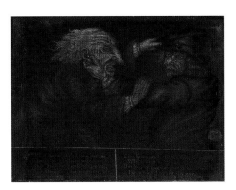

Collier, John 1708–1786
Altercation
oil on canvas 43.5 x 53.5
PCF12

Collier, John 1708–1786
Choir
oil on canvas 58 x 47.5
PCF8

Collier, John 1708–1786
Human Passions
oil on canvas 62 x 92
PCF3

Collier, John 1708–1786
Human Passions
oil on canvas 40 x 70 (E)
PCF7

Collier, John 1708–1786
Mrs Charles Collier
oil on canvas 21.5 x 17
T2732

Collier, John 1708–1786
No.3 Human Passions
oil on canvas 57.1 x 86.3
128A

Collier, John 1708–1786
No.28 Human Passions
oil on canvas 53 x 83
128B

Collier, John 1708–1786
Portrait of a Man
oil on canvas 26.5 x 22.5
1

Collier, John 1708–1786
Portrait of a Man
oil on board 37.5 x 32.2
45

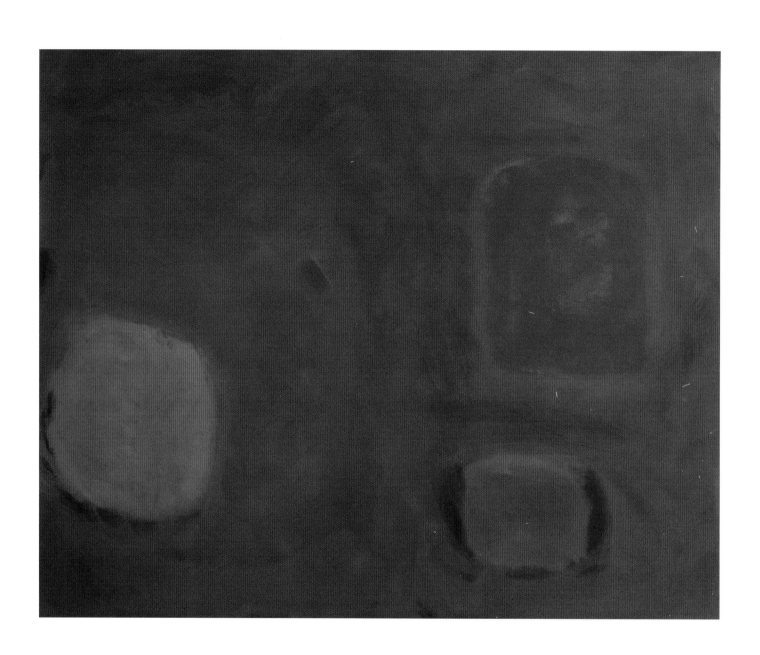

Collier, John 1708–1786
Portrait of the Artist's Son
oil on canvas 52 x 42.5
140

Collier, John 1708–1786
Portrait of the Artist Wearing an Iron Mask
oil on canvas 51.5 x 46
139

Collier, John 1708–1786
Pulling Teeth
oil on canvas 75 x 62.3
138

Collier, John 1708–1786
Sarah Collier, the Artist's Daughter
oil on canvas 29 x 22
T2726

Collier, John 1708–1786
Self Portrait
oil on canvas 42 x 28
44

Collier, John 1708–1786
Two Faces
oil on canvas 46.5 x 61
PCF13

Collier, John 1708–1786
Two Figures
oil on canvas 58 x 72
PCF4

Collier, John 1850–1934
Dr J. R. Ashworth 1908
oil on canvas 122 x 91.5
731

Collier, John 1850–1934
Meditation 1921
oil on canvas 76.2 x 63.5
636

Facing page: Heron, Patrick, 1920–1999, *Scarlet and Green in Brown, November, 1961*, Gallery Oldham, (p. 22)

Collins, William 1788–1847
The Sale of the Pet Lamb 1813
oil on canvas 54 x 66.5
233

Constable, John (circle of) 1776–1837
Study of Cumulus Clouds
oil on canvas 25.2 x 34.3
743

Constable, John (follower of) 1776–1837
Landscape (Stream with a Bank of Trees)
oil on canvas 23.5 x 30
744

Conti, Tito 1842–1924
Day Dreams
oil on canvas 42.5 x 52.5
258

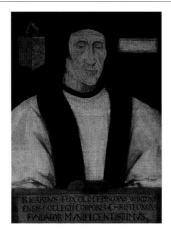

Corvus, Hans (follower of) active 1512–
after 1544
Richard Foxe (c.1448–1528)
oil on panel 54 x 40
1226

Cook, Job
Rural Scene
oil on canvas 96 x 93.5
1391

Cooke, Edward William 1811–1880
*Danish Craft on the Elbe, Blankenese,
Germany, Low Water* 1872
oil on canvas 88 x 137
184

Cooper, Byron 1850–1933
Across the Moorland c.1870
oil on canvas 61.5 x 91.5
194

Cooper, Thomas Sidney 1803–1902
Mountain Sheep 1862
oil on canvas 76.8 x 107
29

Cooper, Thomas Sidney 1803–1902
Cattle in a Meadow, Evening 1875
oil on canvas 75.5 x 108
234

Cooper, Thomas Sidney 1803–1902
*Sheep on the Marshes, near Folkestone,
Kent* c.1875
oil on panel 59 x 44.5
459

Cooper, Thomas Sidney 1803–1902
Landscape 1881
oil on canvas 27 x 39
773

Cope, Charles West 1811–1890
*Hope Deferred, and Hopes and Fears that
Kindle Hope* before 1877
oil on panel 76 x 62
207

Cordall, William active late 19th C
Village Scene
oil on panel 47 x 67.3
1068

Cot, Pierre Auguste 1837–1883
The Last Support
oil on canvas 139.5 x 99
198

Coutts, Gordon 1868–1937
A Merchant of Tangiers
oil on canvas 66.5 x 91.9
501

Crabtree, Jack b.1938
The Pressure of One's Environment (1) c.1960
oil on canvas 92 x 71
803

Crabtree, Jack b.1938
The Speaker 1962
oil on canvas 137 x 122
802

Cranach, Lucas the elder (circle of)
1472–1553
*The Reformers Radisponen and G. Wolf
(Frederick 'The Wise', 1463–1525, and (...)*
oil on panel 30.5 x 20.8
1224

Creswick, Thomas 1811–1869 & **Frith,
William** 1819–1909
Lancaster Sands, Lancashire 1848
oil on canvas 106 x 154
76/2

Critchlow, Jeremy b.1951
Crawling Woman, Benares, India 1981
oil on canvas 120 x 159
1276

Crome, John (attributed to) 1768–1821
Landscape
oil on canvas 23.5 x 30.5
522

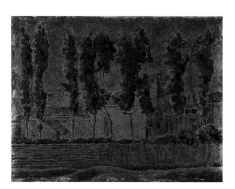

Crossley, Bob 1912–2010
Landscape near Mestre, Venice 1940–1945
oil on board 38.5 x 51
1499

Crossley, Bob 1912–2010
The Spin before the Fling 1962
oil on board 119.4 x 88.9
1477

Crossley, Bob 1912–2010
Westwards 1979
acrylic on canvas 213 x 152
1496

Crossley, Bob 1912–2010
North Sea Oil Rig 1987
acrylic on canvas 108 x 162.5
1479

Crossley, Bob 1912–2010
Sharks Feeding 1989
acrylic on canvas 100.3 x 153.6
1478

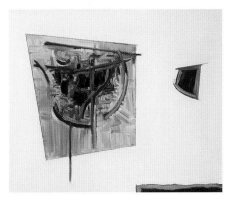

Crossley, Bob 1912–2010
Scholar 2002
oil on canvas 99 x 120.6
1476

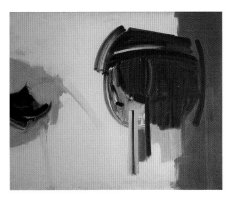

Crossley, Bob 1912–2010
Aggressive Blacks
oil on canvas 101.5 x 127.5
879

Cunaeus, Conradyn 1828–1895
Deerhounds and Dead Game 1851
oil on canvas 82.5 x 117
24

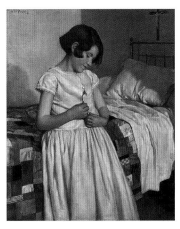

Cundell, Nora Lucy Mowbray 1889–1948
The Patchwork Quilt 1919
oil on card 70 x 58
712

Davis, Henry William Banks 1833–1914
Thorn Trees on a Breconshire Hillside 1904
oil on canvas 91.5 x 182.5
548

Dawson, Henry 1811–1878
Sunrise at Sea 1861–1866
oil on canvas 50 x 75.5
209

Dawson, Henry 1811–1878
Waiting for the Tide, Sunset 1866
oil on canvas 74.5 x 104
210

Day, H. R.
*Amen Corner (A Bit of Old Rochdale,
Lancashire)*
oil on canvas & board 25 x 18
1070

De Léon y Escosura, Ignacio 1834–1901
The Artist's Studio 1876
oil on wood 48.5 x 60
264

Deutsch, Ludwig 1855–1935
An Arab Schoolmaster 1889
oil on panel 54.4 x 47.4
496

Dickinson, Lowes Cato 1819–1908
John Bright (1811–1889) 1873
oil on canvas 237 x 147
575

Dicksee, Thomas Francis 1819–1895
Ophelia 1873
oil on canvas 141.6 x 101
125

Dierckx, Pierre Jacques 1855–1947
The Knitting Lesson
oil on canvas 71 x 113
259

Dollman, John Charles 1851–1934
'Marquis', a Gordon Setter
oil on canvas 38.5 x 48.6
48

Dugdale, Thomas Cantrell 1880–1952
The Bathing Cove 1903
oil on canvas 116 x 66
57

Dunlop, Ronald Ossory 1894–1973
Memory of Honfleur, France
oil on canvas 55.5 x 152.5
808

Dunlop, Ronald Ossory 1894–1973
Southwold, Suffolk
oil on canvas 102.3 x 127
622

Dunstan, Bernard b.1920
The Zip Fastener
oil on board 50 x 67
806

Earl, George 1824–1908
Excelsior 1870
oil on canvas 124 x 153.5
599

Eastman, Frank S. 1878–1964
A Little Sleep c.1906
oil on canvas 107 x 91
557

Ellis, Edwin (attributed to) 1841–1895
Picking Berries
oil on canvas 153 x 183
1492

Elmore, Alfred 1815–1881
Charles V at the Monastery of Yuste 1856
oil on canvas 46.7 x 64
211

Etchells, Jessie 1892–1933
Flowers before 1914
oil on canvas 46 x 35.5
517

Eurich, Richard Ernst 1903–1992
Mousehole, Cornwall 1938
oil on canvas 63.5 x 76
623

Faed, Thomas 1826–1900
Highland Lassie 1871
oil on canvas 74.5 x 51
435

Fagnani, Giuseppe 1819–1873
Richard Cobden (1804–1865) 1861
oil on canvas 101 x 81
1072

Fagnani, Giuseppe 1819–1873
John Bright (1811–1889), and Richard Cobden (1804–1865)
oil on canvas 68.5 x 86.4
1053

Falk, Alan b.1945
Bedroom Piece
oil on canvas 44 x 59.5
PCF2

Farquharson, David 1839–1907
Early Morning on Beer Common, South Devon 1872/1873
oil on canvas 117 x 183
235

Farquharson, Joseph 1846–1935
Through the Crisp Air 1902
oil on canvas 98 x 153
576

Federov, A. A.
Russia (copy of Ivan Shishkin) 1935
oil on canvas 111 x 168
673

Feyen, Jacques Eugène 1815–1908
Oyster Fishers (Cleaning the Oysters after the Catch)
oil on wood 30.3 x 45
499

Fidler, Harry 1856–1935
Energy
oil on canvas 78 x 82
598

Fildes, Luke 1843–1927
Lady Royds (1846–1925) 1908
oil on canvas 128 x 92.2
533a

Fisher, Horace 1861–1934
Autumn, Capri, Italy
oil on canvas 102 x 72
558

Fisher, Mark 1841–1923
Sheep Shearing 1892
oil on canvas 44.5 x 58.5
515

Facing page: Dicksee, Thomas Francis, 1819–1895, *Ophelia*, 1873, Rochdale Arts & Heritage Service (p. 96)

Fisher, Mark 1841–1923
Farm Work c.1904
oil on canvas 36 x 52
70

Fishwick, Janet active 1909–1913
Amen Corner, Rochdale, Lancashire 1909
oil on canvas 35.5 x 25.5
137

Fishwick, Janet active 1909–1913
Belfield Hall, Rochdale, Lancashire
oil on canvas 21.5 x 29.2
286

Flemish (Antwerp) School
The Adoration of the Magi c.1600
oil on panel 89 x 64.7
1237

Flemish School 17th C
Portrait of a Monk
oil on canvas 47 x 41.3
1216

Flint, William Russell 1880–1969
Maruja the Strong
oil on canvas 87 x 137.5
593

Francis, Eva 1887–1924
Snowdrops and Violets 1903
oil on canvas 15.2 x 20
71

French School
*Philippe le Bon (1396–1467), Duc de
Bourgogne* c.1500
oil on panel 41 x 29.2
1227 ※

French School
Philip II (1527–1598), King of Spain c.1600
oil on panel 43.5 x 33.3
1235

Freud, Lucian b.1922
Woman's Head with a Yellow Background 1963
oil on canvas 32 x 23
1278

Frost, William Edward 1810–1877
Aurora and Zephyr 1852
oil on canvas 90 x 69.5
212

Fry, Roger Eliot 1866–1934
Studland Bay, Dorset 1911
oil on canvas 62 x 92
516

Gabain, Ethel Leontine 1883–1950
The Dancer and the Canary late 1940s
oil on canvas & board 50.5 x 41
724

Gauld, John Richardson 1885–1961
The Students c.1949–1950
oil on canvas 46 x 40.7
721

Gertler, Mark 1891–1939
The Bokhara Coat 1920
oil on canvas 71 x 71
799

Giovanni di Paolo 1403–1482
The Crucifixion 1423–1426
oil on panel 31 x 49.7
1240

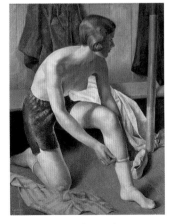

Glasson, Lancelot Myles 1894–1959
The Young Rower 1932
oil on canvas 102 x 76
585

Gledhill, David b.1959
Unidentified Street, Rochdale, Lancashire 2006
oil on canvas 91.7 x 142.3
1494

Glehn, Wilfrid Gabriel de 1870–1951
Shadows on the Wall, Cannes, France
oil on canvas 73 x 60.5
592

Goodall, Frederick 1822–1904
Rebekah 1867
oil on canvas 152.5 x 224
213

Goodall, Frederick 1822–1904
The Marriage Procession 1870
oil on panel 62 x 45.1
50

Goodall, Frederick 1822–1904
Shepherdess and Her Flock at a Pool Left by the
Subsiding of the Overflow of the Nile
oil on canvas 36.5 x 89.5
49

Gorbatov, Konstantin Ivanovich 1876–1945
A Sunny Terrace 1930
oil on canvas 90.5 x 95.4
606

Gotch, Thomas Cooper 1854–1931
Mother Goose c.1908
oil on canvas 88 x 60.8
114

Graham, Peter 1836–1921
Highland Mists 1891
oil on canvas 59.5 x 85.1
273

Graham, Peter 1836–1921
Highland Landscape
oil on canvas 50.6 x 76.5
272

Grant, Duncan 1885–1978
Fort St Louis, Toulon, France 1937
oil on canvas 55 x 73
631

Grant, Keith b.1930
Snow Drift, Clear Sky (polyptych, panel 1 of 4)
1974
oil on canvas 121.5 x 91.2
1022/1

Grant, Keith b.1930
Snow Drift, Clear Sky (polyptych, panel 2 of 4)
1974
oil on canvas 121.5 x 91.2
1022/2

Grant, Keith b.1930
Snow Drift, Clear Sky (polyptych, panel 3 of 4)
1974
oil on canvas 121.5 x 91.2
1022/3

Grant, Keith b.1930
Snow Drift, Clear Sky (polyptych, panel 4 of 4)
1974
oil on canvas 121.5 x 91.2
1022/4

Green, Anthony b.1939
*Our Tent, the Fourteenth Wedding
Anniversary* 1975
oil on board 243.8 x 182.9
1005

Greenwood, E.
W. Atkinson
oil on canvas 91 x 71
T8315

Gregory, Edward John 1850–1909
*A Study of Boulter's Lock, Maidenhead,
Berkshire*
oil on canvas 77 x 51
186

Grundy, Cuthbert Cartwright 1846–1946
Fresh and Breezy
oil on canvas 92 x 112.5
245

Gunn, Herbert James 1893–1964
Pauline (d.1950), Wife of the Artist c.1930
oil on canvas 91.5 x 72
577

Gunn, Herbert James 1893–1964
Gracie Fields (1898–1979) c.1938
oil on canvas 126 x 100.5
620

Hacker, Arthur 1858–1919
By the Waters of Babylon
oil on canvas 267.4 x 168.5
236

Hackert, Jacob Philipp 1737–1807
Landscape 1767
oil on copper 29 x 39.5
770

Hackert, Jacob Philipp 1737–1807
Landscape
oil on copper 30.3 x 41
771

Hague, Joshua Anderson 1850–1916
Summer Flowers c.1913
oil on canvas 76.2 x 103
279

Haite, George Charles 1855–1924
A Venetian Fruit Stall 1896
oil on canvas 66.5 x 102
260

Halswelle, Keeley 1832–1891
On the Thames
oil on canvas 38 x 57.5
523

Harding, James Duffield 1798–1863
An Italian Coast Scene c.1840
oil on canvas 43 x 58.5
51

Hardy, Frederick Daniel 1827–1911
The Solo 1874
oil on canvas 66 x 51
261

Hardy, Frederick Daniel 1827–1911
Waiting for Mother 1883
oil on canvas 62 x 43
214

Hardy, Heywood 1842–1933
Hunting Scene 1899
oil on canvas 109 x 166.5
262

Harmar, Fairlie 1876–1945
Cheyne Walk, Chelsea, London
oil on canvas 66.5 x 87.5
711

Haughton, Benjamin 1865–1924
Church Hill Wood
oil on canvas 62.5 x 55
607

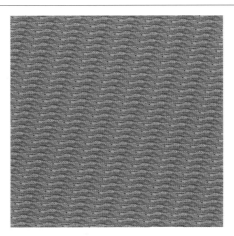

Havers, Alice 1850–1890
End of Her Journey 1875
oil on canvas 113 x 182
14

Hayes, Edwin 1819–1904
Falmouth Harbour, Cornwall 1873
oil on canvas 44.5 x 80
215

Hayllar, Jessica 1858–1940
The Robin 1910
oil on canvas 40 x 32
246

Haynes-Williams, John 1836–1908
A Spanish Warrior 1873
oil on canvas 53.5 x 37.5
28

Haynes-Williams, John 1836–1908
A Spanish Matador 1880
oil on canvas 82 x 51
124

Heath, Frank Gascoigne 1873–1936
The Gentleness of Heaven Is on the Sea c.1912
oil on canvas 71.5 x 92
280

Heffner, Karl 1849–1925
The Aqueduct of Claudius, Rome c.1881
oil on canvas 119 x 166
197

Heineman, T.
Preparing the Meal 1920s
oil on canvas 51 x 61.2
545

Heineman, T.
The Quayside 1920s
oil on canvas 46 x 61
546

Hemingway, Harold 1908–1976
Rochdale, Lancashire, 1856 1956
oil on board 54 x 80
804

Hemingway, Harold 1908–1976
Rochdale, Lancashire, 1956 1956
oil on board 54 x 79.5
805

Hemy, Charles Napier 1841–1917
The Armed Merchant Man 1912
oil on canvas 180 x 212.6
534

Henry, James Levin 1855–1929
*In Winter Quarters (Hayle Harbour,
Cornwall)* 1902
oil on canvas 60 x 69.5
84

Henshaw, Frederick Henry 1807–1891
A Forest Glade
oil on canvas 122 x 212.1
550

Hepple, Norman 1908–1994
Early Morning, Lake Garda, Italy
oil on canvas 101.6 x 127
807

Hepple, Norman 1908–1994
Spring Flowers
oil on board 51.5 x 41.5
780

Herkomer, Hubert von 1849–1914
Clement Royds (1842–1916), CB 1908
oil on canvas 155.5 x 99.3
533b

Herman, Josef 1911–2000
Miners against a Mountain
oil on canvas 59.5 x 113
1290

Herring, John Frederick II 1815–1907
Farmyard Scene
oil on canvas 61.5 x 92
439

Hewit, Forrest 1870–1956
Mount Orgueil, Jersey
oil on canvas 71.6 x 91.5
630

Hill, Robert W. 1932–1990
The Wave 1968
oil on canvas 122 x 122.7
876

Hiller, Susan b.1940
Gulf 1 1991
dispersion oil on wallpaper & canvas
110 x 104
1428

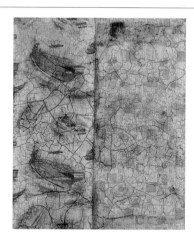

Hiller, Susan b.1940
Gulf 2 1991
dispersion oil on wallpaper & canvas
110 x 94.3
1429

Hillier, Tristram Paul 1905–1983
Las lavanderas 1965
oil on canvas 61 x 81
863

Hitchens, Ivon 1893–1979
Sussex, Spring 1933
oil on canvas 68.6 x 95.6
1442

Hitchens, Ivon 1893–1979
Open Terrace 1958
oil on canvas 52 x 117
800

Hoggatt, William 1879–1961
Top of the 'Howe Glen'
oil on canvas 89.6 x 122
1087

Holl, Frank 1845–1888
Newgate, Committed for Trial 1878
oil on canvas 71 x 97
185

Hollinrake, J.
*Hare Hill Road Corner, Littleborough,
Lancashire* 1902
oil on card 37.5 x 50.2
1416

Holmberg, August Johann 1851–1911
The Connoisseur
oil on canvas 112 x 145
287

Holt, Charlie b.1947
Sacred Books 1998
acrylic & gouache on paper & hardboard
98.5 x 129
1449

Horley, S.
Capri, Italy
oil on canvas 34 x 44
E:225.17

Facing page: Vauchelet, Théophile Auguste, 1802–1873, *The Birth of Cain*, 1831, Stockport Heritage Services (p. 194)

Hornel, Edward Atkinson 1864–1933
Among the Lilies 1905
oil on canvas 100 x 76.2
83 ✻

Horsley, John Callcott 1817–1903
St Valentine's Morn 1863
oil on canvas 43.5 x 51.1
32 ✻

Horsley, John Callcott 1817–1903
Going to a Party 1866
oil on canvas 112 x 87
216

Hughes, Arthur 1832–1915
The Sluggard, Market Women, Brittany, France 1876
oil on canvas 80 x 134
818

Hughes, Edward 1829–1908
The Alarm 1867
oil on card & panel 45 x 61
26

Hughes, Talbot 1869–1942
A Court Belle, 1770
oil on canvas 105 x 80
217 ✻

Hughes, Talbot 1869–1942
The Morning of the Duel
oil on canvas 110.5 x 76.3
218

Hulme, Frederick William 1816–1884
Bolton Abbey, North Yorkshire 1858
oil on canvas 60.4 x 91
219

Hunter, Alexis b.1948
Passionate Instincts No.13 1984
oil on canvas 109.8 x 99.5
1393

Hutchinson, Betty active 1964–1965
View from Okenrod School, Rochdale,
Lancashire 1964
oil on canvas 49 x 72
1092

Inskip, John Henry 1864–1947
Walmer, Kent 1905
oil on canvas 13.7 x 22
73

Inskip, John Henry 1864–1947
Whitstable, Kent
oil on canvas 16 x 21.7
74

Irmer, Carl 1834–1900
The Edge of a Bavarian Forest, Germany 1874
oil on canvas 76.2 x 116.3
21

Italian School 17th C
St Ignatius of Loyola (1491–1556)
oil on canvas 52.1 x 39.4
1225

Italian School 19th C
Madonna and Child
oil on panel 78 x 58.5
1238

Jackson, Frederick William 1859–1918
A Welcome Visitor 1893
oil on canvas 76 x 152.5
512

Jackson, Frederick William 1859–1918
Sunday Morning 1900
oil on canvas 61 x 57
1104

Jackson, Frederick William 1859–1918
Rushbearing at Middleton, Rochdale,
Lancashire 1900–1918
oil on canvas 113 x 235.5
1024

Jackson, Frederick William 1859–1918
At Venice 1905
oil on canvas 33.6 x 41
72

Jackson, Frederick William 1859–1918
A. G. C. Hanley, President of the Liberal Association
oil on canvas 76.5 x 64.5
1094

Jackson, Frederick William 1859–1918
Cattle in a Meadow
oil on canvas 61 x 91.6
1095

Jackson, Frederick William 1859–1918
Farm Scene
oil on board 26.6 x 36.5
1096

Jackson, Frederick William 1859–1918
Landscape, Farm Scene
oil on canvas 69 x 92.2
480

Jackson, Frederick William 1859–1918
Middleton Wakes, Rochdale, Lancashire
oil on wood panel 22.3 x 27.7
1101

Jackson, Frederick William 1859–1918
The High Tide, Runswick Bay, North Yorkshire
oil on board 37.9 x 44.7
1098

Jackson, Frederick William 1859–1918
The Last of the Hand Loom Weavers
oil on canvas 37.5 x 53.3
1099

Jackson, Frederick William 1859–1918
The Old Weaver
oil on canvas 51.7 x 61.3
1103

Janssens van Ceulen, Cornelis (follower of) 1593–1661
Portrait of a Young Nobleman 17th C
oil on panel 68 x 52.8
1222

Jaray, Tess b.1937
Remain
acrylic on canvas 213 x 192.6
1366

Jervas, Charles (circle of) c.1675–1739
James Thomson (1700–1748)
oil on canvas 70.5 x 64.3
1234

Jiménez Aranda, José 1837–1903
El santo óleo 1871
oil on canvas 52.5 x 78.8
187

John, Augustus Edwin 1878–1961
Eve Kirk (1900–1969) c.1940
oil on canvas 91.5 x 60
682 🐝

Johnson, Andrew
Flowers c.1961
oil on board 68 x 59.5
811

Johnson, Charles Edward 1832–1913
Cub Hunting in the Midlands 1886
oil on canvas 139 x 243.2
188

Jones-Hughes, Michelle b.1944
Migration c.1976
oil on canvas 116 x 114
1013

Jones-Hughes, Selwyn b.1943
Upright Edges Leading to the Sea 1976
oil on canvas 80 x 78.7
1012

Kay, Phil
'Mr Manchester', Tony Wilson (1950–2007)
oil on canvas 101 x 76
PCF1

Kelly, Gerald Festus 1879–1972
Saw Ohn Nyun IV 1932–1944
oil on canvas 106.5 x 73
652

Kemp-Welch, Lucy 1869–1958
Hill Folk c.1910
oil on canvas 102 x 127.3
542

Kennedy, Cecil 1905–1997
June Arrangement
oil on canvas 50 x 40.5
817

Kern, Hermann 1839–1912
Old Man Shelling Peas c.1880
oil on panel 30 x 45
440

Kershaw, Walter b.1940
Rochdale Arts Festival, 1971 1971
acrylic on canvas 123 x 123
893

King, Henry John Yeend 1855–1924
River Banks and River Blossoms 1909
oil on canvas 131.5 x 183
221

Kingsley, Harry 1914–1998
The Cooling Tower, Stockport, Cheshire 1960
oil on canvas & hardboard 57 x 77
878

Kingsley, Harry 1914–1998
New Street 1961
oil on hardboard 57.5 x 67.4
877

Kingsley, Harry 1914–1998
Embryo, Moss Side, Manchester 1965
oil on canvas & board 61 x 91.5
1403

Kingsley, Harry 1914–1998
Cambridge Street, Hulme, Manchester, 1946
oil on canvas & board 60 x 97
1259

Knight, George active 1872–1892
Seascape
oil on canvas 25.5 x 45.8
764

Knight, George active 1872–1892
Seascape
oil on canvas 25.4 x 45.7
765

Knight, Harold 1874–1961
The Young Seamstress 1907
oil on canvas 61.2 x 51.2
115

Knight, Laura 1877–1970
The Elder Sister c.1907
oil on canvas 32.5 x 25
100

Knight, Laura 1877–1970
The Trick Act
oil on canvas 102 x 127
619

La Thangue, Henry Herbert 1859–1929
Packing Cherries in Provence, France c.1923
oil on canvas 87.3 x 75
518

La Thangue, Henry Herbert 1859–1929
The Festa
oil on canvas 73 x 84.5
641

Ladell, Edward 1821–1886
Still Life with Fruit c.1880
oil on canvas 25.3 x 30.5
493

Lamb, Henry 1883–1960
Late News 1953
oil on canvas 140.5 x 201
737

Lance, George 1802–1864
Still Life
oil on panel 22 x 27.9
769

Landini, Andrea 1847–1912
A Distinguished Guest 1880s
oil on canvas 50.5 x 61.8
1411

Landini, Andrea 1847–1912
Contentment 1880s
oil on canvas 46.5 x 38.3
1412

Landini, Andrea 1847–1912
Une bonne bouteille 1880s
oil on canvas 46.5 x 38.3
1413

Lavery, John 1856–1941
Schooling the Pony 1929
oil on canvas 77 x 103
597 🐝

Le Bas, Edward 1904–1966
The Misericordia, Venice c.1949
oil on canvas 76.6 x 101.2
708

Leader, Benjamin Williams 1831–1923
Ben Vorlich 1858
oil on canvas 93.5 x 140.5
569

Facing page: Burne-Jones, Philip Edward, 1861–1926, *An Unfinished Masterpiece*,
Rochdale Arts & Heritage Service (p. 85)

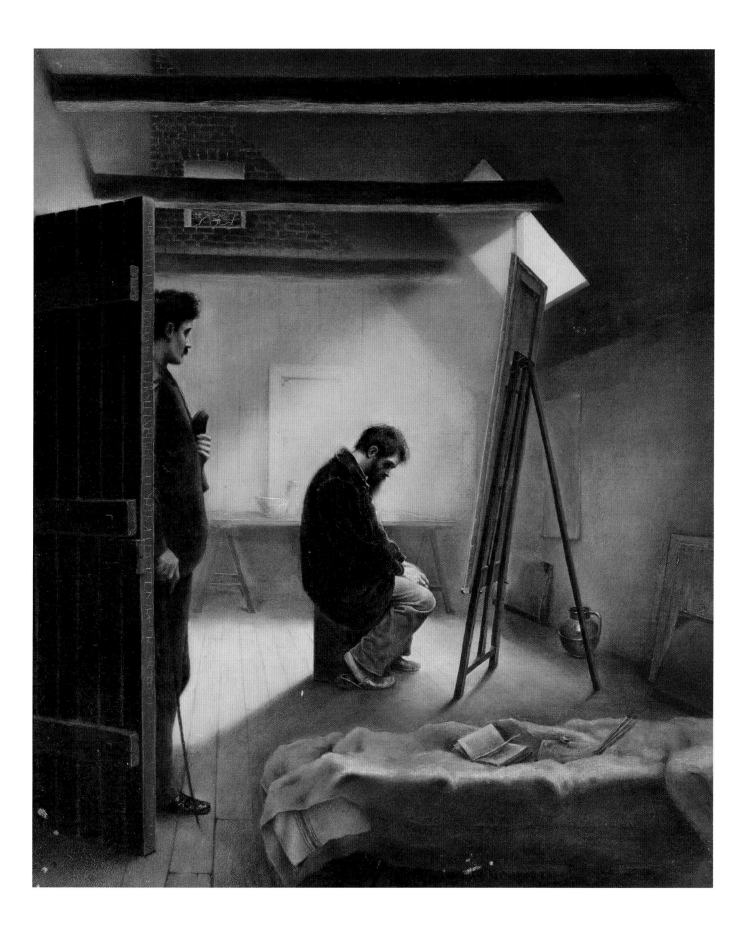

Leader, Benjamin Williams 1831–1923
Scene on the Llugwy with Moel Siabod in the Distance 1870
oil on panel 40 x 60
437

Leader, Benjamin Williams 1831–1923
The Stream through the Birch Woods 1871
oil on canvas 90 x 136.2
672

Leader, Benjamin Williams 1831–1923
Glyder Fawr, Snowdon Range 1881
oil on canvas 122 x 184
196

Leader, Benjamin Williams 1831–1923
Haymaking 1881
oil on canvas 41 x 60
263

Learoyd, Barbara
Conflict c.1965
oil on hardboard 104.8 x 73.7
843

Lee, Sydney 1866–1949
The Norman Column 1905
oil on canvas 97.5 x 64
81

Leighton, Edmund Blair 1852–1922
Hales Old Hall, Hales Green, near Norwich, Norfolk 1913
oil on panel 24 x 35
434

Leslie, George Dunlop 1835–1921
The Gardener's Daughter 1876
oil on canvas 71 x 55.5
189 ✿

Lessore, Thérèse 1884–1945
Hop Gardens, Kent 1935
oil on canvas 61 x 50.5
693

Levene, Ben 1938–2010
Green Still Life
oil on hardboard 122 x 111
1370

Lhermitte, Léon-Augustin 1844–1925
Rue, Mont-Saint-Père, France
oil on canvas 35 x 45.5
511

Linnell, James Thomas 1826–1905
Redstone Wood, Spring 1879
oil on canvas 71.5 x 101.6
222

Linnell, William 1826–1906
O'er the Muir among the Heather
oil on canvas 89 x 168
451

Lloyd, Walker Stuart 1875–1929
A Mile from the Sea, Newton Ferrers, River Lynter, South Devon
oil on canvas 93.5 x 180.5
199

Lord, W.
St Chad's, Rochdale, Lancashire 1904
oil on canvas 61 x 77
1107

Lorimer, John Henry 1856–1936
Hush 1905–1906
oil on canvas 101.6 x 144.8
99

Lowry, Laurence Stephen 1887–1976
Our Town 1943
oil on canvas 43 x 62
665

Lucas, John 1807–1874
'Love', Portrait of a Lady ('Grace was in all her steps. Heaven in her eye, in every gesture dignity and love') (from John Milton's (...)
oil on canvas 123 x 97
35

Lyons, John C. M. b.1933
Performance 2000
oil on canvas 106 x 76.2
1452

MacWhirter, John 1839–1911
The Fisherman's Haven, St Monans, Fifeshire 1872
oil on canvas 120 x 188
223

MacWhirter, John 1839–1911
Over the Border c.1880
oil on canvas 96.6 x 175.2
118

MacWhirter, John 1839–1911
The Lake
oil on canvas 101.4 x 153
1108

Magarshack, Stella active 1964–1968
Interior, Night c.1964
oil on canvas on board 92 x 76
824

Magarshack, Stella active 1964–1968
Portrait of the Artist 1967
oil on board 94.6 x 124.8
874

Mann, Cathleen 1896–1959
Flowers in a Vase and a Statuette 1953
oil on canvas 77 x 64
790

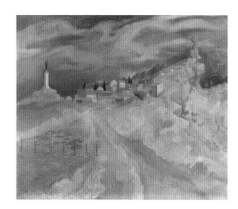

Mason, Bateson 1910–1977
Châteauneuf, France c.1946
oil on canvas 61 x 77
684

Mason, Bateson 1910–1977
Venice c.1968
oil on wood 76.2 x 122
873

McEvoy, Ambrose 1878–1927
Mrs Julian Lousada c.1920
oil on canvas 112 x 99
757

McEvoy, Ambrose 1878–1927
Daphne (The Honourable Daphne Baring,
1904–1986, Wife of the Sculptor) c.1924
oil on canvas 101.6 x 76.6
703

McGlynn, Terry 1903–1973
Italian Beach c.1958
acrylic on card 34.3 x 46.8
786

Meade, Arthur 1863–1948
The Wreck (After the Storm) 1920
oil on canvas 122.6 x 183.5
556

Methuen, Paul Ayshford 1886–1974
Neuville-les-Avignon and Mont Ventoux,
France
oil on canvas 82 x 122.2
782

Mignard, Pierre I (circle of) 1612–1695
Cardinal Richelieu (1585–1642) 17th C
oil on canvas 45.8 x 36.9
1217

Miller, Roy b.1938
The Field from Above 1960
oil on hardboard 59.5 x 120.7
812

Montezin, Pierre Eugène 1874–1946
Soleil d'automne c.1920
oil on canvas 60.6 x 73.7
613

Morales, Luis de (follower of) c.1509–c.1586
Ecce Homo
oil on panel 40 x 26.6
1215

Morland, George (studio of) 1763–1804
Interior with Sheep
oil on canvas 63 x 76.6
1229

Morreau, Jacqueline b.1929
Sisyphus 1989–1990
acrylic on canvas 122 x 152.4
1447

Morris, Philip Richard 1836–1902
The End of the Journey c.1870
oil on canvas 88 x 149
224

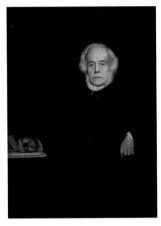

Morris, William Bright 1844–1912
John Bright (1811–1889)
oil on canvas 127.5 x 102.3
519

Mostyn, Thomas Edwin 1864–1930
The Tryst c.1904
oil on canvas 91.5 x 71
69 🐝

Mostyn, Thomas Edwin 1864–1930
Lieutenant Colonel Henry Fishwick (1835–1914), FSA 1906
oil on canvas 127.5 x 101.5
95

Mostyn, Thomas Edwin 1864–1930
The Sanctuary c.1910
oil on canvas 51 x 68.5
549

Mostyn, Thomas Edwin 1864–1930
The Valley of Sunshine
oil on canvas 51 x 68.5
110

Müller, Leopold Carl 1834–1892
Tric-Trac Players 1886
oil on canvas 73 x 122
271

Murillo, Bartolomè Esteban (follower of)
1618–1682
The Crucifixion c.1650
oil on canvas 56 x 34
1232

Murray, David 1849–1933
Loch Linnhe at Port Appin, Argyllshire 1884
oil on canvas 99 x 157
225

Nardi, Angelo (attributed to) 1584–1665
The Martyrdom of St Bartholomew
oil on canvas 101 x 76
1463

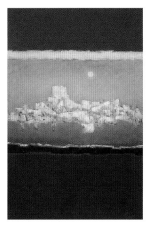

Neep, Victor 1921–1979
Winter Sea c.1967
oil on canvas 91.9 x 61.5
865

Nevinson, Christopher 1889–1946
After the Recapture of Bapaume, France 1918
oil on canvas 71 x 94
544 🐝

Nevinson, Christopher 1889–1946
The Old Harbour
oil on canvas 40.5 x 51
791 🐝

Newton, Algernon Cecil 1880–1968
Port
oil on panel 38 x 61
792

Nicholls, Bertram 1883–1974
Easby Abbey, Richmond, North Yorkshire
1929
oil on canvas 55 x 80
629

Noble, John Sargeant 1848–1896
Out in the Cold c.1890
oil on wood 52.6 x 32.6
226 🐝

Norbury, Frank
Carpet-Making Factory 1970–1979
oil on board 122 x 141
1493

North, John William 1842–1924
Over Hedges and Ditches c.1890
oil on canvas 66 x 99
119

Nurse, C. W.
*Old Farmhouse, Syke, Rochdale,
Lancashire* 1915
oil on board 21 x 49
1113

**Nuvolone, Carlo Francesco (attributed
to)** 1608–1665
Hagar in the Wilderness
oil on canvas 59 x 47
1218

Oakes, John Wright 1820–1887
*Mountain Stream, Glen Derry, Aberdeenshire,
'Like time the restless waters rush along'* 1873
oil on canvas 119 x 164
120

Ogden, Charles
'Swinger' c.1838
oil on canvas 36 x 42
T8148

Olsson, Albert Julius 1864–1942
Off The Needles, Isle of Wight c.1905
oil on canvas 61 x 76.5
77/1

Olsson, Albert Julius 1864–1942
Sunset at Land's End, Cornwall
oil on canvas 59 x 74
489

Parrott, William 1813–after 1891
The Fountain, Port of Genoa, Italy 1855
oil on canvas 113 x 97
265

Partington, John Herbert Evelyn 1843–1899
Old Salts, Whitby, North Yorkshire 1879
oil on canvas 128 x 102
23

Passini, Alberto 1826–1899
A Moorish Market Place
oil on canvas 39 x 54.5
268

Payne, Steve b.1949
Landscape 1981
oil on paper 73 x 55
1314

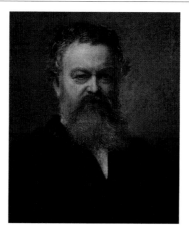

Pearson, Christine
'Tate' Shapes, Night 1998
acrylic on canvas 45.5 x 45.6
1506

Percy, William 1820–1893
Edwin Waugh (1817–1890) 1876
oil on canvas 62 x 50
116

Petker, J. (attributed to)
Landscape c.1820
oil on canvas 87 x 110
763

Pettie, John 1839–1893
*Distressed Cavaliers Turned
Highwaymen* 1861
oil on canvas 56.5 x 87.6
227

Phillip, John 1817–1867
The Convent Dole
oil on canvas 84 x 103
266

Phillip, John 1817–1867
The Spanish Widow
oil on canvas 48 x 36
768

Pickering, James Langsdale 1845–1912
*From English Seas (White Nose Cliff, the
Highest in Dorset)* c.1910
oil on canvas 83.5 x 124
193

Pickersgill, Frederick Richard 1820–1900
Ferdinand and Miranda (from William
Shakespeare's 'The Tempest') 1863
oil on canvas 74 x 52
31

Piper, John 1903–1992
Rievaulx Abbey, North Yorkshire
oil on linen 70 x 88
725

Pissarro, Lucien 1863–1944
A Muddy Lane, Hewood, Dorset 1940
oil on canvas 46 x 56
643

Potter, Charles 1832–1907
*Samuel Bamford (1788–1872), 'The Radical',
Silk Weaver of Middleton*
oil on canvas 60.5 x 56
1196

Priestman, Arnold 1854–1925
The Windmill 1911
oil on canvas 77.2 x 127
278

Priestman, Bertram 1868–1951
A Cotswold Village 1945
oil on canvas 50 x 60
674

Pyne, James Baker 1800–1870
Norwegian Scene
oil on card & wood 20.9 x 29.2
717

Radford, Gordon b.1936
Untitled
oil on board 24.1 x 34
1410

Facing page: Clouet, François (circle of), c.1515–1572, *Hercule François de Valois-Angoulême, Duc d'Alençon
et d'Anjou (1555–1584)*, 16th C, Rochdale Arts & Heritage Service (p. 87)

Rankle, Alan b.1952
Untitled Painting I (Calder Heights) 2009
oil on canvas 152 x 213.5
1507

Reckelbus, Louis Joseph 1864–1958
Canal near Bruges, Belgium, Autumn
tempera on card 59 x 69
490

Reid, Flora Macdonald 1860–c.1940
French Politicians, Royalist and Republican
1903
oil on canvas 92.5 x 133
56

Reynolds, Hettie Tangye active 1914–1934
Roses 1930s
oil on canvas 91.5 x 101.7
591

Richter, Herbert Davis 1874–1955
Reflections in a Silver Ball c.1932
oil on canvas 92.2 x 71.4
580

Roberts, David 1796–1864
Ruins of the Temple, Kom Ombos, Upper Nile,
Egypt 1842/1843
oil on canvas 108.5 x 150
52

Roberts, David 1796–1864
Milan Cathedral, Italy 1863
oil on canvas 130 x 107
121

Rose, Gerard de 1918–1987
Wrestlers 1956
oil on canvas 135 x 106.5
785

Rötig, Georges Frédéric 1873–1961
Sangliers allant boire 1903
oil on canvas 198 x 167
1120

Royds, John J.
The Critics
oil on panel 24.5 x 30
294

Rutherford, Harry 1903–1985
Rochdale, Lancashire 1960s
oil on board 52 x 75
1490

Sadler, Walter Dendy 1854–1923
Experientia docet 1884
oil on canvas 76.4 x 110.8
267

Sadler, Walter Dendy 1854–1923
Played Out c.1885
oil on canvas 85 x 121
450

Sant, James 1820–1916
The First Sense of Sorrow 1862
oil on canvas 115 x 142
53

Schedoni, Bartolomeo 1578–1615
La carità
oil on canvas 187 x 145
80

Schlesinger, Henry Guillaume 1814–1893
Peine perdue
oil on canvas 92.1 x 73.7
123

Schmaltz, Herbert Gustave 1856–1935
Queen of the May 1884
oil on canvas 128 x 72
228

Schofield, G. P. S.
Hill Top Farm c.1953
oil on canvas & board 24.3 x 39.6
740

Schofield, John 1853–1928
In a Little Difficulty 1900
oil on canvas 84 x 72
91

Schofield, John 1853–1928
Blackstone Edge, Hollingworth Lake in the Distance, Rochdale, Lancashire 1920
oil on canvas 58.4 x 88.3
1417

Schofield, John 1853–1928
Lydgate, Lancashire 1921
oil on canvas 30 x 44.5
535

Schofield, John 1853–1928
Going to the Meet
oil on canvas 59 x 44
1357

Scognamiglio, Antonio (attributed to) active 1879–1900s
Vesuvius in Eruption, 7 April 1906 1906–1909
oil on canvas 45.7 x 91.5
1394

Seemann, Enoch the younger (attributed to) 1694–1744
Bridget Domville (d.1750), Daughter of Sir Thomas Domville
oil on canvas 122.2 x 100
1219

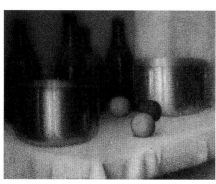

Segal, Arthur 1875–1944
Aluminium Pans and Oranges 1930
oil on canvas 71.2 x 91
745

Sephton, George Harcourt 1860–1923
Ducklings 1898
oil on canvas 106 x 85.9
1125

Shackleton, William 1872–1933
Christ at Jerusalem 1907
oil on canvas 97.2 x 109.2
298

Shackleton, William 1872–1933
Phryne at Eleusis 1907
oil on canvas 100.5 x 140.5
584

Sharp, Dorothea 1874–1955
Low Tide
oil on canvas 71.2 x 81.6
573

Shayer, William 1788–1879
A Group of Gypsies 1870s
oil on canvas 64.5 x 74.5
500a

Sickert, Walter Richard 1860–1942
The Fair, Dieppe, France c.1902
oil on canvas 129.5 x 97.2
642

Simcock, Jack b.1929
Rockside, Mow Cop, Staffordshire 1969
oil on board 34.5 x 48
890

Simpson, Kate A.
Sister of Kate Simpson, Eyla Laurence 1894
oil on canvas 58 x 46
1127

Skeaping, Kenneth Mathieson 1857–1946
Richard Heape 1911
oil on canvas 152.5 x 112
547

Skeaping, Kenneth Mathieson 1857–1946
Robert Taylor Heape (1848–1917) 1911
oil on canvas 108 x 83
397

Skeaping, Kenneth Mathieson 1857–1946
*Lord Byron (George Gordon Byron, 6th Baron
Byron of Rochdale, 1788–1826)*
oil on canvas 91.5 x 71.2
117/2

Smith, George 1829–1901
Obliging the Company c.1879
oil on canvas 98.3 x 168
190

Smith, George 1829–1901
An Interior
oil on wood 43 x 50
27

Smith, Matthew Arnold Bracey 1879–1959
Blue Vase with Fruit 1950s
oil on canvas 63.5 x 76.5
801

Somerset, Richard Gay 1848–1928
Mountain Pasture, Snowdonia c.1908
oil on canvas 101.2 x 152.5
113

Sosnica, Jerzy active 1963–1965
Rochdale, Lancashire, Fording the Roche (copy
of an earlier painting) 1963
oil on hardboard 109 x 139.5
826

Southern German School
The Crucifixion c.1500
oil on panel 43 x 32
1365

Spencer, Gilbert 1892–1979
Sheep in a Field
oil on canvas 45.7 x 55.9
547a 🐝

Spencer, Stanley 1891–1959
Bellrope Meadow, Cookham, Berkshire 1936
oil on canvas 92 x 130
640 🐝

Spenlove-Spenlove, Frank 1866–1933
*The Light at the Door, a January Night in
Flanders (No.96)* 1907
oil on canvas 91 x 71
136

Steer, Philip Wilson 1860–1942
Richmond Castle through the Trees, North Yorkshire c.1939
oil on canvas 64.9 x 76.5
670

Steinthal, Emeline Petrie 1855–1921
John Petrie, Engineer 1900–1910
oil on canvas 84 x 58.2
1131

Stephen, Dan b.1921
The Painter's Studio 1961
oil on canvas 88 x 114
809

Stevens, Norman 1937–1988
Castle Garden
oil on canvas 152 x 182.5
1258

Stott, Edward William 1859–1918
Ploughing, Early Spring c.1890
oil on canvas 25.5 x 39
882

Stott, Edward William 1859–1918
The Horse Pond c.1890
oil on canvas 60.9 x 76.2
608 🐝

Stott, Edward William 1859–1918
Sunrise in Winter c.1891
oil on canvas 25.4 x 34.2
706

Stott, Edward William 1859–1918
The Fold c.1895
oil on canvas 60 x 55.5
882a 🐝

Stott, Edward William 1859–1918
There Was No Room in the Inn c.1910
oil on canvas 82.6 x 66
231

Stott, Edward William 1859–1918
Approaching Night c.1917
oil on canvas 27.5 x 41
883

Stott, Edward William 1859–1918
Self Portrait
oil on canvas 30.4 x 20.9
609

Stott, William 1857–1900
The Two Sisters 1882
oil on canvas 183.5 x 214
463

Stroudley, James 1906–1985
First-Floor Front 1959
oil on board 100.3 x 75
797

Stroudley, James 1906–1985
The Sun from the West, Saltdean, East Sussex c.1968
oil on board 71.6 x 91.5
875

Taylor, Arnold 1892–1951
Wellfield Old Mill, Rochdale, Lancashire 1937
oil on canvas 53.5 x 41
610

Taylor, Arnold 1892–1951
Brierley's Mill, Rochdale, Lancashire c.1950
oil on board 51 x 69
730

Taylor, Arnold 1892–1951
Miller Bridge, Kendal, Cumbria
oil on board 37.5 x 51.5
590a

Taylor, Charles Donald 1922–2005
Hey Head 1955
oil on board 32 x 44.5
760

Facing page: Rankle, Alan, b.1952, *Untitled Painting I (Calder Heights)*, 2009, Rochdale Arts & Heritage Service (p. 128)

Taylor, Charles Donald 1922–2005
*The Construction of College Bank Flats,
Rochdale, Lancashire* 1966
oil on board 68.3 x 99
1495

Taylor, Leonard Campbell 1874–1969
Still Life c.1932
oil on canvas 41 x 36.5
581

Taylor, Walter active 1952–1955
Mill Lodge 1952
oil on board 57.8 x 69.3
741

Taylor, Walter active 1952–1955
*Salmon Nets at Cocker Sands,
Lancashire* 1955
oil on card 40.6 x 69.8
761

Ten Kate, Herman Frederik Carel 1822–
1891
A Royal Musical Party 1860
oil on board 50 x 70
220

Teniers, David II (follower of) 1610–1690
The Alchemist 17th C
oil on panel 39.5 x 26
1364

**The Master of the Countess of Warwick
(attributed to)** active c.1560–c.1570
*Margaret of Austria (1522–1586), Duchess of
Parma* 1570
oil on panel 63 x 49
1228

Thornton, R.
Welding 1989/1990
oil on board 120 x 89.9
1488

Tibble, Geoffrey Arthur 1909–1952
Graham Bell (1910–1943)
oil on canvas 56.2 x 45.9
626a

Topham, Frank William Warwick 1838–
1924
The Story of Ruth and Boaz 1894
oil on canvas 82 x 114.2
20 🐝

Turley, Keith John b.1950
Gracie Fields (1898–1979) 1998
oil on canvas 59 x 49
E178

unknown artist 17th C
Travellers Leaving a Hostelry, Dawn
oil on canvas 30.8 x 41
1220

unknown artist
Portrait of a Woman 1830–1870
oil on canvas 75 x 62
T8232

unknown artist
*Alderman Fred Lord Kay, Mayor of Middleton
Borough (1935–1936)*
oil on canvas 58.5 x 44
PCF5

unknown artist
*Alderman William Cuncliffe, JP, OBE, Mayor
of Rochdale (1911–1913)*
oil on canvas 128 x 102
1161

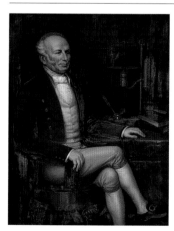

unknown artist
Benjamin Heape, Son of Robert Heape
oil on canvas 142 x 112
1163

unknown artist
Benjamin Heape, Son of Robert Heape
oil on canvas 67.4 x 59.6
1164

unknown artist
Capri, Italy
oil on canvas 49 x 54
T14176

unknown artist
Interior of the Town Hall, Rochdale,
Lancashire
oil on canvas 61 x 51
1173

unknown artist
James Wild, 'Jem Jarvis', Fought at the Battle
of Waterloo, Drummer in the 2nd Life Guards
oil on canvas 90 x 70 (E)
109

unknown artist
John Ashworth
oil on canvas 59 x 49
11

unknown artist
Joseph Henry, MD
oil on canvas 61 x 53
T8277

unknown artist
Landscape
oil on canvas 87 x 102.5
PCF15

unknown artist
Mill in a Valley
oil on canvas 26.5 x 36.3
1170

unknown artist
Old Rochdale, Lancashire
oil on canvas 63 x 75
1180

unknown artist
Portrait of a Man
oil on canvas 76 x 64
1185

unknown artist
Portrait of an Unknown Lady
oil on canvas 91 x 70
T8309

unknown artist
Portrait of an Unknown Man
oil on canvas 74.5 x 61
PCF14

unknown artist
Portrait of an Unknown Man
oil on board 19 x 13.5
PCF17

unknown artist
Portrait of an Unknown Man
oil on canvas 68 x 58.5
T8257

unknown artist
Portrait of an Unknown Man
oil on canvas 81 x 60
T8316

unknown artist
Portrait of an Unknown Man
oil on canvas 59 x 49
T8324

unknown artist
Portrait of an Unknown Mayor
oil on canvas 127 x 100
T8263

unknown artist
Portrait of an Unknown Woman
oil on canvas 49 x 41
T8176

unknown artist
Seascape
oil on canvas 49 x 63
PCF6

unknown artist
Seascape
oil on canvas 19 x 29
PCF10

unknown artist
Still Life with Fruit
oil on canvas 61 x 73
T8233

unknown artist
Textile Industry
oil on canvas 135 x 205
PCF16

unknown artist
The Reverend William Seaton
oil on canvas 52.5 x 40.5
T8167

unknown artist
'Tim Bobbin', John Collier (1708–1786)
oil on canvas 46 x 32
507

Vanni, Francesco (attributed to) 1563–1610
Saint Catherine of Siena Receiving the Stigmata
oil on canvas 176.5 x 137.2
1233

Vause, William Allan 1903–1987
Gracie Fields (1898–1979) 1978
oil on canvas 76.2 x 58.4
1424

Vergé-Sarratt, Henri 1880–1966
Île d'Yeu, France
oil on canvas 54 x 65.5
733

Vespignani, Renzo 1924–2001
Paesaggio urbano 1958
oil on canvas 64.5 x 90
815

Von Ambros, Raphael 1855–1895
An Eastern Doorway; At the Moslem Chief's Door 1887
oil on wood 41 x 33.2
612 ✳

A. V. W.
Belfield Bridge, Rochdale, Lancashire 1909
oil on canvas 34 x 49.4
1206

A. V. W.
Idlers' Corner 1928
oil on board 31.5 x 37
1204

G. H. W.
Landscape with Sheep
oil on canvas 24 x 29.5
PCF9

Waldron West, Ernest 1904–1994
Cyril Smith (1928–2010), MP 1975
oil on canvas 101.6 x 89
1030

Walters, George Stanfield 1838–1924
Fishing Boats off Gorleston, Norfolk
oil on canvas 37.5 x 55
671

Walton, Allan 1891–1948
Landscape
oil on canvas 51 x 56
574

Wane, Richard 1852–1904
Ebb Tide
oil on canvas 67 x 122
521

Wane, Richard 1852–1904
Tywyn near Conway
oil on canvas 87.5 x 138.6
520

Ward, Henrietta Mary Ada 1832–1924
The Princes in the Tower 1861
oil on canvas 61 x 54.5
30

Waterhouse, John William 1849–1917
In the Peristyle c.1874
oil on canvas 67.3 x 52.1
122

Waterlow, Ernest Albert 1850–1919
Mending the Nets, Newlyn, Cornwall 1882
oil on canvas 61.5 x 91
229

Watson, Derek 1934–1992
A Well-Earned Rest 1988
oil on canvas 24.8 x 29.2
1404

Watson, George Spencer 1869–1934
Three Wise Kings c.1920
oil on canvas 152 x 152
464

Weatherby, William
Edgar Brierley 1927
oil on canvas 60 x 49.5
T8282

Webb, James 1825–1895
Namur, Belgium 1876/1877
oil on canvas 92 x 153.2
237

Webb, James 1825–1895
Evening Scene
oil on canvas 73 x 125
710

Weight, Carel Victor Morlais 1908–1997
The Library c.1970/1971
oil on canvas 46 x 32.5
888

Weisbrod, Richard 1906–1991
Winter, near Clitheroe, Lancashire 1955
oil on paper 48 x 61
787

West, George
River Roch at Midge Hall, Lancashire
oil on canvas 45 x 31.5
887

Whaite, Henry Clarence 1828–1912
Mountains in Wales 1867
oil on canvas 102 x 180
66

White, Noreen b.1948
Akhtar and a Kameez 2002
oil on canvas 58 x 49
1465

Whittle, Thomas c.1842–after 1900
The Next Field 1889
oil on canvas 30.5 x 46
767

Whittle, Thomas c.1842–after 1900
Arundel Castle, Sussex 1890
oil on canvas 31 x 45.6
766

Wilkinson, Norman 1878–1972
Below Tilbury, Essex
oil on canvas 61 x 81.5
825

Williams, Terrick John 1860–1936
Low Tide, St Ives, Cornwall c.1934
oil on canvas 76.3 x 101.9
590

Williams, Terrick John 1860–1936
A Silvery Sky
oil on canvas 34.3 x 44.5
611

Willis, William 1841–1923
Pilchard Fishers 1901
oil on canvas 35 x 53
34

Wilson, Richard 1714–1787
Landscape
oil
774

Wilson, Susan b.1951
Self Portrait with a Clematis Wreath 1996
oil on canvas 126.4 x 75.5
1431

Winstanley, Hamlet 1694–1756
Sir Darcy Lever (1703–1742) 1733
oil on canvas 130 x 103
1213

Winstanley, Hamlet 1694–1756
Frances Lever
oil on canvas 124 x 104
1212

Winstanley, Hamlet 1694–1756
John Lever of Alkrington
oil on canvas 129 x 103
1213A

Winstanley, Hamlet (attributed to) 1694–
1756
John Lever 1735
oil on canvas 76.5 x 64
1060

Winstanley, Hamlet (attributed to) 1694–
1756
*Dame Dorothy Lever with Her Daughter,
Martha*
oil on canvas 125 x 100.5
1211

Wonnacott, John b.1940
*Crescent Road II (The Artist and His
Grandfather)* 1963–1976
oil on plywood 176 x 183
1042

Wood, Edgar Thomas 1860–1935
San Remo, Italy 1925
oil on paper & board 22.2 x 27
1267

Facing page: Freud, Lucian, 1922–2011, *Woman's Head with a Yellow Background*, 1963,
Rochdale Arts & Heritage Service (p. 101)

Wood, Edgar Thomas 1860–1935
*View from Campo dei Fiori, Varese,
Italy* c.1925
oil on wood 21.5 x 27
1419

Wood, Edgar Thomas 1860–1935
Italian Landscape
oil on board 25.4 x 21
1283

Wood, Edgar Thomas 1860–1935
The Artist's Father
oil on canvas 60 x 49
T8158

Woods, Brian b.1938
The Rainbow 1997–2000
acrylic on board 69 x 89.5
1450

Wright, John Michael 1617–1694
Miss Butterworth of Belfield Hall 1650–1670
oil on canvas & board 129 x 103.5
276

Wright, John Michael 1617–1694
Miss Butterworth of Belfield Hall 1650–1670
oil on canvas 129 x 103.5
277

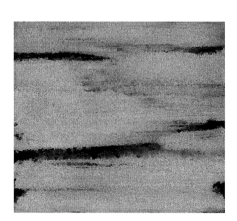

Wyndham, Richard 1896–1948
Head of a Boy c.1920
oil on canvas 40.8 x 31
543

Yadegar, Manijeh b.1951
C6-04 2004
oil on canvas 37 x 41.6
1504

Ziem, Félix François Georges Philibert
1821–1911
Venice in Flood
oil on wood 68.5 x 53.4
494

Rochdale Town Hall

Percy, William 1820–1893
Jacob Bright (1821–1899) 1856
oil on canvas 120 x 94
PCF2

unknown artist
Alderman Edward Taylor (1813–1895)
oil on canvas 126 x 100
PCF1

Westcott, Philip 1815–1878
C. L. Ashworth (1823–1873)
oil on canvas 220 x 143
PCF3

Saddleworth Museum and Art Gallery

Saddleworth Museum opened in 1962 as an independent museum located in part of what was Victoria Mill, Uppermill. The main aim was to preserve the local heritage of the Saddleworth area which, at the time, was starting to change. The collections were initially built up through donations from local people and focused particularly on the history of the area; this inevitably included a number of paintings with local significance.

In 1979 the Museum underwent a development which included a purpose-built gallery area, allowing regular art exhibitions of local, regional and national artists; the Gallery also allowed us to make stronger links with the local Saddleworth Group of Artists.

Not all the paintings in the Gallery collection relate directly to the Saddleworth area. They may have been collected because the artist was born in Saddleworth, or was inspired by visiting and working in the area.

Two significant early paintings in the collection are *Frenches Mill, Greenfield, Saddleworth, Yorkshire*, painted c.1840 and attributed to John Carse, which presents a record of one of the local villages before the valley bottom was industrialised; the other historically-significant painting is *Rushcart Festival at Saddleworth Church, Yorkshire*, painted c.1826 by John Holland before the church (St Chad's) was rebuilt from 1831 to 1833. This painting records the annual rushbearing ceremony (recently revived) when rushcarts processed from the various villages and assembled outside the church.

The most significant collection of works showing the contemporary Saddleworth landscape are by John McCombs, an artist born in Manchester who came to work in the area in 1967 and continues to record all aspects of the local landscape, focusing mainly on the village of Delph. He describes his work as an artist as 'being interested in the nature of landscape; its sense of permanence but seen under a fleeting light.'

Though our Collection is relatively small, consisting of no more than 150 works in all media, we strongly feel that it has significance. The Museum still actively collects and purchases works to add to the Gallery collection.

Peter Fox, Curator

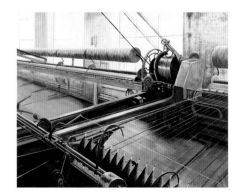

Bowie, Janis b.1956
Mule Spinning Frame 2008
acrylic on canvas 82 x 110.5
2009.35.1

Bradley, Helen 1900–1979
Market Place behind Stockport Road 1916
oil on canvas 33.3 x 43.5
1993.17.1

Carse, John (attributed to) b.1821 (?)
Frenches Mill, Greenfield, Saddleworth, Yorkshire c.1840
oil on canvas 42 x 65.5
2010.41.1

Holland, John c.1805–1880
Rushcart Festival at Saddleworth Church,
Yorkshire c.1826
oil on canvas 50 x 75.7
2001.73.1

Mansel, Lowell Dobbs
Sunday Wedding at Heights Chapel, Delph,
Saddleworth, Greater Manchester 2009
acrylic on canvas 59 x 95
2009.34.1

McCombs, John b.1943
Saddleworth Viaduct, Uppermill, Greater
Manchester c.1990
oil on canvas 35.4 x 29.5
1993.18.6

McCombs, John b.1943
Afternoon Sunlight, Summer, Delph,
Saddleworth, Greater Manchester 2000
oil on canvas 32 x 44.5
2002.93.1

McCombs, John b.1943
Saddleworth Parish Church, Greater
Manchester, Summer 2000
oil on canvas 33 x 43.5
2002.89.1

McCombs, John b.1943
Fletcher's Mill from Tanner's Dam, Greenfield,
Saddleworth, Greater Manchester 2001
oil on canvas 31.5 x 44
2002.91.1

McCombs, John b.1943
The Square, Dobcross, Saddleworth, Greater
Manchester 2001
oil on canvas 32.5 x 44
2002.95.1

McCombs, John b.1943
Wade Lock, Uppermill, Saddleworth, Greater
Manchester 2001
oil on canvas 32 x 44
2002.97.1

McCombs, John b.1943
Winter, Denshaw Church, Saddleworth,
Greater Manchester 2001
oil on canvas 31 x 43
2002.94.1

McCombs, John b.1943
Morning Sunlight, Austerlands, Saddleworth, Greater Manchester 2002
oil on canvas 30.5 x 43.5
2002.92.1

McCombs, John b.1943
Morning Sunlight, Clough Lane, Grasscroft, Saddleworth, Greater Manchester 2002
oil on canvas 32 x 44
2002.90.1

McCombs, John b.1943
The Manns, Friezland, Saddleworth, Greater Manchester 2002
oil on canvas 32 x 44.5
2002.98.1

McCombs, John b.1943
Winter Sunlight, Diggle, Saddleworth, Greater Manchester 2002
oil on canvas 32 x 44.5
2002.96.1

unknown artist
Saddleworth, Yorkshire c.1850
oil on canvas 22.7 x 41.8
2001.87.1

unknown artist
John Andrew (d.1856), Huntsman c.1854
oil on canvas 48 x 36.5
2001.72.1

Stockport Heritage Services

Stockport Metropolitan Borough Council's first fine art collections date from the earliest years of Vernon Park Museum, when one of its two founding MPs, John Benjamin Smith, placed on loan his private collection of approximately 47 paintings which he purchased during his grand tour of Italy in the first half of the nineteenth century. The Museum, situated in Vernon Park, opened in 1860 with a museum gallery on the lower floor and a picture gallery on the upper floor, but without any pictures to hang on the walls. Smith had acquired a collection of oils in Rome some 20 years earlier, and they had remained in their crates ever since. He agreed that they be placed on loan to the Museum and, with remarkable insight for the period, 'that proper blinds be fitted to shield them from the sun'. When Smith died in 1879, the loan was converted to a bequest and the 'Smith Collection' became the core of Stockport's fine art collection.

The Collection grew significantly in 1925, when the War Memorial and Art Gallery were built to remember the dead from the First World War. The Art Gallery called for donations of paintings for the permanent displays and the response was very favourable, with a number of notable paintings being donated. For some years the 'Museum' collection (mostly the Smith Collection) and the 'Art Gallery' collection were regarded as separate, but in recent years they have been fully integrated.

Bramall Hall has a number of paintings by the Victorian genre painter Herbert Gustave Schmalz, including *Where Is the Lord, My King?* and *Rabboni*. There are also some good early-naïve paintings of the Hall and surrounding parkland, which provide important insights into the history and evolution of the house.

On loan to Abney Hall, former home of the Watts family, are two large canvases which remain *in situ* now that the house is no longer a public building. One very large picture on the main staircase is by Frederick Newenham and depicts Cromwell dictating a letter to his secretary, Milton. On the first floor landing another large canvas depicts *The Birth of Cain*, painted in 1831 by Théophile Auguste Vauchelet.

The Stockport Story Museum in the town centre provides the ideal location for the display of local topographical views in a variety of media, and has an important early view of *Stockport Market Place, Cheshire* by the local artist William Shuttleworth, as well as a depiction of St Mary's Parish Church of about the same period. Local mills are also depicted in early industrial landscape views of the late eighteenth and early nineteenth centuries, including two small oils by Shuttleworth of *Hope Hill Mill, Stockport, Cheshire* and the mill owner's house, which were recently conserved with the assistance of the Museums, Libraries and Archives Council's Museum Development Fund, along with an amusing naïve oil on canvas picture, by an unknown artist, depicting an early nineteenth-century race meeting.

Also of great local interest is the conservation of seven oil portraits (all by unknown artists) from Marple Hall. The portraits are possibly of members of the Bradshaw family who lived at the Hall. One seventeenth-century portrait is reputed to be the infamous Judge John Bradshaw, who was elected president of the court which condemned Charles I to death and consequently signed the King's death warrant. This was an important conservation project which, as well as conserving seven oil on canvas portraits by unknown artists, also led to the discovery of three original and rare silver gilt frames. All seven portraits are now on display in Staircase House in the Market Place in Stockport.

The fine art collection now numbers in the region of approximately 900 paintings, prints and other media, and is housed across Stockport's heritage sites. The Collection mainly consists of pictures which have a local significance, either in subject matter, artist or association, and though modest in size, the Collection is well-suited to the variety of display locations across the borough, including temporary exhibitions in gallery spaces and period room settings within Stockport's historic houses.

Katie Cavanagh, Collections Officer

Allori, Cristofano (copy of) 1577–1621
Judith Holding the Head of Holofernes
oil on canvas 137 x 110.5
STOPM: 2010.222

Amorosi, Antonio 1660–1738
*Two Men Playing Cards Outdoors, Watched by
a Youth*
oil on canvas 44.4 x 52.8
STOPM: KX.54

Amorosi, Antonio 1660–1738
*Two Youths Gambling Outdoors, Watched by
a Third*
oil on canvas 32.5 x 41.8
STOPM: KX.55

Austin, Alfred R. active 1873–1899
The Farmer's Supper 1890–1899
oil on canvas 29 x 24
STOPM: 2007.282

Austin, Alfred R. active 1873–1899
*Game of Crib (Oliver Goldsmith, Dr Samuel
Johnson and David Garrick)*
oil on canvas 39 x 59
STOPM: 2007.364

Barabino, Simone c.1585–c.1620
Christ in the Carpenter's Shop
oil on canvas 123.5 x 173.2
STOPM: KX.40

Barber, Alfred R. 1841–1925
Four Rabbits 1895
oil on canvas 34 x 44
RD.11899

Bates, Frederick Davenport 1867–1930
Portrait of a Gentleman 1896
oil on canvas 112 x 86.8
STOPM: 2005.60

Bates, Frederick Davenport 1867–1930
Alderman William Lees 1908
oil on canvas 101.9 x 91.8
STOPM: 2004.252

Facing page: Giovanni di Paolo, 1403–1482, *The Crucifixion*, 1423–1426,
Rochdale Arts & Heritage Service (p. 101)

Bates, Frederick Davenport 1867–1930
Frank Brown c.1925
oil on wood 50 x 39
STOPM: 2008.73

Batoni, Pompeo (circle of) 1708–1787
The Penitent Magdalen
oil on canvas 84.5 x 103
STOPM: KX.1

Belgian School 19th C
The Cock Fight
oil on canvas 59.7 x 75
STOPM: 2007.188

Bell, W. H.
Portrait of a Gentleman 1807
oil on canvas 74 x 62
STOPM: 2004.369

Bell, W. H.
Portrait of a Lady 1807
oil on canvas 79 x 63
STOPM: 2004.370

Boar, J. active 1903–1904
The Bridge 1903
oil on canvas 42 x 50
RD.2108

Boar, J. active 1903–1904
Rural Cottage 1904
oil on canvas 42 x 50
RD.2107

Browning, Amy Katherine 1881–1978
Block Makers
oil on canvas 62 x 75
STOPM: 1982.65.1

Browning, Amy Katherine 1881–1978
Shaping the Hats
oil on canvas 76.2 x 91
STOPM: 1982.65.2

Browning, Amy Katherine 1881–1978
At the Sewing Machines
oil on canvas 63.3 x 76.5
STOPM: 1982.65.3

Browning, Amy Katherine 1881–1978
Hatting Factory Workers
oil on canvas 76.8 x 103
STOPM: 1982.65.4

Browning, Amy Katherine 1881–1978
Packing the Hats
oil on canvas 50.4 x 76.1
STOPM: 1982.65.5

Brueghel, Abraham c.1631–1690
*Flowers in a Pewter Vase, Grapes and
Peaches* 1650 (?)
oil on canvas 33.5 x 26
STOPM: KX.41

Burgess, M.
Steelworks 1975
oil on canvas 72.5 x 118.5
STOPM: 2010.77

Bygate, Joseph E. active c.1890
Durham City
oil on canvas 99 x 159
STOPM: 2010.258

Cairo, Francesco del 1607–1665
The Salutation (The Visitation) 1650 (?)
oil on panel 69.3 x 44.3
STOPM: KX.27

Callcott, Augustus Wall 1779–1844
Coastal Scene
oil on canvas 50 x 68
STOPM: 2007.246

Carlieri, Alberto (attributed to)
1672–after 1720
*Architectural Capricci with Tobias and the
Angel*
oil on canvas 99 x 57
STOPM: KX.36

Carlieri, Alberto (attributed to)
1672–after 1720
Tobias Curing Tobit's Blindness
oil on canvas 99 x 56.5
STOPM: KX.37

Carmichael, John Wilson (attributed to) 1800–1868
Seascape
oil on canvas 84 x 127.5
STOPM: 2005.61

Carrington, James Yates 1857–1892
Dog Playing the Piano 1888
oil on canvas 60 x 44
STOPM: 1948.1.4

Castiglione, Giovanni Benedetto (follower of) 1609–1664
Saint Jerome
oil on canvas 72 x 96
STOPM: KX.22

Castiglione, Giovanni Benedetto (follower of) 1609–1664
Saint Onuphrius
oil on canvas 87.5 x 111.5
STOPM: KX.21

Chettle, James Patchell 1871–1944
Old Swanage, Dorset 1936
oil on canvas 49 x 60
STOPM: 2008.119

Chettle, James Patchell 1871–1944
Above the Valley 1943
oil on canvas 62 x 75
STOPM: 2010.206

Chialiva, Luigi 1842–1914
Summer Time
oil on canvas 34 x 52
RD.11189

Chirnside, J.
Self Portrait 1979
oil on canvas 71.5 x 55
STOPM: 2008.184

Christie, James Elder (attributed to)
1847–1914
Old Man with Gold Coins
oil on canvas 75 x 61.5
STOPM: 2004.326

Clark
The Farmyard
oil on canvas 23 x 30.7
STOPM: 2005.219

Clarke, J. (attributed to)
English Landscape
oil on canvas 30 x 55.6
STOPM: KX.66

Clater, Thomas 1789–1867
The Proposal 1825
oil on canvas 59.5 x 49
STOPM: 2007.249

Clegg, H. active 1888–1889
Arden Hall, Bredbury, Cheshire 1888
oil on canvas 45.5 x 55.5
STOPM: 2004.222

Clegg, H. active 1888–1889
St Paul's Church, Portwood, Stockport, Cheshire 1889
oil on canvas 47 x 35
STOPM: 1958.24.1 (P)

Cobbett, Edward John 1815–1899
Science
oil on canvas 60 x 49.5
STOPM: 2007.253

Cole, John
The Wallace Monument, Stirling
oil on panel 59.8 x 69.8
STOPM: 2005.425

Collier, John 1708–1786
Portrait of a Jovial Young Man
oil on canvas 46 x 35.5
STOPM: 1955.25

**Colombo, Giovanni Battista Innocenzo
(attributed to)** 1717–1793
Travellers Ambushed in a Wood
oil on canvas 54 x 69.5
STOPM: KX.19

Cooper, Thomas Sidney 1803–1902
Landscape with Sheep
oil on canvas 36 x 50
STOPM: 2008.182

Corbishley, M. M.
Bridge in the Park 1908
oil on canvas 30.5 x 41
STOPM: 2004.211

Cotman, John Sell 1782–1842
The Mill (copy of Rembrandt van Rijn)
oil on canvas 80.3 x 111.2
STOPM: 2005.63

Cottrell, Mary
VE Street Party, 1945 1992
oil on canvas 44 x 53.8
STOPM: 2005.221

Cowley, Mollie
Old and New, Lancashire Hill
oil on board 67 x 60
STOPM: 2007.231

Cresti, Domenico (circle of) 1559–1638
The Visitation
oil on canvas 149.1 x 98
STOPM: KX.31

Davies, James Hey 1844–1930
The Stackyard
oil on canvas 70.9 x 91.5
STOPM: 2005.6

De Luna, Charles b.c.1812
À Mlle Floranet 1895
oil on board 23.5 x 13.3
STOPM: 2007.291

Desubleo, Michele (circle of) c.1601–1676
The Madonna Adoring the Sleeping Child
oil on canvas 65 x 46
STOPM: KX.39

Detti, Cesare Augusto 1847–1914
A Garden Party
oil on board 46 x 66
STOPM: 2007.256

Domenichino (style of) 1581–1641
Virgin and Child with Saint John
oil on canvas 50.5 x 62.7
STOPM: 2004.265

Dunstan, Bernard b.1920
Girl Holding a Blue Nightdress 1972
oil on board 25 x 32
STOPM: 2005.233

Eastlake, Charles Lock 1793–1865
Held for Ransom
oil on canvas 113.5 x 144.2
STOPM: 2005.112

Eisler, Georg 1928–1998
Stockport, Cheshire 1991
oil on panel 29.5 x 39.5
STOPM: 2005.469

Eley, William b.1938
Fall 1968
oil on board 101 x 80
STOPM: 2007.190

Ellis, Edwin 1841–1895
The Harbour
oil on canvas 39 x 75
STOPM: 2007.280

Eyre, C.
Henry Walker, Mayor
oil on canvas 74 x 48.5
STOPM: 1994.458

Fidanza, Francesco (follower of) 1747–1819
A Galley in a Mediterranean Harbour
oil on canvas 46.2 x 36.7
STOPM: KX.52

Fidanza, Francesco (follower of) 1747–1819
A Mediterranean Harbour
oil on canvas 56.8 x 48
STOPM: KX.16

Fidanza, Francesco (style of) 1747–1819
A Mediterranean Inlet at Sunrise
oil on panel 31.3 x 36.4
STOPM: KX.44

Fox, Allan H. b.1859
Henry Bell 1878
oil on canvas 96 x 76.2
STOPM: 2004.371

Fox, Allan H. b.1859
Portrait of an Unknown Lady 1878
oil on canvas 76 x 64
STOPM: 2004.357

Fox, Allan H. b.1859
John Andrew 1893
oil on board 52 x 44.8
STOPM: 1961.41

Fox, Allan H. b.1859
Portrait of an Unknown Lady
oil on canvas 76.5 x 63.5
STOPM: 2004.358

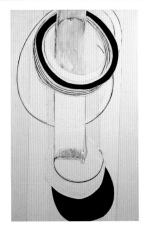

Frost, Terry 1915–2003
Black and White 1979
oil & collage on canvas 149.3 x 95.2
STOPM: 2008.495

Gagliardi, Filippo d.1659
Architectural Capricci
oil on canvas 110 x 155
STOPM: KX.9

Gagliardi, Filippo d.1659
Architectural Capricci
oil on canvas 110 x 155
STOPM: KX.10

Garbutt, S.
'The Crown' Inn
oil on board 41.8 x 52.3
STOPM: 1997.780

Gessard, V.
Lady at a Window
oil on panel 29 x 19
RD.12087

Goodall, Frederick 1822–1904
Ready for the Journey
oil on canvas 48.5 x 35
STOPM: 2007.257

Gough, Thomas b.1858
Prestbury Church, Cheshire
oil on canvas 60 x 50
STOPM: 2007.505

Grant, Ian 1904–1993
Margaret Reading 1954
oil on canvas 60 x 75
STOPM: 2007.545

Green, Ewart
From a Stockport Window
oil on board 55.9 x 44.5
STOPM: 2005.389

Gregory, Jessica
Dawn 1974
oil on paper 31.3 x 43.2
STOPM: 2005.276

Grimbleby, David
Chaos Ground
acrylic on board 70 x 90.5
STOPM: 2007.177

Grozier, R.
Girl and a Baby 1862
oil on canvas 51 x 41
RD.11192

Guercino (follower of) 1591–1666
A Sibyl 18th C
oil on canvas 107 x 85
STOPM: KX.6

Hague, Joshua Anderson 1850–1916
Burdock
oil on canvas 76.3 x 63.8
STOPM: 2005.442

Hague, Joshua Anderson 1850–1916
Coast near Deganwy, Conwy
oil on canvas 49 x 75
STOPM: 2007.309

Hague, Joshua Anderson 1850–1916
In the Mold Valley, Flintshire
oil on canvas 105.2 x 135.7
STOPM: 2005.194

Hague, Joshua Anderson 1850–1916
Late Autumn
oil on canvas 41.5 x 51
STOPM: KX.70

Hague, Joshua Anderson 1850–1916
The Mill Stream
oil on canvas 126 x 95
STOPM: 2010.230

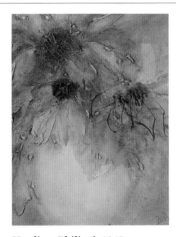

Harding, Philip b.1962
Flower Study 8
oil on canvas 22 x 17.3
STOPM: 2007.118

Harding, Philip b.1962
Flower Study 14
oil on canvas 22 x 17.3
STOPM: 2007.119

Facing page: Weight, Carel Victor Morlais, 1908–1997, *The Library*, c.1970/1971,
Rochdale Arts & Heritage Service (p. 142)

Hardy, James II 1832–1889
Gaming Birds
oil on canvas 19.5 x 28.5
RD.12729

Harvey, Douglas c.1821–after 1900
Nymphs, Cherubs and Swans
oil on canvas 90.7 x 137.3
STOPM: 2005.22

Haughton, Benjamin 1865–1924
Winter Wonderland 1907
oil on canvas 66 x 61.2
STOPM: 2005.448

Haworth, Mike
Oswaldtwistle Landscape, Lancashire 1974
oil & hessian on canvas 58 x 90
STOPM: 2007.225

Hemy, Charles Napier 1841–1917
Seascape
oil on canvas 31 x 55
STOPM: 2007.306

Henzell, Isaac 1815–1876
Village Gossip 1864
oil on canvas 102.8 x 138
STOPM: 2005.116

Heusch, Jacob de (after) 1657–1701
*An Italianate Landscape with Three Banditti
and a Dog*
oil on canvas 80.5 x 100.8
STOPM: KX.8

Heusch, Jacob de (circle of) 1657–1701
*A Rocky Mediterranean Coast with Peasants
and a Galley*
oil on canvas 48 x 73.5
STOPM: KX.18

Hirst, John
Root III 1968
oil on board 120 x 89
STOPM: 2010.201

Holder, Edward Henry 1847–1922
Pastoral Scene 1886
oil on canvas 112 x 139
STOPM: 2010.259

Horlor, George William active 1849–1891
Calves and Lambs 1888
oil on canvas 44 x 59.5
STOPM: 2007.255

Houlston, Helen C. b.1927
1st Age, the Infant 1981–1982
oil on canvas 90 x 60
STOPM: 2007.397

Houlston, Helen C. b.1927
2nd Age 1981–1982
oil on canvas 90 x 60
STOPM: 2007.388

Houlston, Helen C. b.1927
3rd Age 1981–1982
oil on canvas 90 x 60
STOPM: 2007.389

Houlston, Helen C. b.1927
4th Age 1981–1982
oil on canvas 90 x 60
STOPM: 2007.390

Houlston, Helen C. b.1927
5th Age, Justice 1981–1982
oil on canvas 90 x 60
STOPM: 2007.391

Houlston, Helen C. b.1927
6th Age, Pantaloon 1981–1982
oil on canvas 90 x 60
STOPM: 2007.392

Houlston, Helen C. b.1927
7th Age, Sans Everything 1981–1982
oil on canvas 90 x 60
STOPM: 2007.393

Hughes-Stanton, Herbert Edwin Pelham 1870–1937
On the French Coast 1917
oil on canvas 41.5 x 53
STOPM: 2007.232

Hunt, Charles 1829–1900
The School Room 1884
oil on canvas 82 x 133.5
STOPM: 2005.62

Hyde-Pinion, A. b.1878
James Watts 1906
oil on canvas 93 x 71
STOPM: 2005.5

Isherwood, James Lawrence 1917–1989
Old Spanish Lady 1972
oil on hardboard 40 x 30
STOPM: 2008.632

Isherwood, James Lawrence 1917–1989
Mijas, Spain 1975
oil on canvas 45 x 51
STOPM: 2010.257

Italian (Roman) School 18th C
The Penitent Magdalen
oil on canvas 92 x 69.5
STOPM: KX.49

Italian (Roman) School (attributed to)
Pope Urban VIII (1568–1644), with His Nephews Cardinal Francesco Baberini (1597–1679), and Cardinal (...) c.1630
oil on canvas 155 x 118
STOPM: KX.29

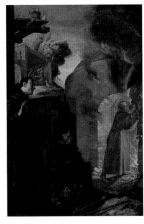

Italian (Tuscan) School (attributed to)
17th C
Saint Francis of Paola Saving a Lime Kiln near Paterno Calabro, Italy
oil on canvas 56 x 42.5
STOPM: KX.59

Italian School 17th C
Saint Ursula Arriving on a Rocky Coast
oil on canvas 50 x 65
STOPM: KX.56

Italian School (attributed to) 17th C
The Adoration of the Magi (after Peter Paul
Rubens)
oil on canvas 168.8 x 233.8
STOPM: KX.30

Jackson, Frederick William 1859–1918
Returning with the Catch 1908
oil on canvas 129 x 218
STOPM: 2010.260

Jennings, Derrick
Reflections 1979
oil on canvas 39 x 49
STOPM: 2007.359

Jervas, Charles (follower of) c.1675–1739
*Anne Masters (1673–1763), 4th Countess of
Coventry*
oil on canvas 350 x 145 (E)
STOPM: 1994.170

Johnson, Charles Edward 1832–1913
The Horse Pond 1890
oil on canvas 88 x 118.5
STOPM: 2005.21

Johnson, Helen
Mountain Scene (A Highland Spate)
oil on canvas 63 x 83
STOPM: 2010.220

Joli, Antonio (circle of) c.1700–1777
The Campo Vaccino, Rome
oil on wooden panel 118 x 112.2
STOPM: KX.65

Keil, Bernhard 1624–1687
A Scene of Sacrifice at an Altar
oil on panel 23
STOPM: KX.58

Keil, Bernhard 1624–1687
The Supper at Emmaus
oil on panel 23
STOPM: KX.57

Kershaw, Joseph Franklin 1885–1917
Renaissance of Spring 1911
oil on canvas 122.2 x 122.2
STOPM: 2005.193

King, Henry John Yeend 1855–1924
A Cottage Garden, Braemar, Aberdeenshire
oil on board 49 x 39.6
STOPM: 2005.423

Kingsley, Harry 1914–1998
The Cooling Tower, Portwood, Stockport, Cheshire 1960
oil on canvas 61.5 x 75
STOPM: 2008.6

Kingsley, Harry 1914–1998
Newbridge Lane, Stockport, Cheshire 1961
oil on canvas 49.5 x 59.5
STOPM: 2008.9

Kingsley, Harry 1914–1998
Storm in a Teacup 1961
oil on board 51.5 x 61
STOPM: 2005.450

Kingsley, Harry 1914–1998
Alpine Road, Stockport, Cheshire 1965
oil on board 57.7 x 67.7
STOPM: 2005.413

Kingsley, Harry 1914–1998
The Old Chimney, Stockport, Cheshire 1965
oil on board 59 x 49
STOPM: 2005.445

Kingsley, Harry 1914–1998
Early Morning, Stockport, Cheshire 1974
oil on board 49 x 59
STOPM: 2008.631

Kingsley, Harry 1914–1998
The Roundhouse, Ancoats, Manchester 1976
oil on canvas 50 x 60
STOPM: 2007.236

Kingsley, Harry 1914–1998
The Cooling Tower, Stockport, Cheshire 1981
oil on board 61 x 75
STOPM: 2005.449

Kitchen, Edna
The Cat's Park, Hillgate, Stockport 1997
oil on canvas 41.7 x 46
STOPM: 2005.424

Kneller, Godfrey 1646–1723
Sir John Egerton of Wrinehill (1658–1729) 1687
oil on canvas 126.6 x 95.5
STOPM: 2005.64

Knight, John William Buxton 1843–1908
Harvest, Eventide
oil on canvas 34 x 50
STOPM: 2007.416

Knighton-Hammond, Arthur Henry 1875–1970
The Crook of Lune
oil on canvas 60 x 80
STOPM: 2009.4

Leader, Benjamin Williams 1831–1923
Harvest Landscape 1869
oil on canvas 56.5 x 82
STOPM: 2005.8

Leader, Benjamin Williams 1831–1923
Mountain Solitude 1873
oil on canvas 109.4 x 170.6
STOPM: 2005.43

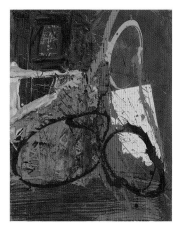

Lee, Moses 1950–1995
Round Flight 1991
acrylic on paper 68 x 54
STOPM: 2007.370

Lee, Moses (attributed to) 1950–1995
Abstract
oil on board 53.5 x 53.5
STOPM: 2007.422

Lees, E. H.
Little Underbank, Stockport, Cheshire 1880
oil on canvas 58.2 x 69.5
STOPM: 1964.19

Lees, E. H.
St Mary's, Stockport, Cheshire
oil on canvas 96.3 x 136.5
STOPM: 2005.115

Lees, Fred
Market Place, Stockport, Cheshire 1889
oil on canvas 32 x 54
STOPM: 2007.353

Lees, Fred
Waiting for the Boats, North Devon 1889
oil on canvas 64.5 x 92
STOPM: 2004.324

Levy, Emmanuel 1900–1986
Maria
oil on canvas 59.3 x 44
STOPM: 2007.149

Liverseege, Henry (circle of) 1803–1832
Thomas Whalley, Esq.
oil on canvas 90 x 69
STOPM: 1994.468

Llatka, Eut L.
Coastal Scene 1897
oil on canvas 23.5 x 39
STOPM: 2004.158

Lowe, Doreen
Tenements with Figures 1973
oil on board 60 x 84.9
STOPM: 2005.440

Lowe, George
Bredbury Old Hall, Stockport, Cheshire 1826
oil on canvas 35.5 x 45.4
STOPM: 2005.384

Facing page: Sickert, Walter Richard, 1860–1942, *The Fair, Dieppe, France*, c.1902,
Rochdale Arts & Heritage Service (p. 131)

Lowe, George
Stockport Market Place, Cheshire, 1809
oil on canvas 50 x 70 (E)
STOPM: HX.582

Lowndes, Alan 1921–1978
Gasworks 1954
oil on board 49 x 35
STOPM: 2007.507

Lowndes, Alan 1921–1978
Stockport Street Scene, Cheshire 1954
oil on board 120 x 185
STOPM: 2009.9 (P)

Lowndes, Alan 1921–1978
In the Park 1956
oil on board 116 x 177
STOPM: 2008.1

Lowndes, Alan 1921–1978
Love Lane Corner 1970
oil on canvas 118 x 87.5
STOPM: 2008.5 (P)

Lowry, Laurence Stephen 1887–1976
Crowther Street, Stockport, Cheshire 1930
oil on board 53.2 x 42.9
STOPM: 2006.288

Lucchesi, Raffaello
La Madonna della sedia (after Raphael)
oil on canvas 71
STOPM: KX.46

Ludlow, Henry Stephen 1859–c.1934
The Gamekeeper's Daughter 1888
oil on canvas 49 x 29
STOPM: 2007.248

Luti, Benedetto 1666–1724
*A Penitent Magdalen Fainting before a Vision
of an Angel*
oil on canvas 74.5 x 51.5
STOPM: KX.50

March y Marco, Vicente 1859–1927
Reading the Will
oil on board 35.7 x 50.8
STOPM: 2007.178

Marchis, Alessio de (follower of) 1684–1752
A Fortified Bridge over a River
oil on canvas 47.5 x 37.5
STOPM: KX.51

Matania, Eduardo 1847–1929
Mother and Child 1874
oil on canvas 29 x 15
RD.12086

Mawson, Elizabeth Cameron 1849–1939
Tintern Abbey, Monmouthshire 1877
oil on canvas 48.5 x 58
STOPM: 2007.279

Mayer-Marton, George 1897–1960
Wet Lane 1954
oil on canvas 69 x 89
STOPM: 2007.242

Mayer-Marton, George 1897–1960
Sea Wall, Blue Anchor, West Somerset 1959
oil on canvas 49 x 60
STOPM: 2007.363

Megget
Portrait of a Lady
oil on canvas 75 x 61.5
STOPM: 2004.368

Miller, Alva
Watts of Abney 1903
oil on canvas 105 x 104.5
STOPM: 2004.305

Mola, Pier Francesco (circle of) 1612–1666
Figures near Classical Ruins
oil on canvas 42.5 x 51.5
STOPM: KX.23

Mola, Pier Francesco (circle of) 1612–1666
Figures near Classical Ruins
oil on canvas 42.5 x 51.5
STOPM: KX.24

Mola, Pier Francesco (circle of) 1612–1666
Saint Francis
oil on canvas 119.5 x 94.5
STOPM: KX.47

Morris, C.
Landscape with a Windmill
oil on canvas 29 x 49
STOPM: 2010.79

Morris, Philip Richard 1836–1902
Home, Sweet Home
oil on canvas 74 x 49
STOPM: 2010.202

Morris, Philip Richard 1836–1902
Lady and a Dog
oil on canvas 75 x 59
STOPM: 2010.219

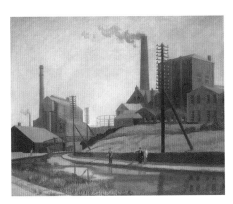

Mort, Marjorie 1906–1989
Factories
oil on canvas 62.5 x 75
STOPM: 2008.8

Mostyn, Thomas Edwin 1864–1930
The Jewel Box 1900
oil on canvas 98 x 104
STOPM: 2007.308

Mostyn, Thomas Edwin 1864–1930
River Scene
oil on canvas 54.5 x 70
STOPM: 2008.175

Newenham, Frederick 1807–1859
Cromwell Dictating to Milton 1850
oil on canvas 200 x 300 (E)
STOPM: 1996.35

Niemann, Edmund John 1813–1876
River Scene with an Angler 1855
oil on canvas 61.5 x 112
STOPM: 2005.2

Niemann, Edmund John 1813–1876
Landscape
oil on canvas 59 x 105.5
STOPM: 2007.142

Nithsdale, John Maxwell
*Councillor Headridge, Mayor of Stockport
(1983)* 1983
oil on board 83.5 x 51.5
STOPM: 2007.369

Nithsdale, John Maxwell
Day at the Museum
acrylic on canvas 47 x 59
RD.21492

Nithsdale, John Maxwell
Lancaster Bombers
acrylic on canvas 28 x 89
RD.21494

Nithsdale, John Maxwell
Selecting the 'Champion of Champions'
oil on canvas 54.5 x 70
STOPM: 2007.141

Nithsdale, John Maxwell
State Occasion
oil on board 89 x 58.5
STOPM: 2010.221

Nithsdale, John Maxwell
The Blackpool Excursion Train
oil on board 59.5 x 90
STOPM: 2008.93

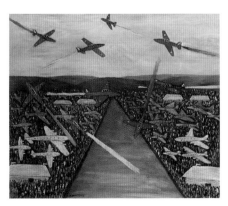

Nithsdale, John Maxwell
The Red Arrows
acrylic on canvas 62 x 74
RD.21493

Noble, John Sargeant 1848–1896
'None but the brave deserve the fare'
oil on panel 24 x 39.5
STOPM: 2007.258

Nomé, François de c.1593–after 1644
Aeneas and Anchises Fleeing the Burning of Troy
oil on canvas 25.5 x 92
STOPM: KX.48

Nowell, Arthur Trevethin 1862–1940
Dr Murray (d.1931)
oil on canvas 74.5 x 62
STOPM: 2010.207

O'Brien, Ivor 1918–2003
St Petersgate, Stockport, Cheshire 1950
oil on canvas 62.5 x 56
STOPM: 2008.211

Oliver, William 1823–1901
Portrait of a Lady 1877
oil on canvas 49.5 x 39.2
STOPM: 2007.250

Osborn, Emily Mary 1828–1925
Sailing Barges 1880
oil on canvas 24 x 70
RD.11186

Owen, Joseph
A Woodland Clearing
oil on canvas 62.5 x 75
STOPM: 2008.176

Partington, John Herbert Evelyn 1843–1899
Girl on a Beach 1880
oil on canvas 71 x 102.9
STOPM: 2005.3

Partington, John Herbert Evelyn 1843–1899
Edward Walmsley (b.1815) 1885
oil on canvas 115.5 x 90.5
STOPM: 2010.133

Partington, John Herbert Evelyn 1843–1899
William Rayner, MD 1885
oil on canvas 108.5 x 84
STOPM: 2010.75

Partington, John Herbert Evelyn 1843–1899
George Cooper
oil on canvas 61 x 50.5
STOPM: 1960.15

Patton, Ernest
River Scene
oil on canvas 78 x 105.5
STOPM: 2010.209

Payne, David c.1844–1891
A Scene on the Wye, near Haddon Hall, Derbyshire
oil on canvas 75 x 127
STOPM: 2005.111

Peel, James 1811–1906
Near Capel Curig, Conwy
oil on canvas 30 x 45
STOPM: 2007.415

Penney, David
Culture Cul-de-Sac 1976
oil on canvas 117 x 154
STOPM: 2010.228

Phillip, John 1817–1867
The Castanet Player 1854
oil on canvas 61.3 x 42.5
STOPM: 2007.300

Phillips, Brian b.1939
A Sluggish Sort of Day near Stockport, Cheshire 1995
oil on canvas 84.5 x 90
STOPM: 2009.8

Phillips, Brian b.1939
'Urry Up You, We've Got to Be at Mi Mother's in 'Alf an Hour 1995
oil on canvas 85 x 89
STOPM: 2010.204

Poole, Paul Falconer 1807–1879
Summer
oil on canvas 58 x 48
STOPM: 2007.251

Priestman, Arnold 1854–1925
A Norfolk Broad 1892
oil on canvas 81.2 x 110.8
STOPM: 2005.192

Przepiora, David Stefan b.1944
People 1974
oil on board 49 x 38.5
STOPM: 2007.358

Ramsay, George S.
Landscape 1905
oil on canvas 100 x 74.5
E1614.1

Redfern, Richard
Still Life with Fruit 1863
oil on canvas 16.5 x 22
RD.12730

Reynolds, Joshua (attributed to) 1723–1792
A Young Bacchus
oil on canvas 101.2 x 126.6
STOPM: 2005.110

Richardson, Edward Harrison 1881–1952
A Corner of My Studio 1924
oil on canvas 37.5 x 32
STOPM: 2007.193

Riding, Harold active from c.1925
The River at Llanyblodwel, Shropshire
oil on canvas 50 x 60
STOPM: 2007.296

Rivers, Leopold 1852–1905
Evening at Beccles, Suffolk
oil on canvas 59 x 89.5
STOPM: 2010.211

Robert, Hubert (attributed to) 1733–1808
Capricci of Classical Ruins
oil on canvas 71 x 96
STOPM: K.35

Robert, Hubert (attributed to) 1733–1808
Capricci of Classical Ruins
oil on canvas 91 x 113
STOPM: KX.38

Romeyn, Willem (circle of) c.1624–1694
Italianate Landscape with Drovers
oil on canvas 31.2 x 48.2
STOPM: KX.25

Romeyn, Willem (circle of) c.1624–1694
Italianate Landscape with Drovers
oil on canvas 30.5 x 48
STOPM: KX.26

Romney, George (attributed to) 1734–1802
*Captain John Joseph Vernon, 3rd Dragoon
Guards*
oil on canvas 75 x 62
STOPM: 2010.226

Roos, Philipp Peter 1657–1706
*Farm Animals in a Landscape with an Old
Man Drinking*
oil on canvas 97 x 134
STOPM: KX.17

Rosa, Salvator 1615–1673
Landscape with Brigands
oil on canvas 60.5 x 50
STOPM: KX.61

Rosa, Salvator (follower of) 1615–1673
Landscape with Brigands
oil on canvas 47.5 x 36.5
STOPM: KX.60

Roscoe, F.
Portrait of an Unknown Gentleman 1877
oil on canvas 73.5 x 61.1
STOPM: 2004.296

Rossi, Pasquale de' 1641–1725
A Jesuit Instructing the Populace
oil on canvas 33.7 x 41.2
STOPM: KX.62

Rossi, Pasquale de' 1641–1725
A Jesuit Instructing Youths
oil on canvas 22.5 x 28.7
STOPM: KX.63

Rothmer, Dorothy b.1926
Cheshire in Autumn 1971
oil on canvas 39.5 x 50
STOPM: 2010.136

Rutherford, Harry 1903–1985
September, Mottram, Cheshire
oil on canvas 59.5 x 49.5
STOPM: 2009.6

Saker, John
Landscape with Sheep
oil on canvas 42.5 x 70
STOPM: 2004.367

Salucci, Alessandro (attributed to) 1590–c.1655
A Capriccio of Classical Buildings in a Port
oil on canvas 37.5 x 46.7
STOPM: KX.33

Schmalz, Herbert Gustave 1856–1935
The Temple of Eros 1883
oil on canvas 106.3 x 213.7
STOPM: 2005.117

Schmalz, Herbert Gustave 1856–1935
Where Is the Lord, My King? 1888
oil on canvas 140 x 330
STOPM: 1998.1068

Schmalz, Herbert Gustave 1856–1935
Beth-El 1890
oil on canvas 45 x 160
RD.11182

Facing page: Breakspeare, William Arthur, 1855–1914, *The Maidservant*, 1881, Tameside Museums and Galleries Service: The Astley Cheetham Art Collection (p. 201)

Schmalz, Herbert Gustave 1856–1935
Shiloh 1890
oil on canvas 45 x 160
RD.11187

Schmalz, Herbert Gustave 1856–1935
Captain T. N. C. Nevill
oil on canvas 162 x 88
RD.11898

Schmalz, Herbert Gustave 1856–1935
Rabboni
oil on canvas 150 x 250
STOPM: 1998.1619

Seiter, Daniel 1649–1705
The Dead Christ, with the Madonna and Saint John the Evangelist
oil on canvas 90 x 175.5
STOPM: KX.11

Selous, Arthur
Coastal Scene, Guernsey 1940–1946 (?)
oil on canvas 74.5 x 105.5
STOPM: 2009.211

Shaw, David Carson b.1942
Mountain at the Sound 1984
oil on board 16 x 16
STOPM: 2008.41

Shaw, Peter 1926–1982
Stockport from Pendlebury Hill, Cheshire 1966
oil on board 89.5 x 112.5
STOPM: 2007.310

Shaw, Peter 1926–1982
Stockport Market, Cheshire 1978
oil on canvas 121 x 90.4
STOPM: 2003.162

Shaw, Peter 1926–1982
Matley Moor, Rowarth, Derbyshire
oil on canvas 75 x 121
STOPM: 2009.5

Short, Frederick Golden 1863–1936
Autumn 1898
oil on canvas 38 x 52
RD.11191

Shuttleworth, William b.1785
Church of St Mary, Stockport, Cheshire 1810
oil on canvas 52 x 74
STOPM: 2005.452

Shuttleworth, William b.1785
Stockport Market Place, Cheshire 1810
oil on canvas 167 x 107
STOPM: 2004.147

Shuttleworth, William b.1785
View of a Town 1838
oil & watercolour on board 55 x 79.5
STOPM: HX.592

Shuttleworth, William b.1785
Hope Hill Mill, Stockport, Cheshire
oil on canvas 52.8 x 71
STOPM: 2004.232

Shuttleworth, William b.1785
Hope Hill Mill, Stockport, Cheshire
oil on canvas 44.7 x 63
STOPM: 2005.403

Smart, Rowley 1887–1934
Chrysanthemums
oil on canvas 45 x 34.8
STOPM: 2005.360

Smith, E. E.
Stockport from Brinksway, Cheshire 1906
oil on canvas 102.1 x 152.2
STOPM: 2005.23

Snyders, Frans (follower of) 1579–1657
A Wild Boar Hunt
oil on canvas 160 x 230 (E)
STOPM: 1994.249

Somerset, Richard Gay 1848–1928
On the Conway
oil on canvas 34 x 51
STOPM: 2007.239

Somerset, Richard Gay 1848–1928
Venice
oil on canvas 49 x 74.5
STOPM: 2007.247

Somerset, Richard Gay 1848–1928
Waterfall
oil on canvas 28.5 x 44
STOPM: 2010.114

Spadino, Giovanni Paolo 1659–c.1730
A Melon and Other Fruit
oil on canvas 39.5 x 50
STOPM: KX.14

Spadino, Giovanni Paolo 1659–c.1730
Fruit and Tendrils
oil on canvas 48.2 x 56.5
STOPM: KX.15

Spadino, Giovanni Paolo 1659–c.1730
Fruit on Stone Steps
oil on canvas 47.3 x 56.5
STOPM: KX.13

Spenlove-Spenlove, Frank 1866–1933
The End of a Weary Day
oil on canvas 72 x 183
STOPM: 2010.225

Stark, James 1794–1859
Landscape with Sheep
oil on canvas 49 x 59
STOPM: 2007.254

Sumner, Roger
Skipping in Bourne Street 1974
oil on board 90.3 x 59.8
STOPM: 2005.447

Swift, Reginald
The Cathedral
oil on board 70 x 90
STOPM: 2008.3

Tassi, Agostino c.1579–1644
Mediterranean Coast with Shipping
oil on canvas 34.5 x 120
STOPM: KX.28

Tassi, Agostino (follower of) c.1579–1644
Mediterranean Coast with Shipping
oil on canvas 34.5 x 119.3
STOPM: KX.53

Ten Kate, Herman Frederik Carel 1822–1891
Cavaliers
oil on canvas 60 x 92.2
STOPM: 2004.323

Thompson, Alan J. b.1940
Moston Evening Landscape, Cheshire
oil on canvas 33 x 45
STOPM: 2008.12

Trowski, Laura
Saint Andrew 1977
tempera & gold leaf on board 15 x 12
STOPM: 2005.277

Trust, Peter 1936–2008
Eye Condemn 1978
acrylic on hessian 105.3 x 104.7
STOPM: 2007.189

Turchi, Alessandro (circle of) 1578–1649
The Pietà 1666
oil on canvas 70.5 x 45
STOPM: KX.43

Turner, William McAllister 1901–1976
Street in Crémieu, France 1972
oil on board 59 x 49
STOPM: 2007.508

unknown artist
Portrait of an Unknown Gentleman (said to be Judge John Bradshaw, 1602–1659) 1750
oil on canvas 76 x 63.2
STOPM: 1996.1004

unknown artist
Portrait of an Unknown Man 1750
oil on canvas 75.5 x 63.5
STOPM: 1996.1006

unknown artist
Portrait of an Unknown Woman 1750
oil on canvas 76.3 x 63.5
STOPM: 1996.1005

unknown artist
Portrait of an Unknown Woman in a Red Dress 1750–1850
oil on canvas 101 x 80.5
STOPM: 2004.304

unknown artist
Stockport Market and Traders, Cheshire 1824
oil on canvas 106 x 166.7
STOPM: 2005.41

unknown artist
Peter Marsland (b.1770) 1825
oil on canvas 74.5 x 62.5
STOPM: 2004.363

unknown artist
Portrait of an Unknown Man 1850
oil on canvas 76.5 x 64.5
STOPM: 1996.1003

unknown artist
Portrait of an Unknown Man 1850
oil on canvas 99.5 x 76.5
STOPM: 1996.1008

unknown artist
Portrait of an Unknown Woman 1850
oil on canvas 91.8 x 77
STOPM: 1996.1007

unknown artist
Mary Ann Howard c.1850
oil on canvas 90 x 70
STOPM: 1994.467

unknown artist
George Cooper Bellman 1865
oil on canvas 40 x 31
STOPM: 1960.15 dup

unknown artist
Seascape 1897
oil on canvas 25 x 40
STOPM: 2008.84

unknown artist early 19th C
The Race Meeting
oil on canvas 86 x 109
STOPM: 2005.4

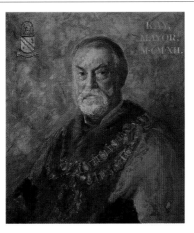

unknown artist
Thomas Kay (1841–1914), Mayor of Stockport 1912
oil on board 56 x 50
STOPM: 2008.627

unknown artist
Chrysanthemums 1913
oil on canvas 90 x 70
STOPM: 2010.208

unknown artist
George Edward Rostron c.1940
oil on canvas 40.5 x 30.5
STOPM: 1994.465

unknown artist
A Group Portrait
oil on canvas 70 x 88
STOPM: 2010.210

unknown artist
A Venetian Scene
oil on canvas 74.5 x 125
STOPM: 2010.224

unknown artist
Augustus Henry Venables-Vernon (1829–1883), 6th Baron Vernon
oil on canvas 110 x 84
STOPM: 2010.129

unknown artist
Boating Scene
oil on canvas 40.5 x 55
STOPM: 2004.223

unknown artist
Bolton Abbey, North Yorkshire
oil on canvas 60.5 x 91
STOPM: 2004.329

unknown artist
Bolton Abbey, North Yorkshire, Side Keep
oil on canvas 60.3 x 91
STOPM: 2004.328

unknown artist
Boy Overlooking the Sea
oil on canvas 43 x 61
STOPM: 2004.221

unknown artist
Bramall Hall, Stockport, Cheshire
oil on canvas 80 x 110 (E)
RD.12209

unknown artist
Bramall Hall, Stockport, Cheshire
oil on paper 34 x 50
STOPM: 2008.625

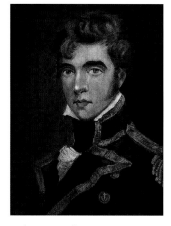

unknown artist
Captain Salusbury Pryce Humphreys (d.1845)
oil on canvas 55 x 45
RD.8543

unknown artist
Cows in a Field
oil on canvas 44.3 x 71
RD.11190

Facing page: Carse, John, b.1821 (?), *Frenches Mill, Greenfield, Saddleworth, Yorkshire*, c.1840, Saddleworth Museum (p. 148)

unknown artist
Dr Calveley Legh (1682–1727)
oil on canvas 90 x 70 (E)
STOPM: 1994.257

unknown artist
East Front of Bramall Hall, Stockport, Cheshire
oil on canvas 69.5 x 93.5
RD.12616

unknown artist
Edward Carrington Howard
oil on canvas 109.5 x 84.5
STOPM: 2010.74

unknown artist
Edwin Rayner, Governor (1880–1921)
oil on canvas 90 x 70
STOPM: 2010.134

unknown artist
Emma Magnus of Fallowfield
oil on canvas 73 x 59
STOPM: 2004.359

unknown artist
Figure of a Woman
oil on canvas 128 x 84
STOPM: 2010.227

unknown artist
Girl in the Wood
oil on canvas 82.5 x 46
STOPM: 2004.354

unknown artist
Italian Pastoral Landscape
oil on canvas 49.7 x 62.5
STOPM: 2004.230

unknown artist
James Leech
oil on canvas 54.5 x 46.5
STOPM: 1994.466

unknown artist
John Roberts
oil on canvas 64 x 53.5
STOPM: 2004.231

unknown artist
Lady with a Child on Her Knee
oil on canvas 142 x 112.1
STOPM: 2005.7

unknown artist
Landscape with a Tree
oil on canvas 74 x 59
STOPM: 2008.341

unknown artist
Man Sitting on a Rock
oil on canvas 175 x 142
STOPM: 2005.42

unknown artist
Martha Brownell
oil on canvas 89.5 x 69.5
STOPM: 2010.76

unknown artist
Miss Lowe
oil on canvas 64 x 47
STOPM: 2010.135

unknown artist
Mother and Child
oil on canvas 125 x 100
RD.12648

unknown artist
Mrs Howard
oil on canvas 90 x 70
STOPM: 1996.980

unknown artist
Old Stockport, Cheshire
oil on canvas 44.5 x 62.5
STOPM: 1948.9.1

unknown artist
Old Stockport, Cheshire
oil on canvas 40.5 x 62.5
STOPM: 1948.9.2

unknown artist
Pitt Outwitted
oil on canvas 27 x 34.5
STOPM: 1992.1449

unknown artist
Portrait of a Bearded Man
oil on canvas 55 x 44
STOPM: 2010.130

unknown artist
Portrait of a Lady
oil on canvas 30.5 x 24.5
STOPM: 2004.150

unknown artist
Portrait of a Man
oil on canvas 53 x 40
RD.11895

unknown artist
Portrait of a Man in a Ruff
oil on board 24.5 x 19
STOPM: 2004.216 (P)

unknown artist
Portrait of a Young Lady
oil on canvas 127.6 x 86.8
STOPM: 2005.44

unknown artist
Portrait of an Unknown Gentleman
oil on canvas 73 x 60
STOPM: 2004.356

unknown artist
Portrait of an Unknown Man
oil on canvas 76.2 x 63.5
STOPM: 1996.1001

unknown artist
Portrait of an Unknown Woman
oil on canvas 63 x 54
STOPM: 1995.1238

unknown artist
Samuel Oldknow (1756–1828)
oil on canvas 75 x 62
E2135

unknown artist
Scene with a Swan
oil on canvas 67 x 94
STOPM: 2010.203

unknown artist
Scene with Putti
oil on canvas 75 x 95
STOPM: 2005.1

unknown artist
Sir Ralph Pendlebury (1790–1861), JP
oil on canvas 109 x 85
STOPM: 2010.132

unknown artist
The Ten Commandments I–IV
oil on board 222 x 129.5
RD.21570

unknown artist
The Ten Commandments V–X
oil on board 222 x 128
RD.21571

unknown artist
Thomas Lees (1826–1897), JP
oil on canvas 112 x 86.1
STOPM: 2004.251

unknown artist
Thomas Pendlebury (1758–1840)
oil on canvas 74 x 48.5
STOPM: 2010.117

unknown artist
William Williamson, Trustee (1861–1879)
oil on canvas 97.5 x 76.5
STOPM: 2010.131

unknown artist
William Wilson Prescott (d.1878)
oil on canvas 71.5 x 64.2
STOPM: 2004.355

unknown artist
Young Musicians
oil on canvas 91 x 65.5
STOPM: 2004.303

Valette, Adolphe 1876–1942
Still Life, Fruit 1912
oil on canvas 44 x 75
STOPM: 2007.252

Vauchelet, Théophile Auguste 1802–1873
The Birth of Cain 1831
oil on canvas 300 x 200 (E)
STOPM: 1996.34

Vermiglio, Giuseppe (circle of) c.1585–after
1668
Saint Apollonia 1668
oil on panel 34 x 28
STOPM: KX.4

Vermiglio, Giuseppe (circle of) c.1585–after
1668
Saint Ursula 1668
oil on panel 34 x 28.2
STOPM: KX.3

Waite, Edward Wilkins 1854–1924
Calm Decay 1896
oil on canvas 132 x 90.5
STOPM: 2005.113

Walker, Peter John active 1974–1978
Winter Landscape, Evening 1974
oil on board 28.5 x 28.5
STOPM: 2005.468

Walker, Peter John active 1974–1978
Rock Formation No.II 1978
oil on canvas 98 x 175.5
STOPM: 2010.205

Wane, Richard 1852–1904
Sea View, Conway
oil on canvas 44.5 x 82
STOPM: 2007.276

Wane, Richard 1852–1904
The Orchard
oil on canvas 49.5 x 75
STOPM: 2008.121

Waterhouse, B.
Boat Pond, Edgeley, Stockport, Cheshire 1906
oil on canvas 49 x 74.5
STOPM: 1950.6.1

Waterhouse, B.
Boat Pond, Edgeley, Stockport, Cheshire 1906
oil on canvas 68 x 92.5
STOPM: 1950.6.2

Waterlow, Ernest Albert 1850–1919.
A Country Scene
oil on canvas 26.5 x 59
STOPM: 2007.414

Watson, William II d.1921
Crossing the Moor
oil on canvas 48.5 x 74.5
STOPM: 2010.116

Webb, James 1825–1895
Snape, Suffolk 1878
oil on board 22 x 45
STOPM: 2008.40

Webb, James 1825–1895
A Sussex Common
oil on panel 18 x 33.5
STOPM: 2005.218

Whistler, James Abbott McNeill (style of) 1834–1903
The Thames, Evening
oil on canvas 44 x 54
STOPM: 2007.233

Wilkinson, Derek 1929–2001
Church
oil on board 66 x 101.5
STOPM: 2008.2

Williams, H. C.
A Sunset 1870
oil on canvas 74.5 x 126
STOPM: 2010.229

Williams, Matti
Harbour Scene 1973
oil on canvas 50 x 39.5
STOPM: 2010.115

Williamson, George
William Crossley 1943
oil on canvas 44 x 35
STOPM: 2008.301

Wimperis, Edmund Morison 1835–1900
Landscape with Sheep 1900
oil on canvas 59.5 x 90
STOPM: 2010.78

Wynne, Anthony
Stockport '67 Triptych (left wing)
oil on board 116 x 52
STOPM: 2008.677.1

Wynne, Anthony
Stockport '67 Triptych (centre panel)
oil on board 116 x 52
STOPM: 2008.677.2

Wynne, Anthony
Stockport '67 Triptych (right wing)
oil on board 116 x 52
STOPM: 2008.677.3

Zoffany, Johann (circle of) 1733–1810
Cupid
oil on canvas 36 x 31.2
STOPM: KX.12

Tameside Museums and Galleries Service: The Astley Cheetham Art Collection

Tameside Museums and Galleries Service consists of six different sites, three of which are art galleries. The Service manages three collections: social history, military history and finally the Astley Cheetham Art Collection.

The Astley Cheetham Art Collection was originally bequeathed to the town of Stalybridge by the Victorian industrialist and mill owner John Frederick Cheetham after his death in 1932.

The Collection comprises over 500 works of art, including works on paper and a small selection of sculptures. It is well-known as an excellent small regional collection and includes works from the fourteenth and fifteenth centuries, as well as by nineteenth-century British painters such as David Cox the elder and Edward Burne-Jones. The Collection has grown with gifts from the National Art Collections Fund, the Contemporary Art Society and purchases by the Gallery throughout the twentieth century.

The Cheetham family's wealth came from John Frederick Cheetham's grandfather, George Cheetham, who established his own mill, Bankside. Due to his success the next generations were able to pursue their social and political interests.

John Frederick Cheetham's father, John Cheetham, was an avid collector of art, acquired on his extensive foreign travels. It is perhaps due to his collecting habits that the Astley Cheetham Art Collection has an internationally important, albeit small, collection of fourteenth- and fifteenth-century Italian icons. Of particular interest is Jacopo di Cione's *Madonna and Child with Angels,* 1350–1400. This central panel of an altarpiece has since been cut and mounted in a nineteenth-century frame.

Another icon of interest is the Master of the Straus Madonna's *Virgin and Child with Angels and Saints.* This small panel depicts the Virgin and Child with angels and on the left St John the Baptist and St Dorothy, and St Julian the Hospitaller on the right. Below the Virgin's feet lies Eve draped in a

translucent material clutching a miniature of the Tree of Knowledge. The artist was named Master of the Straus Madonna after a Virgin and Child painting, which once belonged to the art collector Percy S. Straus and is now held at the Museum of Fine Art, Houston. The Florentine artist had a penchant for elaborate decorations and shared stylistic traits with Masolino.

John Frederick Cheetham was born in 1835. His father's interest in travel may have inspired John Frederick to also spend several years travelling as far as India and the Himalayas, as well as yearly trips to the Alps. We know from his own sketches, some from early childhood, that he was an accomplished amateur artist with a keen eye for architectural details.

In 1887, Cheetham married Beatrice Emma Astley. She was the sister of Mrs A. W. Nicholson, Lady of the Manor of Dukinfield. She was also the great-granddaughter of successful society portrait painter John Astley who had married Lady Daniel Dukinfield. His son Francis Dukinfield-Astley was a businessman with great interest in coal-mining, leaving Beatrice financially secure.

John Frederick and Beatrice funded the Astley Cheetham Library. The building was opened on 14th January 1901. The room which now houses the Astley Cheetham Art Gallery was originally used for public lectures, funded by a donation from John Frederick's elder sister Mrs Ellen Barnes.

The family was to bestow another gift on Stalybridge. As the couple had no children, when John Frederick Cheetham passed away in 1916 most of his estate was settled between Beatrice and John Frederick's sister Agnes Cheetham, who was still living at the family home Eastwood House. Beatrice continued to live in Bournemouth, where the couple had built another Dukinfield Lodge, outliving her husband by seven years. Frederick Cheetham had stipulated that upon her death, everything, including the land and the house accommodating the art collection, was to be bequeathed to the Stalybridge Corporation. Agnes passed away in 1931 aged 99, at the time the oldest living resident in Stalybridge.

Tameside Museums and Galleries Service continues to collect art for the Astley Cheetham Art Collection with a focus on art relevant to Tameside, and art which compliments work already in the Collection.

Being a part of The Public Catalogue Foundation's project has enabled us to make this stunning regional Collection available to a much larger audience. The Public Catalogue Foundation has raised awareness of the Collection and for this we are grateful.

Marie Holland, Curator of Art

Facing page: Forbes, Stanhope Alexander, 1857–1947, *The Drinking Place*, 1900, Gallery Oldham (p. 15)

Allori, Alessandro (circle of) 1535–1607
Portrait of a Gentleman 16th C
oil on panel 120.5 x 94
ASTAC1932.1

Andrew, A.
Golden Lake Scene 1840–1880
oil on canvas 21.5 x 32
ASTAC1992.9

Astley, John 1724–1787
Portrait of a Lady
oil on canvas 60.5 x 50
ASTAC1983.2

Barrow, Leslie
Rainy Day, Uppermill, Yorkshire 1955–1959
oil on board 39 x 49
ASTAC1959.3

Bigg, William Redmore 1755–1828
Charity 1780–1828
oil on canvas 38 x 30.5
ASTAC1932.23

Bissill, George William 1896–1973
Kirkhallen Farm
oil on canvas 73 x 91
ASTAC1965.3

Bone, Stephen 1904–1958
Gibraltar from Gaucín 1925
oil on panel 23.5 x 33
ASTAC1965.2

Bonington, Richard Parkes 1802–1828
Near Rouen, France
oil on panel 25.5 x 32.5
ASTAC1932.26

Bradshaw, Arthur (attributed to)
*First Town Council, Borough of
Dukinfield* 1899
oil on canvas 126 x 201
PCF6

Breakspeare, William Arthur 1855–1914
The Maidservant 1881
oil on canvas 39 x 28.5
ASTAC1951.2

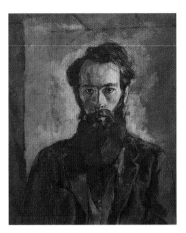

Bridge, Anthony active 1925–1939
Self Portrait
oil on board 61 x 50
ASTAC1992.15

Burne-Jones, Edward 1833–1898
Saint Nicholas 1870–1898
oil on canvas 140.4 x 55.6
ASTAC1932.2

Chuhan, J. b.1955
Dipak Chauhan (1934–2006) 2003
oil on canvas 63 x 50
ASTAC2004.1

Churchill, Gwendeline 1885–1941
Landscape
oil on canvas 34 x 44.5
ASTAC1963.2

Cleve, Joos van c.1464–c.1540
Portrait of a Gentleman in a Landscape
oil on canvas 52 x 44
ASTAC1932.5

Collier, John 1850–1934
Francis Dukinfield Astley (b.1853?) 1881
oil on canvas 57 x 45.5
ASTAC1979.7

Collier, John 1850–1934
William Nicholson
oil on board 77 x 62.5
ASTAC1979.8

Collins, William 1788–1847
Boys Fishing 1824
oil on canvas 44.5 x 56.8
ASTAC1932.21

Collins, William 1788–1847
Rustic Shed
oil on canvas 38.5 x 49
ASTAC1932.20

Connolly, Leo
The Glade 1958–1959
oil on paper 55.5 x 75
ASTAC1959.6

Cox, David the elder 1783–1859
A Road by a Common, Windy Day 1840–1859
oil on panel 20 x 30
ASTAC1932.25

Danby, James Francis 1816–1875
Ship on Fire 1873
oil on canvas 38 x 63.5
ASTAC1935.1

Danby, James Francis 1816–1875
Isle of Arran
oil on panel 16 x 24
ASTAC1932.19

Danby, James Francis 1816–1875
Lake Scene
oil on canvas 26 x 42
ASTAC1932.24

Danby, Thomas c.1818–1886
Lake Scene with a Fishing Boat
oil on canvas 90 x 150.5
ASTAC1992.86

Deane, Frederick b.1924
Harry Rutherford (1903–1985) c.1965
oil on canvas 70 x 43
ASTAC1985.28

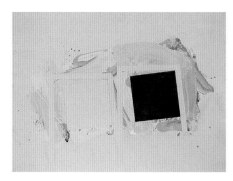

Delaney, Barbara b.1941
Acrylic/Paper January III 76 1976
acrylic & wax on paper 57.5 x 78.5
ASTAC1986.18

Della Monica, Gennaro 1836–1917
Incident in the Life of Garibaldi
oil on canvas 81 x 161.5
ASTAC1992.83

Flemish School
Portrait of a Man 1551
oil on panel 48.5 x 36
ASTAC1932.6

Garside, Ben
Joseph Rayner Stephens (1805–1879) 1839
oil on canvas 112 x 86
ASTAC1992.17

Geeraerts, Marcus the elder (attributed to) c.1520–before 1604
Portrait of a Lady
oil on panel 52.5 x 39.6
ASTAC1932.11

Gertler, Mark 1891–1939
Daffodils c.1914
oil on panel 60.1 x 44.5
ASTAC1954.1

Giulio Romano 1499–1546
The Holy Family with Saint Anne and Saint John (copy of Raphael)
oil on canvas 35 x 27.5
ASTAC1932.9

Grant, Duncan 1885–1978
The Harbour, King's Lynn, Norfolk 1932
oil on canvas 48 x 90
ASTAC1938.1

Halsband, Gertrude 1917–1981
Breakfast at Seaview
oil on canvas 52 x 72.5
ASTAC1983.4

Hattemore, Archibald 1890–1949
Interior, the Mantelpiece
oil on canvas 92 x 69
ASTAC1962.9

Hattemore, Archibald 1890–1949
The Dead Flamingo, Interior of Bethnal Green Museum
oil on canvas 116.8 x 89.7
ASTAC1962.1

Hewit, Forrest 1870–1956
Portrait of a Woman 1920–1935
oil on board 39.5 x 29.5
ASTAC1992.10

Hewit, Forrest 1870–1956
Portrait of an Italian Gentleman 1920–1935
oil on board 39.5 x 29.5
ASTAC1992.8

Hewit, Forrest 1870–1956
Malay Boy 1922
oil on board 39.5 x 29.5
ASTAC1992.7

Hines, Theodore c.1860–1889
A Distant View of Balmoral Castle, Aberdeenshire
oil on canvas 59.5 x 39
ASTAC1939.1

Hines, Theodore c.1860–1889
Luss, Loch Lomond
oil on canvas 39.5 x 59.5
ASTAC1939.4

Hines, Theodore c.1860–1889
Stirling Castle
oil on canvas 59.5 x 39.5
ASTAC1939.3

Hines, Theodore c.1860–1889
The Boat Pier, Loch Katrine, Stirling
oil on canvas 39 x 59.5
ASTAC1939.2

Hodgkinson, George 1914–1997
The Immigrant 1960–1980
oil on canvas 59.5 x 50
ASTAC1992.4

Hodgkinson, George 1914–1997
The Old Farm, Lancashire 1960–1980
oil on wood 24.5 x 44.5
ASTAC1992.3

Hodgkinson, George 1914–1997
Winter, Stalybridge, Cheshire 1980–1984
oil on canvas 45 x 65.5
ASTAC1985.31

Hodgkinson, George 1914–1997
Self Portrait
oil on board 44 x 37.5
ASTAC2000.1

Holder, Edward Henry 1847–1922
Rephidim, Desert of Sinai 1877
oil on canvas 59.5 x 100
ASTAC1932.46

Italian (Florentine) School
Virgin and Child with Saints (triptych) 1380–
1400
oil on panels 43 x 44.5
ASTAC1932.42

Italian School
Madonna and Child with Saints c.1600
oil on panel 39 x 64
ASTAC1932.8

Jacopo di Cione c.1320–1400
Madonna and Child with Angels 1350–1400
tempera on wood 103.8 x 59.5
ASTAC1932.3

Key, Geoffrey b.1941
Hillside Woods 1986
oil & mixed media on paper 47.5 x 67
ASTAC1987.1

Kingsley, Harry 1914–1998
Werneth Low War Memorial, Cheshire 1954
oil on board 39 x 44.5
ASTAC1992.39

Kingsley, Harry 1914–1998
Broadbottom, Cheshire 1957
oil on wood 19 x 30.5
ASTAC1983.3

Kingsley, Harry 1914–1998
Blue Jeans, Moss Side, Manchester 1965
oil on board 62 x 74.5
ASTAC1992.6

Kingsley, Harry 1914–1998
The Gateway, Moss Side, Manchester 1967
oil on board 48.5 x 74
ASTAC1992.5

Kingsley, Harry 1914–1998
The Playground, Dukinfield, Cheshire 1971
oil on wood 91.5 x 60
ASTAC1980.1

Knight, Joseph 1837–1909
The Corn Field 1886
oil on canvas 28 x 40
ASTAC1932.17

Lawson, Cecil Gordon 1851–1882
Landscape
oil on canvas 14 x 19
ASTAC1932.68

Lees, John
*St George's Church, Stalybridge,
Cheshire* 1820–1840
oil on board 34.5 x 49.5
ASTAC1992.21

Linnell, John 1792–1882
Sheep at Rest, Minding the Flock 1840–1880
oil on canvas 15.5 x 22.5
ASTAC1932.27

Liverseege, Henry 1803–1832
Enjoying a Pipe
oil on canvas 44.5 x 34
ASTAC1935.5

Facing page: Frost, Terry, 1915–2003, *59/60*, 1959/1960, Gallery Oldham (p. 15)

Liverseege, Henry 1803–1832
The Betrothed
oil on canvas 74 x 62
ASTAC1936.2

Luini, Bernadino (after) c.1480–c.1532
Saint Catherine of Alexandria
oil on panel 75 x 64.5
ASTAC1932.7

MacDiarmid, John 1865–1942
River Scene 1890
oil on canvas 42 x 52
ASTAC1986.23

Maclaurin, Robert b.1961
Mountain Journey 1988
oil on canvas 183 x 243.5
PCF5

Marinari, Onorio (attributed to) 1627–1715
Eleanor of Toledo (1522–1562)
oil on canvas 51 x 38.5
ASTAC1932.10

Master of the Straus Madonna c.1385–1415
Virgin and Child with Angels and Saints
tempera & gold on panel 70 x 47.5
ASTAC1932.43

Morris, Cedric Lockwood 1889–1982
Llangennith Church, Swansea c.1930
oil on canvas 63.5 x 79.5
ASTAC1935.2

Morris, Cedric Lockwood 1889–1982
Heron 1941
oil on canvas 50 x 75
ASTAC1946.2

Mura, Frank b.1863
White Roses
oil on panel 35 x 25.5
ASTAC1935.4

Newton, Marie
Dutch Triumph 1958–1959
oil on board 47 x 60.5
ASTAC1959.4

Nicholls, Bertram 1883–1974
San Andrea, Volterra, Italy 1924
oil on canvas 29.5 x 42
ASTAC1935.6

Ousey, Buckley 1850–1889
A Welsh Cottage 1884
oil on canvas 45.5 x 61.8
ASTAC1967.1

Ousey, Buckley 1850–1889
Cronies 1884
oil on canvas 50.5 x 76
ASTAC1964.1

Padwick, Philip Hugh 1876–1958
Littlehampton Front, West Sussex
oil on board 26.5 x 35.5
ASTAC1935.8

Palmer, Martin b.1958
Hartshead Pike, Cheshire 2007
acrylic on board 29.3 x 59.7
PCF2

Peppercorn, Arthur Douglas 1847–1926
The Estuary
oil on canvas 24 x 44
ASTAC1962.3

Pier Francesco Fiorentino
1444–1445–after 1497
*Madonna Adoring the Christ Child, with Saint
John the Baptist and Angels* 1480–1500
oil on panel 105 x 65
ASTAC1932.41

Radford, Gordon b.1936
Passing Storm
oil on canvas 38.5 x 38.5
ASTAC1978.4

Raphael, Wendy active 1988–2011
Clown 1988–1989
oil on canvas 34.5 x 24.5
ASTAC1996.2

Raphael, Wendy active 1988–2011
Cossack Rider 1988–1989
oil on board 47.5 x 36.5
ASTAC1996.1

Ratcliff, Sonia active 1976–1978
Oldham Market, Lancashire 1976
oil on wood 14 x 13
ASTAC1978.5

Ray-Jones, Raymond 1886–1942
Lorna Beadle
oil on canvas 102 x 76
ASTAC1996.4

Ray-Jones, Raymond 1886–1942
*The Artist's Wife, Effie Irene Ray-Jones
(1899–1996)*
oil on canvas 86 x 66
ASTAC1996.3

Rigby, J.
*Landscape with a Lake, Mountains and a
Sailing Boat* 1894
oil on glass 14 x 19.5
ASTAC1992.29

Royle, Herbert F. 1870–1958
Ashurst Lane
oil on canvas 39.5 x 29.5
ASTAC1955.1

Royle, Herbert F. 1870–1958
Castle Berg Scar, Nessfield-in-Wharfedale
oil on canvas 62 x 75
ASTAC1955.3

Royle, Herbert F. 1870–1958
Hay Harvesting
oil on canvas 30 x 40
ASTAC1955.2

Royle, Herbert F. 1870–1958
Haytime, Halsall Moss, Lancashire
oil on canvas 39.5 x 49.5
ASTAC1955.4

Royle, Stanley 1888–1961
Wintertime 1926
oil on canvas 70 x 90
ASTAC1940.2 🐝

Royle, Stanley 1888–1961
Fishing Gear, Brittany, France
oil on canvas 50.5 x 60.5
ASTAC1963.3 🐝

Rutherford, Harry 1903–1985
S. Ashworth 1929
oil on canvas 66.5 x 55.5
ASTAC1985.24

Rutherford, Harry 1903–1985
The Hollander c.1930
oil on canvas 34.3 x 29
ASTAC1985.7

Rutherford, Harry 1903–1985
Flight Sergeant Donald S. Mitchell (1922–1945) 1949
oil on canvas 48.5 x 38
ASTAC1976.2

Rutherford, Harry 1903–1985
Marion Rutherford (1899–1976) (recto)
1950s
oil on canvas 62 x 92
ASTAC2005.1a

Rutherford, Harry 1903–1985
House on Fire (verso) 1950s
oil on canvas 52 x 82
ASTAC2005.1b

Rutherford, Harry 1903–1985
Rue des Arquebusiers, Paris 1960
oil on board 53 x 34
ASTAC1985.4

Rutherford, Harry 1903–1985
Ashton Market, Tameside c.1960
oil on canvas 35.6 x 45.8
ASTAC1985.10

Rutherford, Harry 1903–1985
Paris Street Scene c.1960
oil on board 36 x 31
ASTAC2003.6

Rutherford, Harry 1903–1985
Sheila Mumford c.1960
oil on canvas 57 x 47
ASTAC1985.18

Rutherford, Harry 1903–1985
Vigo, Spain c.1960
oil on board 26.5 x 35.5
ASTAC2003.5

Rutherford, Harry 1903–1985
Yorkshire Street, Oldham, Lancashire 1965
oil on canvas 35.5 x 25.5
ASTAC1976.1

Rutherford, Harry 1903–1985
The Square, Hyde, Lancashire c.1970
oil on canvas 39.5 x 49.5
PCF1 (P)

Rutherford, Harry 1903–1985
Tap Room, Hyde, Lancashire 1975
oil on board 34.5 x 24
ASTAC1978.2

T. S.
Early Summer, River Scene with a Farmhouse
1886
oil on canvas 61 x 92
ASTAC1992.18

Sabela, H. J. active 1905–1907
Still Life with Fruit 1907
oil on canvas 35.5 x 46
ASTAC1986.21

Sánchez Coello, Alonso (circle of)
c.1531–1588
Portrait of a Lady
oil on canvas 71.5 x 56
ASTAC1932.4

Scott, David Montagu 1945–2001
Avenue, Broughton 1965–1975
oil on canvas 38.5 x 48.5
ASTAC1975.1

Sellaio, Jacopo del c.1441–1493
Virgin and Child in a Landscape
tempera on panel 98 x 60
ASTAC1932.13

Shackleton, William 1872–1933
Leda and the Swan 1928
oil on canvas 96.8 x 68.3
ASTAC1951.1

**Sicciolante da Sermonta, Girolamo
(attributed to)** 1521–c.1580
Virgin and Child before a Green Curtain
oil on panel 53.2 x 45.4
ASTAC1932.12

Sidley, Samuel 1829–1896
Mrs Gillingham Smith 1895
oil on canvas 124.5 x 81.5
ASTAC1986.13

Sidley, Samuel 1829–1896
Family Group
oil on canvas 206 x 140
ASTAC1986.25

Slack, H. N.
Stalybridge Market Place, Greater Manchester
1974
oil on board 44 x 60
ASTAC1974.1

Soyer, Paul Constant 1823–1903
The Mother 1868
oil on panel 45 x 37
ASTAC1935.3

Stokes, Adrian Durham 1902–1972
Olive Terraces
oil on canvas 62.5 x 75.1
ASTAC1972.1

Stokes, Adrian Durham 1902–1972
Olive Trees, Torre del Benaco, Italy
oil on canvas 75.5 x 63.4
ASTAC1968.1

Swinnerton, B. R.
Goldfish and Horse 1927
oil on panel 33.5 x 28
ASTAC1962.2

Taylor-Heap, Frank active 1950–1959
On Dartmoor, Devon 1950–1958
oil on board 35.5 x 45
ASTAC1959.2

Thompson, Alan J. b.1940
Bushes on a Hillside 1976
oil on canvas 34.5 x 44.5
ASTAC1979.6

Thompson, Alan J. b.1940
Mushrooms 1978
oil on canvas 29 x 39.5
ASTAC1979.5

Thornley, B. R.
Fishing Boats in a Harbour 1908
oil on canvas 60.5 x 91.5
ASTAC1992.97

Topolski, Feliks 1907–1989
The City (Married Life) 1946
oil on canvas 82.5 x 101.5
ASTAC1965.1

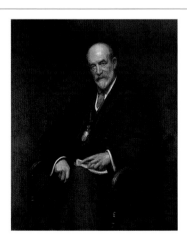

Townsend, Ernest 1885–1944
George Henry Kenyon (1840–1917) 1915
oil on canvas 125 x 105
PCF3 (P)

unknown artist
Edward Hyde (c.1650–1712), Governor of North Carolina (1710–1712) 1685–1695
oil on canvas 60 x 50
ASTAC1936.1

unknown artist
Italian Landscape (detail) 1800–1820
oil on canvas 135.5 x 150
ASTAC1992.84

unknown artist
Francis Dukinfield Astley in Procession as High Sheriff 1806–1807
oil on canvas 90 x 152
ASTAC1979.13

unknown artist
Portrait of a Gentleman 1815–1830
oil on canvas 100 x 158
ASTAC1986.24

unknown artist
Landscape with a River and Cliffs 1820–1860
oil on canvas 55 x 64
ASTAC1992.23

unknown artist
Scottish Woman and Child in a Landscape 1830–1840
oil on canvas 30.5 x 39
ASTAC1992.42

unknown artist
Joseph Hall, Master of the Staley Hunt 1840–1860
oil on canvas 186 x 91.5
ASTAC1956.4

unknown artist
Figures Outside a Cottage Dated 1720 1840–1870
oil on canvas 72 x 92
ASTAC1992.37

unknown artist
Landscape with a River and a Fisherman 1850–1880
oil on canvas 61 x 106.5
ASTAC1992.16

unknown artist
W. G. Bayley (1802–1891), Charter Mayor of Stalybridge (1857–1860?) 1857
oil on canvas 91.5 x 71
ASTAC1988.2

unknown artist
Besom Jack 1860–1870
oil on canvas 43 x 53.5
ASTAC1986.2

unknown artist
Chapel Street Sunday School, Stalybridge, Cheshire 1860–1880
oil on board 29 x 39.5
ASTAC1992.45

unknown artist
Portrait of a Woman with a Cameo
1860–1900
oil on canvas 31.5 x 21.5
ASTAC1992.12

unknown artist
Two Sheep and a Ram in a Barn 1870–1890
oil on board 40 x 32
ASTAC1992.92

unknown artist
Four Sheep and Two Lambs in a Barn
1870–1900
oil on board 40 x 32
ASTAC1992.93

unknown artist
Bamburgh Castle, Northumberland
1880–1910
oil on canvas 51 x 109.5
ASTAC1992.109

unknown artist
First Town Council, Borough of Dukinfield
1899
oil on canvas 192.5 x 60
ASTAC1992.85

A. W.
St Lawrence's Church, Denton, Lancashire 1901
oil on board 40.5 x 58
ASTAC1992.46

Facing page: Prinsep, Valentine Cameron, 1838–1904, *At the First Touch of Winter, Summer Fades Away*, 1897, Gallery Oldham (p. 42)

Walker, Edward Bent 1860–1917
The Musician
oil on canvas 57 x 49
ASTAC1941.1

Watts, George Frederick 1817–1904
Sir Perceval 1860–1904
oil on panel 55 x 24.5
ASTAC1932.22

Webb, James 1825–1895
View on the South Coast 1868
oil on canvas 92 x 153
ASTAC1936.3

Webb, William J. c.1830–c.1904
The Lost Sheep 1864
oil on canvas 76 x 61
ASTAC1932.45

Webbe, Jenny active 1983–1990
Model in a Yellow Gown 1983
oil on canvas 59 x 61
ASTAC1985.32

Webbe, Jenny active 1983–1990
Paula Sitting on the Radiator 1983–1986
oil on canvas 93.5 x 70
ASTAC1990.1

Wells, Henry Tanworth 1828–1903
J. F. Cheetham (1835–1916) 1880–1890
oil on canvas 111 x 85.5
ASTAC1932.56

Whitehead, F. (Mrs)
Dukinfield Old Hall Congregational Chapel, Cheshire 1980
oil on board 18.5 x 29.5
ASTAC1980.2

Wilde, Fred active 1961–1981
Wet Whit Walk 1975–1980
oil on canvas 24 x 36
ASTAC1981.1

Wilde, Fred active 1961–1981
'An dese teef ah ma own teef'
oil on board 43.5 x 65.2
ASTAC1981.3

Wilde, Fred active 1961–1981
'T'bull's getten loose'
oil on canvas 49.5 x 38
ASTAC1981.2

Wilson, Richard (follower of) 1714–1787
A Classical Landscape
oil on canvas 41.5 x 52
ASTAC1932.18

Wolfe, Edward 1897–1982
Hassan
oil on board 63.2 x 47.4
ASTAC1946.1

The Rutherford Gallery

The Rutherford Gallery is the newest art gallery in Tameside and aims to celebrate the artistic life of Harry Rutherford, a local artist with a national reputation, identified as one of the unsung heroes of the Lowry generation.

Upon the artist's death in 1985, Tameside Museums and Galleries Service were bequeathed approximately 80 works. The Collection now totals over 100 works on paper and canvas. In 2008 a special gallery was built to house and display the Collection as well as part of the artist's studio.

Much has been made of Rutherford's links with Walter Sickert, who himself named Rutherford as his natural follower. But it was his wit and quick eye for detail which has given him a place in the heart of Tameside residents and indeed everyone who has since come into contact with his work and character.

On permanent display is *Northern Saturday* from 1948, a painting of Hyde Market and a particular favourite among locals. The scene is a buzzing hive of activity and in the background are the hills and chimneys so reminiscent of northern towns.

Another favourite on permanent display is *Mill Girls, Ashton, Lancashire* which was the front cover for *John Bull Magazine* in 1948. Here, four giggling mill girls are leaving the mill after a long day's work. The four girls are, in fact, based on one muse: Bewley Fletcher, a local girl and a popular model for the artist.

It is Rutherford's depictions of streets rendered iridescent by the rain, the white-grey sky and the men in flat caps which really stand out. The simple colour palette matches the simple scenes from his studio window in Hyde. It is in these scenes that Harry Rutherford excels, always a believer in the importance of art with a local colour.

Harry Rutherford is perhaps better known for his television career which spans three decades, from the 1930s to the 1950s. Originally Rutherford was employed by BBC producer, Cecil Maddern, to sketch the variety acts live on his *Cabaret Cartoons* programme. It was not until the 1950s that he was able to showcase his natural wit and narrative talent with his own children's show *Sketchbook*. On the fifteen-minute programme he toured the nation's cities, sketching live and presenting his own script. The Rutherford Gallery owns two complete sets of these sketches depicting Lancaster and Bradford, and a selection are always on display.

Harry Rutherford painted less in his later years due to ill health, but some of his most significant and insightful paintings of local life are from this time. His work is of national importance due to his significant place in the development of British twentieth-century art and the contribution he made to the history of television.

Marie Holland, Curator of Art

Rutherford, Harry 1903–1985
The Model, Sickert's Class 1925
oil on canvas 51 x 40.5
L: ASTAC2009.10 (P)

Rutherford, Harry 1903–1985
The Comedians (Hyde Theatre) c.1926
oil on canvas 53.4 x 43
ASTAC1985.19

Rutherford, Harry 1903–1985
Theatre Royal, Hyde, Tameside c.1926
oil on canvas 61.5 x 51
ASTAC1985.23

Rutherford, Harry 1903–1985
Comedian's Corner 1932
oil on board 67 x 52
L: ASTAC2009.11 (P)

Rutherford, Harry 1903–1985
Great Yarmouth, Norfolk 1932
oil on board 92 x 123
L: ASTAC2009.2 (P)

Rutherford, Harry 1903–1985
*Sir John Barbirolli Conducting the Hallé
Orchestra* c.1945
oil on canvas 60.8 x 84
ASTAC1985.2

Rutherford, Harry 1903–1985
The Custodian 1947
oil on canvas 60 x 49.8
ASTAC1985.1

Rutherford, Harry 1903–1985
Mill Girls, Ashton, Lancashire 1948
oil on canvas 51 x 40.5
ASTAC1985.30

Rutherford, Harry 1903–1985
Northern Saturday 1948
oil on board 62 x 75
ASTAC1948.3

Rutherford, Harry 1903–1985
Blackpool Sands, Lancashire (study) c.1950
oil on board 13 x 19.5
ASTAC1985.9

Rutherford, Harry 1903–1985
*View from the Studio Window, Hyde,
Lancashire* c.1952
oil on board 55 x 46
ASTAC1985.21

Rutherford, Harry 1903–1985
The Red Caravan 1957
oil on board 30 x 44.5
ASTAC1985.6

Rutherford, Harry 1903–1985
Borneo Landscape, Indonesia 1958
oil on board 69 x 79.5
L: ASTAC2009.4 (P)

Rutherford, Harry 1903–1985
Bar Parlour c.1960
oil on canvas 47.5 x 37.8
ASTAC1985.7

Rutherford, Harry 1903–1985
Joan Hughes c.1960
oil on canvas 57 x 40.5
ASTAC1985.12

Rutherford, Harry 1903–1985
Near Bredon Hill, Worcestershire 1960s
oil on canvas 26.5 x 35.5
ASTAC2003.7

Rutherford, Harry 1903–1985
The Domino Players (recto) 1960s
oil on board 64 x 54
L: ASTAC2009.5 (P)

Rutherford, Harry 1903–1985
Street Scene (verso) 1960s
oil on board 54 x 64
L: ASTAC2009.5a (P)

Rutherford, Harry 1903–1985
Clarendon Hotel, Interior c.1965
oil on board 23.5 x 33.5
ASTAC1985.8

Rutherford, Harry 1903–1985
Conversation Piece, Rochdale, Lancashire
1967
oil on board 49.3 x 74.7
ASTAC1985.3

Rutherford, Harry 1903–1985
The Green Door 1968
oil on canvas 59.7 x 49.2
ASTAC1978.1

Rutherford, Harry 1903–1985
The Opening of the Chartists' Meeting House,
Hyde, Lancashire
oil on canvas 59.7 x 90.6
ASTAC1989.1

Facing page: Poole, Paul Falconer, 1807–1879, *Summer*, Stockport Heritage Services (p. 178)

Paintings Without Reproductions

This section lists all the paintings that have not been included in the main pages of the catalogue. They were excluded as it was not possible to photograph them for this project. Additional information relating to acquisition credit lines or loan details is also included. For this reason the information below is not repeated in the Further Information section.

Gallery Oldham

Ansdell, Richard 1815–1885, *Mother Love*, 30.4 x 50.8, oil, 5.54/2, gift from Mrs Deen, 1954, not available at the time of photography

Ashton, Andrew 1811–1883, *Old Mill, near Heywood, Lancashire*, oil, 7.9, unknown acquisition method, not available at the time of photography

J. B. *'Derelict in the Downs' Being Towed into Port*, oil, 10.55/8, gift from Mrs Comley, 1955, not available at the time of photography

Bates, John Stanley b.1871, *View behind the Parish Church, Oldham, Lancashire*, 1913, 67 x 45.5, oil on canvas, 2.81/108, purchased from the executors the estate of Lilian A. Bates, not available at the time of photography

Beattie, Christine *Untitled*, 79.5 x 123.5, acrylic on board, 3.83/12, unknown acquisition method, not available at the time of photography

Bornanelli (after) *Head of a Woman*, oil, 3.67/8, gift from Miss Ethel A. Mills, 1967, not available at the time of photography

Bottomley, Richard Oastler 1843–1886, *Startled Fox*, c.1870, oil on canvas, 63.37/2, gift from Charles L. Taylor, 1937, not available at the time of photography

Breanski, Alfred Fontville de 1877–1957, *Sunrise in a Welsh Valley*, 75 x 50, oil on canvas, 4.57, gift from Messrs Booth & Middleton, not available at the time of photography

Carse, James Howe 1819–1900, *Oldham Church from Goldburn, Oldham, Lancashire, 1760*, c.1860, 57 x 44.5, oil on canvas, 3.16/1, gift from Thomas Heywood, 1916, not available at the time of photography

Carse, James Howe 1819–1900, *Cherry Valley*, 75 x 62, oil on canvas, 71.33/1, gift from Mrs Whittaker, 1933, not available at the time of photography

Chesters, Stephen active 1885, *George Wainwright, Mayor of Oldham (1875–1876)*, 84.5 x 69, oil on canvas, 4.02, gift from Mrs Boger, 1902, not available at the time of photography

Dillon, Frank 1823–1909, *The Statues of Memnon*, 117.5 x 67.5, oil on canvas, 1.9, gift from William Agnew, 1890, not available at the time of photography

Elias, Alfred E. active 1875–1911, *In an Orchard*, 114 x 79, oil, 5.05, purchased from the artist, 1905, not available at the time of photography

Gordon, Jan (Godfrey Jervis) 1882–1944, *Regent Street, London*, oil, 56.37, purchased from the artist, 1937, not available at the time of photography

Hague, John Haughton 1842–1934, *An Old Waterway, Ashton-under-Lyne, Lancashire*, 1909, oil on canvas, 10.39, gift from F. Cummings, 1939, not available at the time of photography

Jackson, Frederick William 1859–1918, *Chew Brook*, c.1890, oil on canvas, 28.54/7, gift from Mr G. B. Taylor, 1954, not available at the time of photography

Pell, C. *Chadderton Park Road*, oil, 4.4, gift from Mrs W. T. Lees, 1940, not available at the time of photography

Pyne, James Baker 1800–1870, *The Meeting of the Severn and the Wye*, oil, 5.54/1, gift from Mrs Deen, 1954, not available at the time of photography

Radcliffe, Paul active 1956, *Nocturne*, oil, 42.56/2, purchased (?) from the artist, 1956, not available at the time of photography

Roche *John Nield*, oil, 11.49/1, gift from Mrs Chadwick, 1949, not available at the time of photography

Somerset, Richard Gay 1848–1928, *Scene, near Conway*, oil, 15.44/1, gift from E. Horrobin, 1944, not available at the time of photography

Steel, Thomas *Collie Dog*, oil, 29.49, acquired, 1949, not available at the time of photography

Stones, Sam active 1890–1891, *Emanuel Whittaker, Mayor of Oldham (1873–1874)*, 126 x 100, oil on canvas, 16.98, gift from the sitter's family, 1898, not available at the time of photography

Stott, William 1857–1900, *Morning in the Alps (White Mountain)*, oil on canvas, 18.53/1, gift from M. D. Stott, 1953, not available at the time of photography

Stott, William 1857–1900, *Road through the Wood, Concarneau, France*, oil on canvas, 9.47/5, gift from Raymond Stott, 1947, not available at the time of photography

Stubbs, Frederick J. *Scene, near Epping Forest*, oil, 1.55/1, gift from Mrs A. Rowbotton, 1955, not available at the time of photography

Tuson, George E. c.1820–1880, *The Right Reverend J. Fraser, Bishop of Manchester (1870–1885)*, 122 x 96.5, oil on canvas, 6.85, gift from Hilton Greaves, 1885, not available at the time of photography

unknown artist *Ellen Nield*, oil, 11.49/2, gift from Mrs Chadwick, 1949, not available at the time of photography

unknown artist *James Halliday*, 65 x 51.5, oil, 11.24, gift from Mrs E. H. Boardman 1924, not available at the time of photography

unknown artist *James Platt, MP for Oldham*, oil, 19.50/3, gift from the directors of Oldham Lyceum, 1950, not available at the time of photography

unknown artist *John Robinson, Mayor of the Borough (1867–1868)*, oil, 6.23, gift from Mrs Wood, 1923, not available at the time of photography

unknown artist *Landscape*, oil, 8.56, unknown acquisition method, not available at the time of photography

unknown artist *Madonna and Child*, oil, 6.75/20, gift from Mrs V. Smith, 1975, not available at the time of photography

unknown artist *Mary Anne Rowntree*, oil, 31.51/1, bequeathed by M. M. Rowntree, 1951, not available at the time of photography

unknown artist *Portrait of an Unknown Lady*, oil, 3.83/10, acquired, 1983, not available at the time of photography

unknown artist *Portrait of an Unknown Lady*, oil on canvas, 3.83/27, unknown acquisition method, not available at the time of photography

unknown artist *Portrait of an Unknown Man*, oil, 3.83/13, unknown acquisition method, not available at the time of photography

unknown artist *Portrait of an Unknown Man*, oil on canvas, G798, unknown acquisition method, not available at the time of photography

Vivian, Jane active 1861–1877, *Venice*, oil, 12.44/5, gift from J. T. Hague, 1944, not available at the time of photography

Walker, Ethel 1861–1951, *Lace Wrap*, 59 x 49, oil on canvas, G692, purchased from R. H. Spurr, not available at the time of photography

Weber, Antony active 1973, *L'Ardèche, France (series II)*, oil, 10.73/3, purchased from the artist, 1973, not available at the time of photography

Whittle, F. *George Wright-Oldham, Huntsman*, 71 x 58.5, oil, 7.21, gift from T. O. Schofield, 1921, not available at the time of photography

Wimpenny, George Henry 1857–1939, *Huntsmen at Hopwood Hall, Lancashire*, 1922, oil on canvas, 10.47, gift from Mr Worsley, 1947, not available at the time of photography

Wimpenny, George Henry 1857–1939, *James Nield*, oil on canvas, 19.50/1, gift from the directors of Oldham Lyceum, 1950, not available at the time of photography

Wimpenny, George Henry 1857–1939, *River Scene*, oil on canvas, 4.72/3, gift from J. W. Whiteley, 1972, not available at the time of photography

Wood, Stanley Llewelyn 1867–1928, *'Halt!', A Battery of Horse Artillery Coming into Position*, 47 x 34, oil on canvas, 2.93, purchased from the artist, 1893, not available at the time of photography

Rochdale Arts & Heritage Service

Collier, John 1708–1786, *Human Passions (The Drunkards)*, 47 x 33.5, oil on canvas, 889, purchased from Henry Spencer & Sons, 1971, not available at the time of photography

Fishwick, Janet active 1909–1913, *Nasturtiums*, oil, 111, not available at the time of photography

Garside, Oswald 1869–1942, *On the Scheldt*, oil, 644a, donated by the executors of the artist's estate, 1943, not available at the time of photography

Gere, Charles March 1869–1957, *Alpine Village in Northern Italy*, oil on canvas, 675, purchased from the artist, 1945, not available at the time of photography

Gallery Oldham

Ansdell, Richard 1815–1885, *Mother Love*, 30.4 x 50.8, oil, 5.54/2, gift from Mrs Deen, 1954, not available at the time of photography

Ashton, Andrew 1811–1883, *Old Mill, near Heywood, Lancashire*, oil, 7.9, unknown acquisition method, not available at the time of photography

J. B. *'Derelict in the Downs' Being Towed into Port*, oil, 10.55/8, gift from Mrs Comley, 1955, not available at the time of photography

Bates, John Stanley b.1871, *View behind the Parish Church, Oldham, Lancashire,* 1913, 67 x 45.5, oil on canvas, 2.81/108, purchased from the executors the estate of Lilian A. Bates, not available at the time of photography

Beattie, Christine *Untitled,* 79.5 x 123.5, acrylic on board, 3.83/12, unknown acquisition method, not available at the time of photography

Bornanelli (after) *Head of a Woman,* oil, 3.67/8, gift from Miss Ethel A. Mills, 1967, not available at the time of photography

Bottomley, Richard Oastler 1843–1886, *Startled Fox,* c.1870, oil on canvas, 63.37/2, gift from Charles L. Taylor, 1937, not available at the time of photography

Breanski, Alfred Fontville de 1877–1957, *Sunrise in a Welsh Valley,* 75 x 50, oil on canvas, 4.57, gift from Messrs Booth & Middleton, not available at the time of photography

Carse, James Howe 1819–1900, *Oldham Church from Goldburn, Oldham, Lancashire, 1760,* c.1860, 57 x 44.5, oil on canvas, 3.16/1, gift from Thomas Heywood, 1916, not available at the time of photography

Carse, James Howe 1819–1900, *Cherry Valley,* 75 x 62, oil on canvas, 71.33/1, gift from Mrs Whittaker, 1933, not available at the time of photography

Chesters, Stephen active 1885, *George Wainwright, Mayor of Oldham (1875–1876),* 84.5 x 69, oil on canvas, 4.02, gift from Mrs Boger, 1902, not available at the time of photography

Dillon, Frank 1823–1909, *The Statues of Memnon,* 117.5 x 67.5, oil on canvas, 1.9, gift from William Agnew, 1890, not available at the time of photography

Elias, Alfred E. active 1875–1911, *In an Orchard,* 114 x 79, oil, 5.05, purchased from the artist, 1905, not available at the time of photography

Gordon, Jan (Godfrey Jervis) 1882–1944, *Regent Street, London,* oil, 56.37, purchased from the artist, 1937, not available at the time of photography

Hague, John Haughton 1842–1934, *An Old Waterway, Ashton-under-Lyne, Lancashire,* 1909, oil on canvas, 10.39, gift from F. Cummings, 1939, not available at the time of photography

Jackson, Frederick William 1859–1918, *Chew Brook,* c.1890, oil on canvas, 28.54/7, gift from Mr G. B. Taylor, 1954, not available at the time of photography

Pell, C. *Chadderton Park Road,* oil, 4.4, gift from Mrs W. T. Lees, 1940, not available at the time of photography

Pyne, James Baker 1800–1870, *The Meeting of the Severn and the Wye,* oil, 5.54/1, gift from Mrs Deen, 1954, not available at the time of photography

Radcliffe, Paul active 1956, *Nocturne,* oil, 42.56/2, purchased (?) from the artist, 1956, not available at the time of photography

Roche *John Nield,* oil, 11.49/1, gift from Mrs Chadwick, 1949, not available at the time of photography

Somerset, Richard Gay 1848–1928, *Scene, near Conway,* oil, 15.44/1, gift from E. Horrobin, 1944, not available at the time of photography

Steel, Thomas *Collie Dog,* oil, 29.49, acquired, 1949, not available at the time of photography

Stones, Sam active 1890–1891, *Emanuel Whittaker, Mayor of Oldham (1873–1874),* 126 x 100, oil on canvas, 16.98, gift from the sitter's family, 1898, not available at the time of photography

Stott, William 1857–1900, *Morning in the Alps (White Mountain),* oil on canvas, 18.53/1, gift from M. D. Stott, 1953, not available at the time of photography

Stott, William 1857–1900, *Road through the Wood, Concarneau, France,* oil on canvas, 9.47/5, gift from Raymond Stott, 1947, not available at the time of photography

Stubbs, Frederick J. *Scene, near Epping Forest,* oil, 1.55/1, gift from Mrs A. Rowbotton, 1955, not available at the time of photography

Tuson, George E. c.1820–1880, *The Right Reverend J. Fraser, Bishop of Manchester (1870–1885),* 122 x 96.5, oil on canvas, 6.85, gift from Hilton Greaves, 1885, not available at the time of photography

unknown artist *Ellen Nield,* oil, 11.49/2, gift from Mrs Chadwick, 1949, not available at the time of photography

unknown artist *James Halliday,* 65 x 51.5, oil, 11.24, gift from Mrs E. H. Boardman 1924, not available at the time of photography

unknown artist *James Platt, MP for Oldham,* oil, 19.50/3, gift from the directors of Oldham Lyceum, 1950, not available at the time of photography

unknown artist *John Robinson, Mayor of the Borough (1867–1868),* oil, 6.23, gift from Mrs Wood, 1923, not available at the time of photography

unknown artist *Landscape,* oil, 8.56, unknown acquisition method, not available at the time of photography

unknown artist *Madonna and Child,* oil, 6.75/20, gift from Mrs V. Smith, 1975, not available at the time of photography

unknown artist *Mary Anne Rowntree,* oil, 31.51/1, bequeathed by M. M. Rowntree, 1951, not available at the time of photography

unknown artist *Portrait of an Unknown Lady,* oil, 3.83/10, acquired, 1983, not available at the time of photography

unknown artist *Portrait of an Unknown Lady,* oil on canvas, 3.83/27, unknown acquisition method, not available at the time of photography

unknown artist *Portrait of an Unknown Man,* oil, 3.83/13, unknown acquisition method, not available at the time of photography

unknown artist *Portrait of an Unknown Man,* oil on canvas, G798, unknown acquisition method, not available at the time of photography

Vivian, Jane active 1861–1877, *Venice,* oil, 12.44/5, gift from J. T. Hague, 1944, not available at the time of photography

Walker, Ethel 1861–1951, *Lace Wrap,* 59 x 49, oil on canvas, G692, purchased from R. H. Spurr, not available at the time of photography

Weber, Antony active 1973, *L'Ardèche, France* (series II), oil, 10.73/3, purchased from the artist, 1973, not available at the time of photography

Whittle, F. *George Wright-Oldham, Huntsman,* 71 x 58.5, oil, 7.21, gift from T. O. Schofield, 1921, not available at the time of photography

Wimpenny, George Henry 1857–1939, *Huntsmen at Hopwood Hall, Lancashire,* 1922, oil on canvas, 10.47, gift from Mr Worsley, 1947, not available at the time of photography

Wimpenny, George Henry 1857–1939, *James Nield,* oil on canvas, 19.50/1, gift from the directors of Oldham Lyceum, 1950, not available at the time of photography

Wimpenny, George Henry 1857–1939, *River Scene,* oil on canvas, 4.72/3, gift from J. W. Whiteley, 1972, not available at the time of photography

Wood, Stanley Llewelyn 1867–1928, '*Halt!', A Battery of Horse Artillery Coming into Position,* 47 x 34, oil on canvas, 2.93, purchased from the artist, 1893, not available at the time of photography

Rochdale Arts & Heritage Service

Collier, John 1708–1786, *Human Passions (The Drunkards),* 47 x 33.5, oil on canvas, 889, purchased from Henry Spencer & Sons, 1971, not available at the time of photography

Fishwick, Janet active 1909–1913, *Nasturtiums,* oil, 111, not available at the time of photography

Garside, Oswald 1869–1942, *On the Scheldt,* oil, 644a, donated by the executors of the artist's estate, 1943, not available at the time of photography

Gere, Charles March 1869–1957, *Alpine Village in Northern Italy,* oil on canvas, 675, purchased from the artist, 1945, not available at the time of photography

Lonsdale, James 1777–1839, *John Entwistle,* 91 x 71.6, oil on canvas, 1106, not available at the time of photography

Partington, John Herbert Evelyn 1843–1899, *Edwin Waugh (1817–1890),* oil on canvas, 7, not available at the time of photography

Sims, Charles 1873–1928, *George Leach Ashworth (1823–1873),* 90 x 70, oil on canvas, 601, not available at the time of photography

Skeaping, Kenneth Mathieson 1857–1946, *Benjamin Heape (1780–1847),* 142.5 x 112, oil on canvas, 1129, not available at the time of photography

Skeaping, Kenneth Mathieson 1857–1946, *Robert Taylor Heape (1848–1917),* 142.7 x 102, oil on canvas, 1128, not available at the time of photography

unknown artist *Benjamin Heape (1780–1847),* oil, 447, gift from Richard Heape, 1919, not available at the time of photography

unknown artist *James Dearden (1774–1825),* oil, 449, gift from Mrs Cryer, 1919, not available at the time of photography

unknown artist *John Ashworth (1813–1875), Author of 'Strange Tales',* oil, 130, purchased, 1908, not available at the time of photography

unknown artist *Richard II (1367–1400), King of England,* 64 x 46.3, oil, 1231, acquired via the Thomas Kay Bequest, 1912; transferred from Heywood, 1974, not available at the time of photography

unknown artist *Sir John Thomas Potter,* oil on canvas, 8, gift from J. Potter, 1878, not available at the time of photography

unknown artist *T. B. Potter,* oil, 12, not available at the time of photography

A. V. W. *Clegg Hall, Rochdale, Lancashire,* 1909, 34 x 49.5, oil on canvas, 1205, not available at the time of photography

STOLEN

Rochdale Arts & Heritage Service

Cooper, Thomas Sidney 1803–1902, *Landscape,* 1890, 41 x 31, oil on canvas, 772, gift from Mrs M. Heath, 1956; stolen, 1991

Wood, Edgar Thomas 1860–1935, *Moroccan Scene (1),* 25.6 x 18.4, oil on board, 1284, transferred from Middleton Library, 1984

Wood, Edgar Thomas 1860–1935, *Moroccan Scene (2),* 17.8 x 24.8, oil on board, 1285, transferred from Middleton Library, 1984

Wood, Edgar Thomas 1860–1935, *Moroccan Scene (3),* 1914, 24.7 x 17.8, oil on board, 1286, transferred from Middleton Library, 1984

Further Information

The paintings listed in this section have additional information relating to one or more of the five categories outlined below. This extra information is only provided where it is applicable and where it exists. Paintings listed in this section follow the same order as in the illustrated pages of the catalogue.

I   The full name of the artist if this was too long to display in the illustrated pages of the catalogue. Such cases are marked in the catalogue with a (…).

II   The full title of the painting if this was too long to display in the illustrated pages of the catalogue. Such cases are marked in the catalogue with a (…).

III   Acquisition information or acquisition credit lines as well as information about loans, copied from the records of the owner collection.

IV   Artist copyright credit lines where the copyright owner has been traced. Exhaustive efforts have been made to locate the copyright owners of all the images included within this catalogue and to meet their requirements. Any omissions or mistakes brought to our attention will be duly attended to and corrected in future publications.

V   The credit line of the lender of the transparency if the transparency has been borrowed. Bridgeman images are available subject to any relevant copyright approvals from the Bridgeman Art Library at www.bridgemanart.com

---

Gallery Oldham

Adam, Patrick William 1854–1929, *Interior, Morning*, purchased from the artist, 1912, photo credit: www.bridgemanart.com

Adams, William Dacres 1864–1951, *Southwark Cathedral, London*, purchased from the artist, 1922

Aikman, George W. 1831–1905, *Weighing the Anchor*, gift from Charles Edward Lees, 1893

Allinson, Adrian Paul 1890–1959, *Somerset Farm*, purchased from R. H. Spurr, 1950, photo credit: www.bridgemanart.com

Anne, Atia Islam b.1962, *Cancer*, purchased from the artist, 2002

Anne, Atia Islam b.1962, *Insulin*, purchased from the artist with the assistance of the British Council

Anrooy, Anton Abraham van 1870–1949, *No.182 Ebury Street, London*, purchased from the artist

Anthony, Henry Mark 1817–1886, *Huge Oak that O'ershadows the Mill*, gift from Mrs Ellen Butler, 1903

Appleton, John H. active 19th C, *William Noton, Mayor of Oldham (1892–1893)*, gift from the sitter, 1898

Ashton, Andrew 1811–1883, *William Johnson Fox (1786–1864), MP*, gift from W. Mackie, 1929

Ashton, Andrew 1811–1883, *James Mellodew, JP, Mayor of Oldham (1874–1875)*, unknown acquisition method

Auerbach, Frank Helmuth b.1931, *E. O. W. on Her Blue Eiderdown*, unknown acquisition method, © the artist

Baker, Christopher b.1956, *Arena*, gift from the Contemporary Art Society, 1986

Banner, Delmar Harmond 1896–1983, *Coniston Fell, Lancashire, from Harter Fell, Cumberland*, gift from Mrs J. Barnes, © the artist's estate

Barnes, Archibald George 1887–1972, *The Red Lacquer Cabinet*, purchased from the Fine Art Society, 1923

Bartlett, William Henry 1858–1932, *Unloading Kelp Weed*, gift from Mrs Hallsworth, 1952

Bates, John Stanley b.1871, *Albion Street, Oldham, Lancashire, 1910*, unknown acquisition method

Baxter, Charles 1809–1879, *Portrait Study (Rose)*, bequeathed by Mrs J. Wilde Clegg, 1918

Bayes, Walter 1869–1956, *A boire*, gift from Charles Hardman, 1920, © the artist's estate, photo credit: www.bridgemanart.com

Bayliss, Wyke 1835–1906, *The Basilica of St Mark's, Venice, Interior*, purchased from the artist, 1892

Beattie-Brown, William 1831–1909, *The River Dochert, at Killin, Perthshire*, purchased from the artist, 1900

Beeton, Alan 1880–1942, *Girl in a Wood*, purchased from the artist, 1926

Bhattacharjee, Shishir b.1960,

Untitled, purchased from the artist, 2002

Birch, Samuel John Lamorna 1869–1955, *The Serpentine Quarry, near Mullion, Cornwall*, purchased from the artist, 1921, © the artist's estate

Blow, Sandra 1925–2006, *Number Seventeen*, purchased from the Gimpel Fils Gallery, 1962, © the artist's estate

Boddington, Henry John 1811–1865, *Morning on the Usk*, gift from Miss Ethel A. Mills

Bold, John 1895–1979, *A North Country Landscape*, purchased from the Tib Lane Gallery, 1961

Bold, John 1895–1979, *Blackstone Edge*, gift from John Brown, 1976

Bomberg, David 1890–1957, *Toledo, Spain*, gift from the Contemporary Art Society, 1944, © the artist's family

Booth, Samuel Lawson 1836–1928, *Tŷ Croes, near Holyhead, Anglesey*, gift from F. Brewer, 1944

Bottomley, Edwin 1865–1929, *The Saddleworth Viaduct, Oldham, Lancashire*, purchased from Mrs Mary MacDonald, 1987

Bottomley, Eric b.1948, *Oldham, Lancashire, Clegg Street Station, 1953*, gift from Mrs Porter, 1998, © the artist

Bottomley, Richard Oastler 1843–1886, *On the Greta, County Durham*, gift from Mrs Wharton, 1935

Bottomley, Richard Oastler 1843–1886, *Chadderton Park,*

Oldham, Lancashire (Road through Nordens), purchased, 1889

Bowie, Janis b.1956, *Spinning Mules 3 and 4*, purchased from the artist, 2006, © the artist

Bradley, Basil 1842–1904, *Hard Times*, purchased from the artist, 1901

Bradley, Helen 1900–1979, *A Special Treat*, purchased at Sotheby's, 2005

Bradley, Helen 1900–1979, *It was early spring...' (Fire on Union Street)*, purchased from the Mercury Gallery, 1970

Bradley, Helen 1900–1979, *'Buckley & Proctor'*, gift from the artist, 1975

Bratby, John Randall 1928–1992, *Sewing Machine, Wife and Baby*, unknown acquisition method, © the artist's estate/Bridgeman Art Library

Brooker, William 1918–1983, *Orange Label*, purchased from Arthur Tooth & Sons, 1966, © the artist's estate

Buckley, John *Yellow Scape*, unknown acquisition method

Budd, Herbert Ashwin 1881–1950, *The Bird Shop*, purchased from the artist, 1922

Bundy, Edgar 1862–1922, *The Puritans*, purchased from the artist, 1898

Burn, Rodney Joseph 1899–1984, *St Brelade's Bay, Jersey*, gift from the S. I. V. Cooke Fund, administered by the Royal Academy, 1989, © the artist's estate

Carse, James Howe 1819–1900,

Oldham, Lancashire, from Glodwick Fields, gift from Thomas Heywood, 1916

Carse, James Howe 1819–1900, *Uppermill from Dobcross, Oldham, Lancashire*, gift from Mrs J. W. Lees, 1927

Carse, James Howe 1819–1900, *Opening Game of the Oldham Subscription Bowling Green, Frankhill, 1860*, gift from George Fletcher

Carse, James Howe 1819–1900, *Medlock Vale in 1866, Oldham, Lancashire*, gift from Dr James Yates, 1907

Carse, James Howe 1819–1900, *Nordens, Oldham, Lancashire*, gift from Mrs Whittaker, 1933

Carse, James Howe 1819–1900, *Sheepwashes Brook*, gift from Thomas Heywood

Chakma, Kanak Chanpa b.1963, *In the Red*, commissioned, 2002

Charles, James 1851–1906, *Hide and Seek*, gift from W. H. Wood, 1924

Charles, James 1851–1906, *Companions*, gift from H. L. Hargreaves, 1908

Charles, James 1851–1906, *Joshua Walmsley Radcliffe, Mayor of Oldham (1884–1887)*, unknown acquisition method

Chevska, Maria b.1948, *Tantamount* (diptych, left panel), gift from the Contemporary Art Society, 1992, © the artist

Chevska, Maria b.1948, *Tantamount* (diptych, right panel), gift from the Contemporary Art

226

Society, 1992, © the artist

Chuhan, J. b.1955, *Cha*, purchased from the artist, 1984, © J. Chuhan

Clausen, George 1852–1944, *Phyllis*, gift from Marjory Lees, 1952, © Clausen estate

Codrington, Isabel 1874–1943, *Old Tramp*, purchased from the artist, 1928

Collier, John 1850–1934, *The Death of Cleopatra*, purchased from the artist, 1891, photo credit: www.bridgemanart.com

Collier, John 1850–1934, *A Street in Jerusalem*, purchased from the artist, 1927

Collier, John 1850–1934, *Samuel Radcliffe Platt, Mayor of Oldham (1887–1889)*, gift from Charles E. Lees, 1893

Colman, Samuel 1780–1845, *Belshazzar's Feast*, gift from J. Mellor, 1895, photo credit: www.bridgemanart.com

Connard, Philip 1875–1958, *A Chelsea Interior*, purchased from the artist, 1914, photo credit: www.bridgemanart.com

Connard, Philip 1875–1958, *Merry England*, purchased from the artist, 1937

Cooper, Thomas Sidney 1803–1902, *Cattle*, bequeathed by Mrs J. Wilde Clegg, 1918

Cope, Charles West 1811–1890, *George Herbert and His Mother*, gift from Mrs G. Taylor, 1910, photo credit: www.bridgemanart.com

Cotman, Frederick George 1850–1920, *Her Ladyship's First Lesson*, purchased from the artist, 1890

Craxton, John 1922–2009, *Beach Scene*, gift from the Contemporary Art Society, 1956, © estate of John Craxton 2011. All rights reserved, DACS

Crossley, Terence active 1975–1981, *And the Blind Eye Creates*, purchased from the artist, 1981

Crossley, Terence active 1975–1981, *Man Sitting in a Pub*, gift from Werneth Labour Club, 1975

Crozier, George 1846–1914, *Reverend R. M. Davies*, gift from Mrs E. Davies, 1908

Cundall, Charles Ernest 1890–1971, *Early Morning, Josselin, France*, unknown acquisition method, © the artist's estate/Bridgeman Art Library

Cundall, Charles Ernest 1890–1971, *La passerelle*, unknown acquisition method, © the artist's estate/Bridgeman Art Library

Darien, Henri Gaston 1864–1926, *Quai Malaquais, Paris, Twilight*, bequeathed by S. Taylor-Whitehead, 1892

Davey, Derek active 1980–2002, *Remembrance Day*, purchased from the artist, 2002

Davidson, T. *Girl with Red Hair*, unknown acquisition method

Davies, James Hey 1844–1930, *Scared*, purchased from the artist,

1888

Davies, John R. 1899–1985, *Sisteron, France*, purchased from the Manchester Academy Exhibition, 1951

Delmard, M. *Goatherd*, unknown acquisition method

Dicksee, Margaret Isabel 1859–1903, *The Children of Charles I*, purchased from the artist, 1896, photo credit: www.bridgemanart.com

Dicksee, Thomas Francis 1819–1895, *Little Florist*, bequeathed by Amy Agnes Goodall, 1969

Dobson, William Charles Thomas 1817–1898, *Wild Flowers*, bequeathed by Mrs J. Wilde Clegg, 1918

Downing, Charles Palmer c.1848–1902, *William Jones, First Mayor of Oldham*, gift from William & James Jones, 1898

Downing, Charles Palmer c.1848–1902, *William Jones, First Mayor of Oldham*, gift from Captain Ashley Jones, 1960

Dunlop, Ronald Ossory 1894–1973, *Chrysanthemums*, purchased from R. H. Spurr, 1950

Dunlop, Ronald Ossory 1894–1973, *Faith*, gift from the Contemporary Art Society, 1933

Durnini, F. *La Madonna della sedia* (copy after Raphael), gift from Miss Ethel A. Mills, 1967

Dvorak, Franz 1862–1927, *Saint Laurence Distributing the Treasures of the Church to the Poor*, purchased from the artist, 1899

Easby, Steve b.1958, *Suspension*, purchased from the artist, 1981, © the artist

East, Alfred 1844–1913, *Autumn in the Valley of the Ouse, Sussex*, purchased from the artist, 1907

Ellis, William 1747–1810, *Cader Idris, Gwynedd*, transferred from Failsworth Library, 1878

Emsley, Walter 1860–1938, *George Hanson, Mayor of Oldham (1902–1903)*, gift from the Union Congregational Sunday School, 1911

Etty, William 1787–1849, *Female Nude*, purchased from the Leger Galleries, 1966

Eurich, Richard Ernst 1903–1992, *The Donkey Boy*, purchased from The Redfern Gallery, 1953, © the artist's estate/Bridgeman Art Library

Fantin-Latour, Henri 1836–1904, *Roses II*, gift from Marjory Lees, 1952

Fidler, Harry 1856–1935, *Work*, purchased from the artist, 1929

Fish, G. W. active 1893–c.1900, *Winston L. S. Churchill (1874–1965), MP for Oldham (1900–1905)*, gift from R. F. Ware, 1903

Fisher, Mark 1841–1923, *The Manor Farm*, purchased from the artist, 1907, photo credit: www.bridgemanart.com

Fisher, Samuel Melton 1859–1939,

Dreams, E dolce dormire, purchased from the artist, 1902, photo credit: www.bridgemanart.com

Fitton, Harvey *Press Conference*, purchased from Thomas Griffiths, 1949

Fitton, James 1899–1982, *Doll on a Chair*, purchased from Miss M. Tate with the assistance of the Museums, Libraries and Archives Council/Victoria and Albert Museum Purchase Grant Fund, 1983, © the artist's estate

Fitton, James 1899–1982, *Tavern Brawl*, unknown acquisition method, © the artist's estate

Fletcher, Geoffrey Scowcroft 1923–2004, *A Summer Afternoon*, acquired from Mr Clegg

Fletcher, William Teulon Blandford 1858–1936, *'O yez, o yez!'*, purchased from the artist, 1890

Foottet, Frederick Francis 1850–1935, *The Orchard*, gift from Miss A. M. Alexander, 1935

Forbes, Stanhope Alexander 1857–1947, *The Drinking Place*, purchased from the artist, 1901, © the artist's estate/Bridgeman Art Library

Foweraker, Albert Moulton 1873–1942, *Bridge of St Bénézet at the Palace of the Popes, Avignon, France*, purchased from the artist, 1909

France, Ada active 1900–1906, *Red Setter*, gift from R. H. Makin, 1977

Frost, Terry 1915–2003, *59/60*, purchased from the Waddington Gallery, 1962, © estate of Terry Frost. All rights reserved, DACS 2011

Gabain, Ethel Leontine 1883–1950, *Adelaide Stanley as Kate in 'The Two Bouquets' (from the play by Herbert Farjeon)*, purchased from the artist, 1937, © the artist's estate

Gertler, Mark 1891–1939, *Tulips and Mimosa*, gift from the Contemporary Art Society, 1935

Gibbs, Thomas Binney 1870–1947, *Samuel Buckley, Mayor of Oldham (1883–1884 & 1889–1891)*, gift from the sitter, 1907

Gibson, William Alfred 1866–1931, *Near Savona, Italy*, purchased from the artist, 1913

Gledhill, James active 1884–1891, *Farm Scene*, purchased from Percy Jones, 1939

Gledhill, James active 1884–1891, *Landscape*, purchased from Ronald Gledhill, 1978

Gledhill, James active 1884–1891, *Landscape with Cattle*, purchased from Percy Jones, 1937

Gledhill, James active 1884–1891, *Turnip Field*, purchased from Ronald Gledhill, 1978

Gledhill, James active 1884–1891, *Welsh Peasants Crossing the Conway, High Spring Tide*, gift from Charles L. Taylor, 1937

Glendening, Alfred Augustus 1840–1921, *On the Thames*, transferred from Failsworth

Library, 1978

Glendening, Alfred Augustus 1840–1921, *View near Kenmore, Loch Tay, Perthshire*, gift from Eli Ormrod, 1939

Gordon, Cora Josephine 1879–1950, *Flatford Pool, Suffolk*, purchased from the artist, 1937

Gosse, Laura Sylvia 1881–1968, *Dieppe, France*, purchased from the Charles Jackson Galleries, 1933, © the artist's estate/Bridgeman Art Library, photo credit: www.bridgemanart.com

Gow, Andrew Carrick 1848–1920, *Napoleon on the Sands at Boulogne, France*, purchased from the artist, 1898

Grassel, Franz 1861–1948, *Weiße Enten in Wasser*, purchased from the artist

Greuze, Jean-Baptiste (attributed to) 1725–1805, *Portrait of a Woman*, unknown acquisition method

Grice, Albert active 1973–1974, *Platting Road, Oldham, Lancashire*, purchased from the artist, 1974

Grice, Albert active 1973–1974, *Hawthorns*, purchased from the artist, 1974

Grice, Albert active 1973–1974, *L. S. Lowry (1887–1796)*, purchased from the artist

Griffith, Thomas *View on Yorkshire Street, Oldham, Lancashire*, purchased from the artist, 1949

Grosvenor, Thomas active 1909, *Houghton Mill on the Ouse*, purchased from the artist, 1909

Gwynne-Jones, Allan 1892–1982, *The Soldier's Daughter*, purchased from the artist, 1932, © the artist's estate/Bridgeman Art Library

Hacker, Arthur 1858–1919, *A Difficulty*, purchased, 1908, photo credit: www.bridgemanart.com

Hague, John Haughton 1842–1934, *Keeper's Cottage, Chadderton Park, Oldham, Lancashire*, purchased from Percy Jones, 1933

Hague, John Haughton 1842–1934, *Oldham Street Sweepers, Lancashire*, bequeathed by Mrs Eva Sherwood, 1933

Hague, John Haughton 1842–1934, *The Chadderton Taxidermist*, unknown acquisition method

Hague, John Haughton 1842–1934, *The Old Bridge, Chadderton Fold, Oldham, Lancashire*, gift from Miss Johnson, 1883

Hague, John Haughton 1842–1934, *Washing Day, Bishop Lakes House, Chadderton, Oldham, Lancashire*, purchased from Henry Nuttall, 1935

Hague, John Haughton 1842–1934, *Weaver and a Magpie*, gift from the artist, 1884

Hague, John Haughton 1842–1934, *Chadderton Fold, Oldham, Lancashire, 1881*, gift from Sir George Allen Mellor, 1926

Hague, John Haughton 1842–1934, *Riversdale, Bardsley, Lancashire*, purchased from Ernest Pennington, 1937

Hague, John Haughton 1842–1934, *John Dodd, President of Oldham Lyceum (1898–1899)*, gift from Oldham Lyceum via Mr Heywood, 1981

Hague, John Haughton 1842–1934, *Strawberry Gardens*, gift from Mr E. Lloyd, 1975, photo credit: www.bridgemanart.com

Hall, H. R. active 1895–1902, *Denizen of the Highlands*, transferred from Failsworth Library, 1978

Hall, H. R. active 1895–1902, *Highland Cattle*, transferred from Failsworth Library, 1978

Hampson, Mark b.1968, *A Brief History of Romance: The Romance of History*, purchased with the assistance of the Museums, Libraries and Archives Council/Victoria and Albert Museum Purchase Grant Fund, 2007, © the artist

Hardy, Frederick Daniel 1827–1911, *Paid Off*, bequeathed by Mrs J. Wilde Clegg, 1918

Hardy, Frederick Daniel 1827–1911, *The Wedding Dress*, bequeathed by Mrs J. Wilde Clegg, 1918

Hare, Julius 1859–1932, *Day Fades*, purchased from Julius Hare, 1888

Harvey, Harold C. 1874–1941, *My Kitchen*, purchased from the artist, 1924, © the artist's estate/Bridgeman Art Library

Hayter, George 1792–1871, *John Fielden (1784–1849)*, purchased from Agnew & Sons Ltd

Hearne, Edward active 1934, *Chamber Hall Barn*, purchased from the artist, 1934

Hearne, Edward active 1934, *The Demolition of Copster Mill, Oldham, Lancashire*, purchased, 2008

Helcke, Arnold c.1843–1912, *Squally Weather, Coast of Guernsey*, purchased from the artist, 1890

Hemy, Charles Napier 1841–1917, *Boat Adrift*, purchased from the artist, 1890

Henderson, William Samuel P. 1816–1876, *A Hard Word*, purchased from M. Newman Ltd, 1965

Herkomer, Hubert von 1849–1914, *Toreador of Valencia*, purchased from the artist, 1913

Heron, Patrick 1920–1999, *Scarlet and Green in Brown, November, 1961*, purchased from the Waddington Galleries, 1962, © Susanna Heron. All rights reserved, DACS 2011

Heywood, Thomas 1846–1919, *Dead Game*, purchased from Percy Jones, 1941

Heywood, Thomas 1846–1919, *Landscape, North Wales (Harvest)*, purchased from the artist

Heywood, Thomas 1846–1919,

Spaniel and Rabbit, purchased from the artist

Hill, Adrian Keith Graham 1895–1977, *Farm at Singleton, Lancashire*, gift from Hesketh Hubbard

Hillier, Tristram Paul 1905–1983, *Trujillo, Spain*, purchased from Arthur Tooth & Sons, 1966, © the artist's estate/Bridgeman Art Library

Hodgkin, Howard b.1932, *Husband and Wife*, presented by the Contemporary Art Society, 1968, © Howard Hodgkin

Hoggatt, William 1879–1961, *In the Lezayre Valley, Isle of Man*, purchased from the artist, 1928

Holland, John 1830–1886, *Crompton from Tandle Hills, Royton, Lancashire*, unknown acquisition method

Holt, S. F. *Sheep in a Stable*, transferred from Failsworth Library, 1978

Hook, James Clarke 1819–1907, *The Mackerel Take*, gift from the family of James Stott, 1923

Hornel, Edward Atkinson 1864–1933, *A Summer Idyll*, purchased from the artist, 1910

Horsley, John Callcott 1817–1903, *Josiah Radcliffe, Mayor of Oldham (1856–1858)*, unknown acquisition method

Houston, George 1869–1947, *An Ayrshire Glen*, purchased from the artist, 1911, © the artist's estate

Hoyland, John b.1934, *Untitled*, gift from the Contemporary Art Society, 1983, © John Hoyland. All rights reserved, DACS 2011

Hutchinson, Michael *Delph Donkey at the Measurements Factory, Oldham, Lancashire*, unknown acquisition method

Hutchison, Robert Gemmell 1855–1936, *The Young Laird*, purchased from the artist, 1919

Ibbotson, Karen *Memory I*, unknown acquisition method

Ince, Charles Percy 1875–1952, *Monuments, Men's Movement, Time's Conquest*, purchased from the artist, 1923

Jackson *Moses Mills (the last Head Constable of Oldham prior to the incorporation of the borough)*, gift from Mrs E. Mills, 1948

Jackson, Frederick William 1859–1918, *In Summer Time*, gift from Mrs Eleanor Deerr, 1960

Jackson, Frederick William 1859–1918, *Runswick Bay, North Yorkshire*, gift from Mrs Walter Maw, 1937

Jackson, Frederick William 1859–1918, *Abraham Crompton, Mayor of Oldham (1871–1872)*, gift from the sitter, 1902

Jackson, Frederick William 1859–1918, *Alfred Waddington, Mayor of Oldham (1897–1898)*, gift

Jackson, Frederick William 1859–1918, *Drinking Trough*, purchased from Percy Jones, 1938

Jackson, Frederick William 1859–1918, *Henry Lees*

Hollingsworth, gift from Mr Boswell, 1955

Jackson, Frederick William 1859–1918, *Herbert Wilde, Mayor of Oldham (1913–1914)*, gift from Mrs H. Wilde, 1915

Jackson, Frederick William 1859–1918, *Jackson Brierley, Mayor of Oldham (1898–1899)*, gift, 1901

Jackson, Frederick William 1859–1918, *James Yates, Mayor of Oldham (1880–1882 & 1904–1905)*, gift from Dr James Yates, 1906

Jackson, Frederick William 1859–1918, *John Armitage, Headmaster of Oldham Technical School*, gift from Oldham Technical Students' Association

Jackson, Frederick William 1859–1918, *Robert Jackson, Organist of St Peter's Church*, gift from Oldham Musical Society, 1907

Jackson, Frederick William 1859–1918, *Robin Hood's Bay, North Yorkshire*, gift from Mrs Eleanor Deerr, 1960

Jackson, Frederick William 1859–1918, *Scene in Capri, Italy*, unknown acquisition method

Jackson, Frederick William 1859–1918, *The Green Tub*, gift from the F. W. Jackson Memorial Committee, 1920

Jackson, Frederick William 1859–1918, *The Harvest of the Sea*, purchased from the artist, 1889

Jackson, Frederick William 1859–1918, *Thomas Bolton, Mayor of Oldham (1908–1909)*, gift from the sitter, 1910

Jackson, Thomas Graham 1835–1924, *View near Morecambe, Lancashire*, gift from Mrs A. Rowbotton, 1955

Jackson, William *Railway Scene*, unknown acquisition method

Jamieson, Alexander 1873–1937, *The Frozen Meadow, Winter 1929*, purchased from the artist, 1931

Jamieson, Robert Kirkland 1881–1950, *Approach to a Cotswold Village*, purchased from the artist, 1939

Jenkins, Paul b.1923, *Phenomena, If Is for Why*, purchased from Arthur Tooth & Sons, 1965, © Paul Jenkins/ ADAGP, Paris and DACS, London 2011

Johnston, W. Herbert active 1882–1892, *William Wrigley, Mayor of Oldham (1872–1873)*, gift from Mrs Wrigley

Jones, Phyllis active 1983, *Dancers on a Chequered Floor*, gift from the artist, 1983

Jones, Phyllis active 1983, *Model in a Room*, gift from the artist

Jones, Wil b.1960, *Eric Sykes (b.1923)*, gift from the artist, 2008, © the artist

Joy, George William 1844–1925, *A Dinner of Herbs*, purchased from the artist, 1905

Keating, John 1889–1977, *Night's Candles Are Burnt Out*, purchased from the artist, 1931, photo credit: www.bridgemanart.com

Kehoe *Sir George William Needham (1843–1928)*, gift from Mrs and Mr Needham, 1995

Kelly, Gerald Festus 1879–1972, *The Burmese Dancer IV*, purchased from the artist, 1922

Kemm, Robert 1830–1895, *Missing*, purchased from the artist, 1889

Kershaw, Joseph Franklin 1885–1917, *Portrait of a South Kensington Model*, gift from Mrs E. Kershaw via Oldham School of Art, 1920

Kershaw, Joseph Franklin 1885–1917, *The Meeting of Spring and Winter*, gift from Mrs Hardman, 1953

Kershaw, Joseph Franklin 1885–1917, *Washing Day*, gift from Mrs Hardman, 1953

King, Henry John Yeend 1855–1924, *Girls Herding Geese*, gift from Miss Whitehead, 1951

King, Henry John Yeend 1855–1924, *The Mill Stream*, gift from Miss Whitehead, 1951

Knight, John William Buxton 1843–1908, *Portsmouth Harbour, Hampshire*, unknown acquisition method

Knight, Joseph 1837–1909, *Meadow Scene*, gift from Miss Ethel A. Mills

Knight, Joseph 1837–1909, *Snowdonia*, purchased from the artist, 1888

Knight, Joseph 1837–1909, *Wood with a Woman, Sheep and a Boy (Meadow Scene)*, gift from Miss Ethel A. Mills, 1967

Knight, Laura 1877–1970, *A Theatre Dressing Room*, purchased from the Fine Art Society, 1956, © reproduced with permission of the estate of Dame Laura Knight, DBE, RA, 2011. All rights reserved

Knight, Patrick active 19th C, *John Platt, MP for Oldham (1865–1872)* (after James Sant), gift, 1898

Knowles, George Sheridan 1863–1931, *Seeking Sanctuary*, purchased from the artist, 1896, photo credit: www.bridgemanart.com

La Thangue, Henry Herbert 1859–1929, *The Last Furrow*, unknown acquisition method, photo credit: www.bridgemanart.com

La Thangue, Henry Herbert 1859–1929, *Packing Stocks*, bequeathed by Mrs K. La Thangue, 1942

La Thangue, Henry Herbert 1859–1929, *The Appian Way*, bequeathed by Mrs K. La Thangue, 1942

La Thangue, Henry Herbert 1859–1929, *A Provençal Morning*, bequeathed by Mrs K. La Thangue, 1942

La Thangue, Henry Herbert 1859–1929, *Trellised Vines*, bequeathed by Mrs K. La Thangue, 1942, photo credit: www.bridgemanart.com

Ladbrooke, John Berney

1803–1879, *Summer Landscape*, bequeathed by Edwin Schofield, 1927

Langley, Walter 1852–1922, 'The tender grace of a day that is dead will never come back to me', purchased from the artist, 1910

Latter, Ruth 1869–1949, *Flowers*, purchased from the artist, 1925

Lawson, Kenneth 1920–2008, *Moon and Sea*, gift from Jean Maudsley, 2009, © the artist's estate

Leader, Benjamin Williams 1831–1923, *Manchester Ship Canal: The Making of Eastham Dock*, gift from Miss Platt, 1927

Leader, Stanley *On the Lledr*, transferred from Failsworth Library, 1978

Leader, Stanley *The Falls at Turnbrill, Perthshire*, transferred from Failsworth Library, 1978

Lee, Terry b.1932, *Near Thing, 1937*, purchased from the Walker Art Gallery, 1964, © the artist

Lee-Hankey, William 1869–1952, *First Steps*, purchased, 1937

Lees, Derwent 1885–1931, *Landscape with a Figure*, gift from the Contemporary Art Society, 1946

Lewis, Charles James 1830–1892, *Our Holiday*, gift from G. Taylor-Whitehead, 1895

Lewis, Neville 1895–1972, *Gipsy Boy*, purchased from the artist, 1923, © the artist's estate

Livens, Horace Mann 1862–1936, *Black and White*, purchased from the artist, 1924

Long, Edwin 1829–1891, *Head*, gift from Mr J. T. Hague

Long, Edwin 1829–1891, *Spanish Beggars*, gift from H. L. Hargreaves, 1908

Lord, Francis *The Battery, New Brighton, Wirral*, gift from W. Gartside, 1939

Loudan, William Mouat 1868–1925, *The Crystal Gazer*, purchased from Mrs L. Cumberland-Jones, 1932

Lowry, Laurence Stephen 1887–1976, *The Procession*, purchased from the Arlington Galleries, 1934, © courtesy of the estate of L. S. Lowry

MacAndrew, E. H. active 1924, *Spanish Lace*, purchased from the artist, 1924

MacDougall, William Brown 1869–1936, *Castle and Priory*, unknown acquisition method

MacKenzie, Alexander 1923–2001, *Flint: White*, purchased from the Waddington Galleries, 1963, © the artist's estate

MacKenzie, Alexander 1923–2001, *Shore*, purchased from the Waddington Galleries, 1963, © the artist's estate

Majid, Aneela b.1963, *Portrait of Two Sisters*, purchased, 2008

Major, Theodore 1908–1999, *Wigan Landscape*, purchased with the assistance of the Museums, Libraries and Archives Council/

Victoria and Albert Museum Purchase Grant Fund, 2009, © the artist's estate

Major, Theodore 1908–1999, *Red Farm*, presented by Dr Mary Major through the Art Fund, 2009, © the artist's estate

Makhoul, Bashir b.1963, *Intifada* (diptych, left panel), unknown acquisition method, © the artist

Makhoul, Bashir b.1963, *Intifada* (diptych, right panel), unknown acquisition method, © the artist

Massani, Pompeo 1850–1920, *The Old Musician*, bequeathed by Mrs J. Wilde Clegg, 1918

Mayor, Patti 1872–1962, *Mill Girl with a Shawl*, bequeathed by Miss A. Mayor, 1982

McBey, James 1883–1959, *Saada*, purchased from the artist, 1937, © the artist's estate

McCombs, John b.1943, *Gateshead Farm, Delph, Lancashire*, purchased from the Manchester Academy of Fine Arts, 1991, © the artist

Mellor, John active 1976, *Moorland Man, the Shadow of the Man*, gift from the artist, 1976

Meninsky, Bernard 1891–1950, *Toddler*, gift from the Contemporary Art Society, 1938, © the artist's estate/Bridgeman Art Library

Messenger, A. J. *Cathedral*, gift from the Contemporary Art Society, 1959

Millais, John Everett 1829–1896, *The Departure of the Crusaders*, bequeathed by Marjory Lees, 1970

Millais, John Everett 1829–1896, *John Joseph Jones (1830–1888)*, on loan from Captain A. Astley Jones

Millais, John Everett 1829–1896, *Thomas Oldham Barlow*, gift from John Joseph Jones, 1888

Millais, John Everett (attributed to) 1829–1896, *Boys Rabbiting*, bequeathed by Edwin Schofield, 1927

Mills, Frank *Portrait of a Spirit Guide*, gift from Steven Lawton, stepson of the artist

Mills, Frank *Portrait of a Spirit Guide*, gift from Steven Lawton, stepson of the artist, 2005

Mills, J. W. active 1939, *Pheasants and a Plover*, gift from the artist, 1939

Mitchell, Arthur Croft 1872–1956, *Interior of a Religious House*, purchased from the artist, 1910, photo credit: www.bridgemanart.com

Mitchell, Pamela *Mick Jagger (b.1943)*, gift from Vivien Bellamy, 1979

Mogford, John 1821–1885, *Cliffs at Barlow*, gift from F. J. Nettlefold, 1948

Mole, John Henry 1814–1886, *Near Tarbert, Loch Fyne, Argyll*, gift from Miss Ethel A. Mills, 1967

Montague, Alfred 1832–1883, *A Breezy Day on the Meuse*, gift from Arthur Newton, 1956

Moore, Henry 1831–1895,

Westward, purchased from the artist, 1893

Morley, Robert 1857–1941, *The Press Gang*, gift from Mrs H. Clegg, 1944, photo credit: www. bridgemanart.com

Morris, Cedric Lockwood 1889–1982, *Harding Down, Llangynwyd, Bridgend*, gift from the Contemporary Art Society, 1931, © trustees of the Cedric Lockwood Morris Estate/ Foundation

Morris, Philip Richard 1836–1902, *Crowd Scene*, purchased from the John Moores Liverpool Exhibition, 1962

Morris, Philip Richard 1836–1902, *The Last Load*, bequeathed by Mrs J. Wilde Clegg, 1918

Mostyn, Thomas Edwin 1864–1930, *A Fisherman's Daughter*, gift from H. L. Hargreaves, 1907

Mostyn, Thomas Edwin 1864–1930, *Morning, Burnham Beeches, Buckinghamshire*, gift from H. L. Hargreaves, 1907

Muckley, William Jabez 1829–1905, *Peonies*, purchased from Dunn and Pilcher Capes, 1967

Muckley, William Jabez 1829–1905, *Apple Blossom*, purchased from Dunn and Pilcher Capes

Muckley, William Jabez 1829–1905, *Oranges*, purchased from Dunn and Pilcher Capes

Muckley, William Jabez 1829–1905, *Water Lilies*, purchased from Dunn and Pilcher Capes

Muirhead, David 1867–1930, *The End of Autumn*, gift from Mr or Mrs Dixon (?), 1934

Munnings, Alfred James 1878–1959, *A White Slave*, purchased from the artist, 1907, © the artist's estate courtesy of Felix Rosenstiel's Widow & Son Ltd

Murphy, Cliff b.1944, *The Beautiful Game*, purchased from the artist, 2003, © the artist

Murray, David 1849–1933, *Silvery Summer, Kennet and Avon Canal, Berkshire*, gift from the executors of the estate of the artist

Murray, David 1849–1933, *Twixt Croft and Creel*, gift from Charles Edward Lees, 1886

Musgrave, E. active c.1900–1985, *Dame Sarah Lees (1842–1935)*, gift from the artist, 1985

Nasmyth, Alexander 1758–1840, *Landscape*, gift from Miss C. Newton, 1983 (?)

Normand, Ernest 1857–1923, *Vashti Deposed*, purchased from Reverend M. B. Williamson, 1896

Ogden, Geoff b.1929, *Cottage Interior*, purchased from the Fishborne Galleries, 1997

Olsson, Albert Julius 1864–1942, *Rising Moon, St Ives Bay, Cornwall*, gift from H. L. Hargreaves, 1908

Olsson, Albert Julius 1864–1942, *Rum from Eigg, Inner Hebrides*, purchased from the artist, 1929

Oppenheimer, Charles 1875–1961, *Artist's Garden*, purchased from the artist, 1931

Orpen, William 1878–1931, *Behind the Scenes*, gift from H. L. Hargreaves, 1910

Orpen, William 1878–1931, *In the Dublin Mountains*, purchased from Professor Michael Sadler, 1920

Padwick, Philip Hugh 1876–1958, *Rye, East Sussex*, purchased from the artist, 1931

Park, John Anthony 1880–1962, *May Pageantry*, purchased from the artist, 1937, © the artist's estate

Parker, Frederick H. A. d.1904, *James Collinge, Mayor of Oldham (1850–1852)*, gift from J. Collinge, 1897

Parr, Edward active before 1910, *Edwin Butterworth (1812–1848), Historian of Oldham*, purchased from Whitehead (?), 1903

Parsons, Alfred William 1847–1920, *Meadows by the Avon*, gift from Charles Edward Lees, 1986, photo credit: www. bridgemanart.com

Parsons, Alfred William 1847–1920, *On the Cotswolds*, purchased from the artist, 1897

Partington, John Herbert Evelyn 1843–1899, *Charles Potter as Amiens in 'As You Like It' at a Calvert Shakespearian Revival*, gift from Percy Jones, 1934

Partington, Richard Lantry 1868–1928, *Edwin Waugh Winter*, gift from the directors of Oldham Lyceum, 1950

Paterson, James 1854–1932, *An East Lothian Village*, purchased from the artist, 1908

Pears, Charles 1873–1958, *The Needles, Isle of Wight*, gift from Joseph Smith, 1920, © the artist's estate

Pegg, John Christopher b.1949, *Street in Oldham, Lancashire*, purchased, 2008, © the artist

Pelham, Thomas Kent c.1831–1907, *Spanish Woman and Child*, gift from J. T. Hague, 1944

Penn, William Charles 1877–1968, *Dr Thomas Fawsitt*, gift from the sitter, 1922, © the artist's estate

Percy, William 1820–1893, *William Bodden, Mayor of Oldham (1877–1878)*, gift from Allen Mellor

Pettie, John 1839–1893, *Charles E. Lees*, bequeathed by Marjory Lees, 1970

Phillip, John 1817–1867, *Ellen Barlow, Wife of Thomas Oldham Barlow*, bequeathed by Miss Jane Lucy Barlow, 1936

Phillip, John 1817–1867, *Return from a Shooting Party in Scotland*, gift from the National Art Collections Fund, 2004

Phillips, Peter b.1939, *Gravy for the Navy*, gift from the Contemporary Art Society, 1964, © Peter and Zoe Phillips

Philpot, Glyn Warren 1884–1937, *Lilacs*, purchased from the artist, 1935

Pickering, James Langsdale 1845–1912, *At Rest*, purchased from the artist, 1907

Pitt, William c.1818–c.1900, *The Village at the Head of the Creek, Helford, Cornwall*, gift from J. S. Tattersall, 1945

Platt, Stella b.1913, *Flowers* (recto), acquired, 1983, © the artist

Platt, Stella b.1913, *Houses in the Valley* (verso), acquired, 1983, © the artist

Potter, Charles 1832–1907, *A Christmas Dawn*, gift from John Ratcliffe, 1888

Potter, Charles 1832–1907, *A Quiet Pool*, purchased from Percy Jones, 1940

Potter, Charles 1832–1907, *A Winter's Tale*, gift from J. F. Tweedale, 1882

Prinsep, Valentine Cameron 1838–1904, *At the First Touch of Winter, Summer Fades Away*, purchased from the artist, 1898, photo credit: www.bridgemanart.com

Purdy, James 1900–1972, *Haircut*, gift from Mrs Purdy, 1978

Purdy, James 1900–1972, *Millbottom (2)*, purchased from the artist, 1936

Purdy, James 1900–1972, *Carnival*, gift from Mrs Purdy, 1978

Purdy, James 1900–1972, *Fisherman*, unknown acquisition method

Purdy, James 1900–1972, *John Edmunds Purdy*, bequeathed by Elizabeth Taylor, 1986

Purdy, James 1900–1972, *Landscape with Sheep*, gift from Mrs Purdy, 1978

Purdy, James 1900–1972, *Moorland Cloud*, gift from Mrs Purdy, 1978

Purdy, James 1900–1972, *Moorland Road*, gift from Mrs Purdy, 1978

Purdy, James 1900–1972, *Mr Waring, Principal of Oldham Technical College*, gift from Dr Holland, 1981

Purdy, James 1900–1972, *Oldham Wakes, Lancashire*, gift from Mrs Purdy, 1978

Purdy, James 1900–1972, *Pennine View*, gift from Mrs Purdy, 1978

Purdy, James 1900–1972, *Reflections*, gift from Mrs Purdy, 1978

Purdy, James 1900–1972, *Rocky Stream*, gift from Mrs Purdy, 1978

Purdy, James 1900–1972, *Self Portrait*, unknown acquisition method

Purdy, James 1900–1972, *Sky Scene*, gift from Mrs Purdy, 1978

Purdy, James 1900–1972, *Snow on the Hills*, gift from Mrs Purdy

Purdy, James 1900–1972, *The Studio*, gift from Mrs Purdy, 1978

Purdy, James 1900–1972, *Unveiling of the War Memorial, Oldham, Lancashire, 28 April 1923*, gift from Mrs C. E. Lees, 1924

Purdy, James 1900–1972, *Wooded Stream*, gift from Mrs Purdy, 1978

Purdy, James 1900–1972, *Woodland Glade*, gift from Mrs Purdy, 1978

Purdy, James 1900–1972, *Woodland Pool*, gift from Mrs Purdy, 1978

Radcliffe, Paul active 1956, *Helen*, purchased from the artist, 1956

Ramsey, David *Portrait of a Young Girl with a Head Sash*, bequeathed by Mrs D. P. Ramsay, 1960

Ranken, William Bruce Ellis 1881–1941, *The Baker's Roundsman, Madeira*, gift from Mrs J. M. R. Thesiger, 1946

Rankle, Alan b.1952, *Fairlight from the Water Meadows*, gift from the Tramman Trust though the Art Fund, 2009, © the artist

Rathans, W. *Landscape*, gift from Angus Butterworth, 1971

Reynolds, Daphne 1918–2002, *Ding Dong Mine*, purchased from the artist, 1969, © the artist's estate

Reynolds, Daphne 1918–2002, *Standing in Tunnels*, purchased from the artist, 1969, © the artist's estate

Richards, Paul b.1949, *Green Apple*, gift from the Contemporary Art Society and the Tom Bendham Bequest, 2007, © the artist

Richardson, A. E. *Failsworth Pole, Oldham, Lancashire*, acquired, 1982

Richter, Herbert Davis 1874–1955, *Summertime, 1930*, purchased from the artist, 1932

Riley, Harold b.1934, *Boating Lake, Alexandra Park, Oldham, Lancashire*, purchased from the artist, 1969

Riviere, Hugh Goldwin 1869–1956, *Dame Sarah Lees (1842–1935)*, gift from the sitter, 1912, © the artist's estate

Roach, J. active 19th C, *William Johnson Fox, MP for Oldham (1847–1856 & 1857–1862)*, gift from Samuel Mellor, 1906

Roberts, Lancelot Percival 1883–1950, *Two More Minutes to Go*, purchased from the artist, 1932

Ronaldson, Thomas Martine 1881–1942, *Ann Todd*, gift from Mrs Ronaldson, 1944, © the artist's estate

Rothenstein, William 1872–1945, *A Corner of the Talmud School*, purchased from the artist, 1908, © the artist's estate/Bridgeman Art Library

Royle, Stanley 1888–1961, *A Derbyshire Landscape*, purchased from the artist, 1927, © the artist's estate/Bridgeman Art Library, photo credit: www.bridgemanart.com

Russell, Walter Westley 1867–1949, *Tying Her Shoe*, purchased from the artist, 1912, photo credit: www.bridgemanart.com

Russell, Walter Westley 1867–1949, *On the Sands*, gift from Joseph Smith, 1913

Rutherford, Harry 1903–1985, *Yorkshire Street, Oldham,*

Lancashire, purchased from the artist, 1949, © the artist's estate

Rutherford, Harry 1903–1985, *Ammon Wrigley (1861–1946)*, gift from the sitter, 1942, © the artist's estate

Salisbury, Frank O. 1874–1962, *Sir Frank Platt (1890–1955)*, gift from Miss Platt, 1981, © estate of Frank O. Salisbury. All rights reserved, DACS 2011

Samsu, S. M. *A Rickshaw Workshop*, purchased from the artist, 2005

Sandby, Paul 1731–1809, *A Woody Landscape*, aquired, 1905

Sandle, Michael b.1936, *Untitled*, purchased from the John Moores Exhibition, Liverpool, © the artist

Sant, James 1820–1916, *John Platt*, unknown acquisition method

Sant, James 1820–1916, *Alice Platt*, unknown acquisition method

Sephton, George Harcourt 1860–1923, *E. Lyneph Stanley, MP for Oldham (1880–1885)*, gift from E. L. Stanley

Shah, Abdus Shakoor b.1946, *Tradition*, purchased from the artist, 2002, © the artist

Shah, Abdus Shakoor b.1946, *She and Chandrabaty*, purchased from the artist with the assistance of the British Council, 2002, © the artist

Shah, Abdus Shakoor b.1946, *The Story of Mahua*, purchased from the artist with the assistance of the British Council, 2002, © the artist

Shannon, James Jebusa 1862–1923, *Robert Whittaker*, gift from the sitter

Shannon, James Jebusa 1862–1923, *Sir J. T. Hibbert*, gift from the Hibbert Testimonial Fund, 1898

Sharp, Dorothea 1874–1955, *Paddlers*, purchased, 1937, photo credit: www.bridgemanart.com

Shayer, William 1788–1879, *Old Farmyard Scene*, gift from Simeon Holden, 1960

Shayer, William 1788–1879, *Coast Scene with Figures*, gift from C. E. Kidd, 1887

Sheringham, George 1884–1937, *The Water Forces Raged against Siegfried*, gift from Mrs P. M. Millard, 1943

Sheringham, George 1884–1937, *The Earth Forces Raged against Siegfried*, gift from Mrs P. M. Millard, 1943

Sickert, Walter Richard 1860–1942, *Barnet Fair, Hertfordshire*, purchased from J. W. Freshfield, 1936, © estate of Walter R. Sickert. All rights reserved, DACS 2011

Simcock, Jack b.1929, *Cottage on a Hillside*, purchased from the Piccadilly Gallery, © the artist

Smith, Jack 1928–2011, *Floating Number 2*, purchased from the Walker Art Gallery, 1966, © the artist's estate

Solomon, Abraham 1824–1862, *A Lesson in the Use of the Fan*, bequeathed by Mrs J. Wilde Clegg,

1918

Solomon, Solomon Joseph 1860–1927, *Joseph Smith, Mayor of Oldham (1893–1894)*, gift from the sitter, 1898

Somerville, Howard 1873–1952, *Alderman Charles Hardman, Mayor of Oldham (1919–1920)*, gift from the sitter, 1921

Somerville, Howard 1873–1952, *Miss Nora Baring*, gift from Miss Adamson, 1955

Somerville, Howard 1873–1952, *The Red Burnous*, purchased from the artist, 1925, photo credit: www.bridgemanart.com

Somerville, Howard 1873–1952, *Zulu with a Black Eye*, gift from Joseph Smith, 1920

Southall, Joseph Edward 1861–1944, *Along the Shore*, gift from the executors of the estate of Mrs A. E. Southall, 1948, © reproduced with permission of the Barrow family

Southall, Joseph Edward 1861–1944, *The Food Queue*, gift from the executors of the estate of Mrs A. E. Southall, 1948, © reproduced with permission of the Barrow family

Spencelayh, Charles 1865–1958, *A Lover of Dickens*, purchased from the artist, 1951, © the artist's estate/Bridgeman Art Library

Spencer, Stanley 1891–1959, *Landscape, near Halifax, West Yorkshire*, gift from the Contemporary Art Society, 1954, © the estate of Stanley Spencer 2011. All rights reserved DACS

Stanaway, Peter b.1943, *Now the Mill Has Gone*, purchased from Todmorden Fine Art, 2006

Stanaway, Peter b.1943, *Helen Bradley's House, Spring Lane, Lees, Lancashire*, gift from Todmorden Fine Art on behalf of the artist, 2006

Stanaway, Peter b.1943, *The House of L. S. Lowry, Mottram, Longdendale, Greater Manchester*, unknown acquisition method

Steele, Jeffrey b.1931, *Scala*, purchased from the Grabowski Gallery, © the artist

Stott, Edward William 1859–1918, *The Ferry*, purchased from the artist, 1889

Stott, Samuel Taylor 1845–1913, *Valley of the Lauterbrunnen, Switzerland*, gift from the artist, 1905

Stott, William 1857–1900, *Wild Flower*, gift from G. Hindley Smith, 1920

Stott, William 1857–1900, *My Father and Mother*, gift from Mrs A. A. Stott, 1938

Stott, William 1857–1900, *Hollyhocks (A Fairy Tale)*, gift from F. Eastbourne Hindley Smith, 1925

Stott, William 1857–1900, *Venus Born of the Sea Foam*, gift from Richard Haworth, 1930

Stott, William 1857–1900, *Hide and Seek in the Garden of Epicurus, Leontium and Ternissa*, purchased

from the executors of the estate of the artist, 1903

Stott, William 1857–1900, *Pastoral*, gift from M. D. Stott

Stott, William 1857–1900, *The White Mountain*, purchased from the executors of the estate of the artist, 1903

Strang, William 1859–1921, *The Feather Fan*, gift from Joseph Smith, 1921

Stuart, Elsie *Oldham Church from Goldbourne, Lancashire*, acquired, 1983

Stubbs, Frederick J. *Old Oldham Church, Lancashire*, unknown acquisition method

Swanwick, Joseph Harold 1866–1929, *Ducks*, purchased from the artist, 1905

Swynnerton, Annie Louisa 1844–1933, *Cupid and Psyche*, gift from Charles Edward Lees, 1892

Talmage, Algernon Mayow 1871–1939, *The Ford*, gift from H. L. Hargreaves, 1908

Tarbet, John A. Henderson 1865–1938, *Highland Landscape*, gift from Mrs C. Henderson, 1939

Thompson, Estelle b.1960, *Spirit*, purchased from the Pomeroy Purdy Gallery, 1991, © the artist

Titcomb, William Holt Yates 1858–1930, *Jubilee Day, St Ives, Cornwall (Good News from the Front)*, gift from Mrs J. A. Titcomb, 1935

Topham, Francis Williams 1808–1877, *Lady of Quality*, gift from Simeon Holden, 1960

Townsend, Ernest 1885–1944, *F. G. Isherwood, Mayor of Oldham (1911–1912)*, gift from the sitter, 1913

Turner, Alice active 1981, *Nicker Brow, Oldham, Lancashire*, gift from the artist, 1981

Tuttle, J. R. active 1897 or earlier, *James Mackensie Maclean, MP for Oldham (1885–1892)*, gift from M. J. Maclean, 1897

Uhlman, Fred 1901–1985, *Two Welsh Cottages*, purchased from the Artists' International Association Exhibition, 1963, © the artist's estate/Bridgeman Art Library

unknown artist *Thomas Henshaw, Founder of the Bluecoat School, Oldham*, gift from H. H. Davenport, 1902

unknown artist early 19th C, *Old Oldham Church, Lancashire*, gift from Miss M. Mackintosh, 1947

unknown artist *Abstract*, unknown acquisition method

unknown artist *Abstract*, unknown acquisition method

unknown artist *Creg-Ny-Baa, Isle of Man*, purchased from Lillian A. Bates, 1980

unknown artist *Dorothy and Marjory Lees*, unknown acquisition method

unknown artist *Edmund Hartley, Mayor of Oldham (1869–1870)*, gift from A. and Anley H. Butterworth, 1898

unknown artist *Eli Lees*, unknown acquisition method

unknown artist *Mrs Eli Lees*, unknown acquisition method

unknown artist *James Buckley of Holleyville*, gift from Uppermill Police Station, 1986

unknown artist *James Wolfenden*, gift from Miss Hannah J. Lees, 1936

unknown artist *John Buckley*, unknown acquisition method

unknown artist *Mrs J. Buckley*, unknown acquisition method

unknown artist *John Jones (1755–1821)*, on loan from Captain A. Astley Jones

unknown artist *John Rowntree the elder*, bequeathed by M. M. Rowntree, 1951

unknown artist *John Rowntree the younger*, bequeathed by M. M. Rowntree, 1951

unknown artist *Joseph Jones (1756–1845)*, on loan from Captain A. Astley Jones

unknown artist *Joseph Jones (1782–1858)*, on loan from Captain A. Astley Jones

unknown artist *Mountain Stream in Flood*, transferred from Failsworth Library, 1978

unknown artist *Pitbank House, Oldham, Lancashire*, gift from Dr Yates

unknown artist *Portrait of a Stockport Worthy*, unknown acquisition method

unknown artist *Portrait of an Unknown Lady*, unknown acquisition method

unknown artist *Portrait of an Unknown Man*, unknown acquisition method

unknown artist *Portrait of an Unknown Man*, unknown acquisition method

unknown artist *Portrait of an Unknown Man*, unknown acquisition method

unknown artist *Portrait of an Unknown Man*, unknown acquisition method

unknown artist *Portrait of an Unknown Man*, unknown acquisition method

unknown artist *Reverend J. F. Walker, Former Incumbent of St James's, Oldham*, gift from J. W. Nague, 1886

unknown artist *Reverend William Winter, Former Incumbent of St Peter's, Oldham (1796–1838)*, gift from H. Clegg, 1886

unknown artist *Samuel Lees*, unknown acquisition method

unknown artist *Mrs Samuel Lees*, unknown acquisition method

unknown artist *Samuel Radcliffe*, gift from the sitter's sons, 1898

unknown artist *Trees*, unknown acquisition method

unknown artist *William Cobbett*, gift from Mrs S. Milne, 1838

unknown artist *William Jones (1759–1833)*, on loan from Captain A. Astley Jones

Verboeckhoven, Eugène Joseph

1799–1881, *Sheep*, bequeathed by Mrs J. Wilde Clegg, 1918

Wadsworth, Edward Alexander 1889–1949, *Imaginary Harbour II*, purchased from the Piccadilly Galleries, 1967, © estate of Edward Wadsworth 2011. All rights reserved, DACS

Wagner, Cornelius 1870–1956, *Low Tide Work*, gift from the artist, 1911

Walker, Ray 1945–1984, *Self Portrait (recto)*, purchased from Anna Walker with the assistance of the Museums, Libraries and Archives Council/Victoria and Albert Museum Purchase Grant Fund, 1987 (?)

Walker, Ray 1945–1984, *Untitled (verso)*, purchased from Anna Walker with the assistance of the Museums, Libraries and Archives Council/Victoria and Albert Museum Purchase Grant Fund, 1987 (?)

Waterhouse, John William 1849–1917, *Circe*, gift from Marjory Lees, 1952, photo credit: www.bridgemanart.com

Watson, Harry 1871–1936, *Morning in a Wood*, gift from Joseph Smith, 1921

Watson, Robert H. active 1894–1920, *Evening in the Highlands*, gift from Mrs Mcphee, 1911

Watson, Robert H. active 1894–1920, *In the Trossachs, Stirling*, gift from Mrs Mcphee, 1911

Watson, Thomas J. 1847–1912, *The Brook*, gift from Miss Ethel A. Mills, 1967

Watts, George Frederick 1817–1904, *Aurora*, bequeathed by Marjory Lees, 1970

Watts, James Thomas 1853–1930, *Autumn's Bravery*, gift from Miss Ethel A. Mills, 1967

Webb, James 1825–1895, *Italian Landscape*, gift from Miss Ethel A. Mills

Webster, Thomas George 1800–1886, *Beating for Recruits (Rocking the Cradle)*, gift from the National Art Collections Fund, 2004

Webster, Walter Ernest 1877–1959, *Rhapsody*, purchased from the artist, 1930

Weight, Carel Victor Morlais 1908–1997, *As I wend to the shores I know not, As I list to the dirge, the voices of men and women wreck'd' (from 'Leaves of Grass' by Walt Whitman)*, gift from the Contemporary Art Society, 1952, © the artist's estate/Bridgeman Art Library

Weir, Linda Mary b.1951, *Still Life with Flying Fish*, purchased, 1986

Wells, William Page Atkinson 1872–1923, *Home across the Sand*, gift from H. L. Hargreaves, 1909

Westcott, Philip 1815–1878, *John Summerscales, First Town Clerk of Oldham (1849–1862)*, gift from Mrs H. Ormerod Hutchinson,

1912

Wetherbee, George Faulkner 1851–1920, *Dawn at the Gate*, purchased from the artist, 1908

Wheelwright, Rowland 1870–1955, *Don Quixote and Maritornes at the Inn (from the novel by Cervantes)*, purchased from the artist, 1905

Whitehead, Richard Henry 1855–1889, *Rhododendrons*, purchased from the Hollingworth sale, 1929

Whitehead, Richard Henry 1855–1889, *The Musician*, gift from Mrs Potter, 1947

Wilkes, Paul *The Clockwork Admiral*, purchased from Arthur Tooth & Sons, 1965

Willaert, Ferdinand 1861–1938, *Béguinage flamand*, purchased from the artist, 1907

Williams, Terrick John 1860–1936, *Cassis, France*, purchased from the artist, 1930

Wimpenny, George Henry 1857–1939, *The Old Fish Market, Oldham, Lancashire*, gift from F. Bradbury, 1937

Wimpenny, George Henry 1857–1939, *Chew Valley, Greenfield, Lancashire*, purchased from P. Jones, 1929

Wimpenny, George Henry 1857–1939, *Italian Grandmother*, gift from H. L. Hargreaves, 1897

Wimpenny, George Henry 1857–1939, *Henry Lister Hargraves (d.1914), Oldham's Leading Quaker*, gift from the artist, 1907

Wimpenny, George Henry 1857–1939, *Memories*, purchased from the artist, 1908

Wimpenny, George Henry 1857–1939, *The Terrace, Haddon Hall, Derbyshire*, gift from J. Wynter, 1932

Wimpenny, George Henry 1857–1939, *Sam Fitton (1868–1923)*, gift from Mrs Annette Dawson, 1907

Wimpenny, George Henry 1857–1939, *Finishing Touches*, gift from G. F. Isherwood, 1956

Wimpenny, George Henry 1857–1939, *The Naturalist*, gift from the artist, 1938

Wimpenny, George Henry 1857–1939, *The Woods, Betws-y-Coed, Conwy*, gift from J. W. Whiteley, 1972

Wimpenny, George Henry 1857–1939, *A Patchwork Quilt*, gift from H. L. Hargreaves, 1908

Wimpenny, George Henry 1857–1939, *Annie Maycock*, gift from J. W. Whiteley

Wimpenny, George Henry 1857–1939, *Chester Cathedral from the Shropshire Canal*, unknown acquisition method

Wimpenny, George Henry 1857–1939, *Chetham's Hospital, Manchester*, gift from G. B. Taylor, 1954

Wimpenny, George Henry 1857–1939, *Farmyard Scene*, gift from A. Musgrave, 1985

Wimpenny, George Henry
1857–1939, *James Dronsfield (Jerry Lichenmoss)*, gift from Ouselwood, 1921

Wimpenny, George Henry
1857–1939, *Summer Garden*, purchased, 1983

Winder, David 1824–1912, *James Ashworth (1815–1889), First Chairman of the Royton Local Board (1863)*, gift from Oldham Leisure Services

Workman, Harold 1897–1975, *A Lancashire Town*, unknown acquisition method

Workman, Harold 1897–1975, *Barge Corner*, purchased from the artist, 1938

Workman, Harold 1897–1975, *Borough Market, Southwark, London*, purchased from the artist, 1938

Workman, Harold 1897–1975, *Bridge Street, Christchurch, Hampshire*, gift from Ronald Makin, 1978

Workman, Harold 1897–1975, *Tower Bridge, London*, purchased from the artist, 1939

Wright, Ethel 1866–1939, *Bonjour, Pierrot!*, purchased from the artist, 1893

Wyllie, William Lionel 1851–1931, *The Pool of London*, purchased from the artist, 1894

Yale, Brian 1936–2009, *A Door and a Window in Acre, Israel*, purchased from the artist, 1998, © the artist's estate/Bridgeman Art Library

Yarnold, Joseph c.1817–1852, *Woodland Scene with a Waterfall*, transferred from Failsworth Library, 1978

Zeba, Fareha b.1961, *Child with Stars and Stripes 2*, purchased from the artist with the assistance of the British Council, 2002, © the artist

Pennine Acute Hospitals NHS Trust

Aston, S. & **Prestwich Creative Living Centre** *View of the Sea*, © the copyright holder

Corbett, Angela & **Prestwich Creative Living Centre** *City*, © the copyright holder

Corbett, Angela & **Prestwich Creative Living Centre** *Firework*, © the copyright holder

Corbett, Angela & **Prestwich Creative Living Centre** *Landscape*, © the copyright holder

Corbett, Angela & **Prestwich Creative Living Centre** *Stormy Sea*, © the copyright holder

Corbett, Angela & **Prestwich Creative Living Centre** *Stormy Sea*, © the copyright holder

Coverdale, Mark *Still Life with Chair*, © the copyright holder

Cymel & **Prestwich Creative Living Centre** *Abstract*, © the copyright holder

Cymel & **Prestwich Creative Living Centre** *Houses by the Sea*, © the copyright holder

the copyright holder

E., Judy & **Prestwich Creative Living Centre** *Flowers*, © the copyright holder

E., Judy & **Prestwich Creative Living Centre** *Pink Flowers*, © the copyright holder

Hepworth, Louise *Still Life with Apples*, © the copyright holder

Johnson, Pat *Stampede*, © the copyright holder

Johnson, Pat *Stampede*, © the copyright holder

Johnson, Pat *Stampede*, © the copyright holder

Johnson, Pat *Stampede*, © the copyright holder

Johnson, Pat *Stampede*, © the copyright holder

Johnson, Pat *Stampede*, © the copyright holder

Johnson, Pat *Stampede*, © the copyright holder

Johnson, Pat *Stampede*, © the copyright holder

Lamb, Nick *Papier-mâché*, © the copyright holder

Prestwich Creative Living Centre *Castle*, © the copyright holder

Prestwich Creative Living Centre *White Cliffs*, © the copyright holder

Prestwich Creative Living Centre & **Riley** *White Cliffs*, © the copyright holder

Prestwich Creative Living Centre & **unknown artist** *Boat at Sea*, © the copyright holder

Prestwich Creative Living Centre & **V., Roma** *Blue Sea*, © the copyright holder

R., J. *Abstract*, © the copyright holder

Spencer, Liam David b.1964, *Crumpsall Hospital*, © the artist

unknown artist *Abstract*, © the copyright holder

unknown artist *Abstract*

unknown artist *Abstract*, © the copyright holder

unknown artist *Abstract Landscape*, © the copyright holder

unknown artist *Abstract Spots*, © the copyright holder

unknown artist *Batik Figures*, © the copyright holder

unknown artist *Cows in a Lane*

unknown artist *Doves*

unknown artist *Ducks in Reeds*

unknown artist *Ducks in Reeds*

unknown artist *Flowers*, © the copyright holder

unknown artist *Garden*, © the copyright holder

unknown artist *Garden with Trees and a Pond*, © the copyright holder

unknown artist *Garden with Waterlilies*, © the copyright holder

unknown artist *Snow Scene*, © the copyright holder

unknown artist *Tardis in a Field*, © the copyright holder

unknown artist *Tree*, © the copyright holder

unknown artist *Trees*, © the copyright holder

unknown artist *Water Lilies*, © the copyright holder

unknown artist *Woodland*, © the copyright holder

unknown artist *Woodland*, © the copyright holder

unknown artist *Woodland*, © the copyright holder

unknown artist *Woodland Waterfall*, © the copyright holder

unknown artist *Yellow Flowers*, © the copyright holder

Greater Manchester Fire Service Museum

Airey, Lilian *Manchester Blitz (Piccadilly), 1940*, © the copyright holder

Banks, Brian *Horse-Drawn Fire Escape*

Rochdale Arts & Heritage Service

Adams, Norman 1927–2005, *The Great Garden*, purchased with the assistance of the Victoria and Albert Museum Purchase Grant Fund, 1974, © the artist's estate

Addison, Alfred Henry *Landscape*, gift from the Contemporary Art Society, 1932

Aelst, Willem van (circle of) 1627–after 1687, *Dead Game*, acquired via the Thomas Kay Bequest, 1912; transferred from Heywood, 1974

Ainscow, George Frederick b.1913, *Celebration*, purchased from the artist, 1997, © the artist

Ainscow, George Frederick b.1913, *The Garden of the Villa Cipressi, Varenna, Lake Como, Italy*, gift from Maud Sulter, 1998, © the artist

Airy, Anna 1882–1964, *July Piece*, purchased from the artist, 1935, © Touchstones Rochdale

Allinson, Adrian Paul 1890–1959, *The Cornish April*, purchased from the Fine Art Society, 1940, © Touchstones Rochdale

Allori, Alessandro 1535–1607, *Isabella Medices Ursina (1542–1576)*, acquired via the Thomas Kay Bequest, 1912; transferred from Heywood, 1974

Anderson, Paul G. *Middleton Library, Rochdale, Lancashire*, purchased from the artist, 1993

Ansdell, Richard 1815–1885, *Dog and a Dead Partridge*, gift from Robert Taylor Heape, 1903

Ansdell, Richard 1815–1885, *Ronda, Spanish Travellers*, gift from Robert Taylor Heape, 1910

Appleyard, Frederick 1874–1963, *A Child's Grief, Called away from School*, purchased from the artist, 1907, © the artist's estate

Archer, Frank Joseph 1912–1995, *Piano Concerto*, purchased from the artist, 1961, © Touchstones Rochdale

Auerbach, Frank Helmuth b.1931, *St Pancras Steps, Station*, purchased from Marlborough Fine Art with

the assistance of the Victoria and Albert Museum Purchase Grant Fund, 1981, © the artist

Aumonier, James 1832–1911, *An Easter Holiday, the Children of Bloomsbury Parochial School in a Wood at Watford*, gift from Robert Taylor Heape, 1911

Ayres, Gillian b.1930, *Mons Graupius*, purchased from the Knoedler Gallery, 1982, © the artist

Bagshaw, Olive *Dorothy Heap*, gift from Yvonne Noble, 1999

Bancroft, Elias 1846–1924, *Rothenburg ob der Tauber, Bavaria, Germany*, gift from William Wiles, 1907

Barber, Charles Burton 1845–1894, *A Special Pleader*, gift from Robert Taylor Heape, 1911, photo credit: www.bridgemanart.com

Barlow, Bohuslav b.1947, *Skull and Birds*, purchased from the artist, 1973, © the artist

Barlow, John Noble 1861–1917, *Early Spring*, purchased from the artist, 1907

Baron, Geoffrey *John Entwistle*

Bartholme, G. L. *Swallow Falls, Betws-y-Coed, Conwy*, bequeathed by J. S. Littlewood, 1919

Bartlett, William Henry 1858–1932, *Fishing off Chioggia, Venice*, gift from Robert Taylor Heape, 1910

Bartlett, William Henry 1858–1932, *Off Greenwich, London*, gift from Robert Taylor Heape, 1913

Beaumont, Edward active 1885–1903, *Oakenrod Hall, Rochdale, Lancashire*

Beaumont, Edward active 1885–1903, *Ashworth Church, Rochdale, Lancashire*, gift from T. Deveney, 1978

Beaumont, Edward active 1885–1903, *Ashworth Chapel and Inn, Rochdale, Lancashire*, presented by H. Silverwood, 1946

Beaumont, Edward active 1885–1903, *St John's Church, Smallbridge, Rochdale, Lancashire*

Beavis, Richard 1824–1896, *Hauling up a Fishing Boat, The Netherlands*, gift from Robert Taylor Heape, 1911

Beggs, Guy b.1947, *The Summer House*, purchased from the Leicester Galleries, 1973, © the artist

Bell, Vanessa 1879–1961, *Interior*, gift from the Friends of Rochdale Art Gallery, 1982, © 1961 estate of Vanessa Bell courtesy Henrietta Garnett

Berchem, Nicolaes (attributed to) 1620–1683, *Cattle, Figures and Landscape*, acquired via the Thomas Kay Bequest, 1912; transferred from Heywood, 1974

Berg, Adrian b.1929, *Gloucester Gate, Regent's Park, London, Summer, Autumn, Winter, Spring*, purchased from the Waddington Galleries with the assistance of the Victoria and Albert Museum

Purchase Grant Fund, 1980, © Adrian Berg

Biddle, Lawrence 1888–1968, *Chinese Bowl and Pansy*, purchased from the Fine Art Society, 1926

Biddle, Lawrence 1888–1968, *Wallflowers and Bluebells in a Bowl*, purchased from M. Newman, 1962

Birch, Samuel John Lamorna 1869–1955, *The Stream at Lamorna, Penzance, Cornwall*, purchased from the artist, 1914, © the artist's estate

Bishop, Henry 1868–1939, *Bedouins Outside a Town*, purchased from Mrs Margaret Wincester, 1940, © Touchstones Rochdale

Bock, Théophile de 1851–1904, *Autumn*, gift from J. S. Crompton, 1921

Bomberg, David 1890–1957, *Underground Bomb Store*, purchased from the Mayor Gallery, 1981, © the artist's family

Booth, James William 1867–1953, *A Country Horse Fair at Hinderwell, North Yorkshire*, transferred from Middleton Library, 1974

Booth, James William (attributed to) 1867–1953, *Weir, Rhodes Wood*, transferred from Middleton Library, 1985

Bowen, Owen 1873–1967, *The Village on the Hill, Appletreewick, North Yorkshire*, purchased from the artist, 1946, © the artist's estate

Brangwyn, Frank 1867–1956, *All Hands Shorten Sail*, gift from Robert Taylor Heape, 1911, © the artist's estate/Bridgeman Art Library

Bratby, John Randall 1928–1992, *Elm Park Gardens, I*, purchased from the artist, 1959, © Touchstones Rochdale

Bratby, John Randall 1928–1992, *Irises and Tulips*, purchased from the artist, 1967, © Touchstones Rochdale

Briscoe, Arthur John Trevor 1873–1943, *The Bowsprit*, purchased from the Fine Art Society, 1931

British (English) School *Portrait of a Nobleman*, acquired via the Thomas Kay Bequest, 1912; transferred from Heywood, 1974

British (English) School *Richard Assheton of Middleton's Son whilst a Child*, gift from Mr Yates to Middleton Library; transferred to Rochdale Art Gallery, 1978

British (English) School *Darcy Lever (1760–1839), with His Son John and Daughters Frances and Emelia Charlotte*, gift from William Logan Horne to the Middleton Corporation; transferred to the Museum, 1974

British (English) School *Robert Turner, JP*, gift from A. W. Kay-Menzies, 1923

British (English) School 19th C, *Napoleon Bonaparte (1769–1821)*, gift from Alfred Seeley, 1948

British School *John Stock, Donor of*

Stock's Charity, gift to Middleton Library from Mrs Alice Kershaw and her stepdaughter, 1935; transferred to Rochdale Art Gallery, 1977

British School *Sir Darcy Lever (1703–1742)*, gift to Middleton Library from Lieutenant Colonel William Logan Home, 1968; transferred to Rochdale Art Gallery, 1977

British School *Reverend William Ashton*, gift to Middleton Library from Lieutenant Colonel William Logan Home; transferred to Rochdale Art Gallery, 1974

British School *J. Lonsdale*, unknown acquisition method

British School *Middleton, Rochdale, Lancashire, in 1835*, transferred from Middleton Library, 1985

British School *John Roby (1793–1850)*, gift from William Fenton Beaumonds, 1876

British School *Robert Taylor Heape (1848–1917)*, unknown acquisition method

British School *Interior of the Town Hall, Rochdale, Lancashire*, unknown acquisition method

British School 19th C, *Seventeenth-Century Half-Timber Building* (formerly standing in Yorkshire Street, Rochdale, Lancashire), gift from Ed Holt

British School *Alderman James Booth*, unknown acquisition method

Brouwer, Adriaen (after) 1605/1606–1638, *A Dutch Tavern Scene*, acquired via the Thomas Kay Bequest, 1912; transferred from Heywood, 1974

Brown, John Alfred Arnesby 1866–1955, *A Fellside Cumberland Village*, purchased from R. H. Spurr, 1939

Brown, Taylor 1869–1924, *Ayrshire Pastoral*, purchased, 1910

Buhler, Robert A. 1916–1989, *Still Life*, gift from the Contemporary Art Society, 1954, © the artist's estate/Bridgeman Art Library

Bundy, Edgar 1862–1922, *The Coffee House Orator*, gift from Robert Taylor Heape, 1911, photo credit: www.bridgemanart.com

Burgess, John Bagnold 1830–1897, *An Irritable Appeal*, gift from Robert Taylor Heape, 1911

Burne-Jones, Philip Edward 1861–1926, *An Unfinished Masterpiece*, gift from Robert Taylor Heape, 1903, photo credit: www.bridgemanart.com

Burr, Alexander Hohenlohe 1835–1898, *The Mask*, gift from Robert Taylor Heape, 1902

Cadell, Francis Campbell Boileau 1883–1937, *Ben More in the Isle of Mull, Inner Hebrides*, purchased from the artist, 1932, photo credit: www.bridgemanart.com

Cameron, David Young 1865–1945, *Head of Loch Ness*, gift from J. S. Crompton, 1921

Cameron, David Young

1865–1945, *The Sanctuary*, purchased from Mr Lockett Thompson, 1930

Carolus, Jean 1814–1897, *The Introduction*, gift from Robert Taylor Heape, 1910

Carpenter, Henry Barrett 1861–1930, *James Ogden*, purchased, 1910

Carter, Samuel John 1835–1892, *Deer and a Fawn*, gift from Robert Taylor Heape, 1911

Carvell, Graham b.1945, *The Mule Spinner*, © the artist

Charles, James 1851–1906, *A Glade*, gift from J. S. Crompton, 1921

Charlton, Alan Bengall 1913–1981, *Landscape*, purchased from the artist, 1933

Charlton, John 1849–1917, *James Griffith Dearden, Lord of the Manor of Rochdale*, gift from Sir C. M. Royds, 1914

Clarkson, Pamela b.1946, *Common Day*, purchased from the artist, 1982, © the artist

Claus, Emile 1849–1924, *Poultry in a Wood*, gift from Robert Taylor Heape, 1911

Clausen, George 1852–1944, *The Golden Barn*, purchased from Mr Lockett Thompson, 1930, © Touchstones Rochdale, photo credit: www.bridgemanart.com

Clays, Paul Jean 1819–1900, *On the Scheldt*, gift from J. S. Crompton, 1921

Clouet, François (circle of) c.1515–1572, *Hercule François de Valois-Angoulême, Duc d'Alençon et d'Anjou (1555–1584)*, acquired via the Thomas Kay Bequest, 1912; transferred from Heywood, 1974

Coker, Peter 1926–2004, *Low Tide, Seascale, Cumbria*, purchased from the artist, 1969, © Touchstones Rochdale

Cole, George 1810–1883, *The Closing Day, Scene in Sussex*, gift from Robert Taylor Heape, 1911

Cole, George Vicat 1833–1893, *A Surrey Cornfield*, bequeathed by J. S. Littlewood, 1919

Cole, George Vicat 1833–1893, *Surrey Hills*, gift from Robert Taylor Heape, 1913

Collier, Edwaert (follower of) c.1640–c.1707, *Memento mori*, acquired via the Thomas Kay Bequest, 1912; transferred from Heywood, 1974

Collier, John 1708–1786, *Self Portrait*, unknown acquisition method

Collier, John 1708–1786, *Man with a Broken Pipe*, purchased from R. Gaskell, 1912

Collier, John 1708–1786, *Man with a Broken Pipe*, purchased from R. Gaskell, 1912

Collier, John 1708–1786, *Human Passions (Two Drunkards, a Glass, a Bottle and a Pipe)*, unknown acquisition method

Collier, John 1708–1786, *Human Passions (Five Heads)*, gift from Richard Heape, 1903

Collier, John 1708–1786, *Human Passions (Three Drunkards and a Bottle)*, unknown acquisition method

Collier, John 1708–1786, *Human Passions (Tooth Pulling)*, unknown acquisition method

Collier, John 1708–1786, *Human Passions (Two Figures, a Lord and a Moneylender)*, unknown acquisition method

Collier, John 1708–1786, *Human Passions (The Parson and the Devil)*, unknown acquisition method

Collier, John 1708–1786, *Altercation*

Collier, John 1708–1786, *Choir*

Collier, John 1708–1786, *Human Passions*

Collier, John 1708–1786, *Human Passions*

Collier, John 1708–1786, *Mrs Charles Collier*

Collier, John 1708–1786, *No.3 Human Passions*, purchased from Alfred Lancaster, 1908

Collier, John 1708–1786, *No.28 Human Passions*, purchased from Alfred Lancaster, 1908

Collier, John 1708–1786, *Portrait of a Man*, unknown acquisition method

Collier, John 1708–1786, *Portrait of a Man*, gift from W. H. Sutcliffe, 1903

Collier, John 1708–1786, *Portrait of the Artist's Son*, gift from Benjamin Taylor, 1909

Collier, John 1708–1786, *Portrait of the Artist Wearing an Iron Mask*, gift from Benjamin Taylor, 1909

Collier, John 1708–1786, *Pulling Teeth*, gift from Albert Earwater, 1909

Collier, John 1708–1786, *Sarah Collier, the Artist's Daughter*

Collier, John 1708–1786, *Self Portrait*, gift from W. H. Sutcliffe, 1903

Collier, John 1708–1786, *Two Faces*

Collier, John 1708–1786, *Two Figures*

Collier, John 1850–1934, *Dr J. R. Ashworth*, gift from Dr Ashworth, 1951

Collier, John 1850–1934, *Meditation*, gift from Lady Turner, 1941

Collins, William 1788–1847, *The Sale of the Pet Lamb*, gift from Robert Taylor Heape, 1911

Constable, John (circle of) 1776–1837, *Study of Cumulus Clouds*, transferred from the General Purchasing Committee to the permanent collection, 1961

Constable, John (follower of) 1776–1837, *Landscape (Stream with a Bank of Trees)*, transferred from the General Purchasing Committee to the permanent collection, 1961

Conti, Tito 1842–1924, *Day Dreams*, gift from Robert Taylor Heape, 1913

Corvus, Hans (follower of) active 1512–after 1544, *Richard Foxe*

(c.1448–1528), acquired via the Thomas Kay Bequest, 1912; transferred from Heywood, 1974

Cook, Job *Rural Scene*, gift from Miss Doris Cook, 1990

Cooke, Edward William 1811–1880, *Danish Craft on the Elbe, Blankenese, Germany, Low Water*, gift from Robert Taylor Heape, 1910

Cooper, Byron 1850–1933, *Across the Moorland*, purchased, 1910

Cooper, Thomas Sidney 1803–1902, *Mountain Sheep*, gift from Robert Taylor Heape, 1902

Cooper, Thomas Sidney 1803–1902, *Cattle in a Meadow, Evening*, gift from Robert Taylor Heape, 1911

Cooper, Thomas Sidney 1803–1902, *Sheep on the Marshes, near Folkestone, Kent*, bequeathed by Robert Schofield, 1920

Cooper, Thomas Sidney 1803–1902, *Landscape*, gift from Mrs M. Heath, 1956

Cope, Charles West 1811–1890, *Hope Deferred, and Hopes and Fears that Kindle Hope*, gift from Robert Taylor Heape, 1911

Cordall, William active late 19th C, *Village Scene*, unknown acquisition method

Cot, Pierre Auguste 1837–1883, *The Last Support*, bequeathed by Mrs Helen Crowther, 1910

Coutts, Gordon 1868–1937, *A Merchant of Tangiers*, purchased from C. P. Chisman, 1922

Crabtree, Jack b.1938, *The Pressure of One's Environment (1)*, purchased from the artist, 1960, © the artist

Crabtree, Jack b.1938, *The Speaker*, gift from the artist, 1962, © the artist

Cranach, Lucas the elder (circle of) 1472–1553, *The Reformers Radisponen and G. Wolf (Frederick 'The Wise', 1463–1525, and John I, 'The Constant', 1468–1532)*, acquired via the Thomas Kay Bequest, 1912; transferred from Heywood, 1974

Creswick, Thomas 1811–1869 & **Frith, William** 1819–1909 *Lancaster Sands, Lancashire*, gift from Robert Taylor Heape, 1905

Critchlow, Jeremy b.1951, *Crawling Woman, Benares, India*, purchased from the artist, 1982

Crome, John (attributed to) 1768–1821, *Landscape*, gift from Mrs Bright, 1925

Crossley, Bob 1912–2010, *Landscape near Mestre, Venice*, gift from Mrs Finlay, 2007

Crossley, Bob 1912–2010, *The Spin before the Fling*, gift from the artist, 2004

Crossley, Bob 1912–2010, *Westwards*, gift from the artist, 2006

Crossley, Bob 1912–2010, *North Sea Oil Rig*, gift from the artist, 2004

Crossley, Bob 1912–2010, *Sharks Feeding*, gift from the artist, 2004

Crossley, Bob 1912–2010, *Scholar*, gift from the artist, 2004

Crossley, Bob 1912–2010, *Aggressive Blacks*, gift from the Contemporary Art Society, 1968

Cunaeus, Conradyn 1828–1895, *Deerhounds and Dead Game*, gift from Robert Taylor Heape, 1902

Cundell, Nora Lucy Mowbray 1889–1948, *The Patchwork Quilt*, purchased from H. B. Brierley, 1950, © Touchstones Rochdale

Davis, Henry William Banks 1833–1914, *Thorn Trees on a Breconshire Hillside*, gift from Philip Bright, 1929

Dawson, Henry 1811–1878, *Sunrise at Sea*, gift from Robert Taylor Heape, 1911

Dawson, Henry 1811–1878, *Waiting for the Tide, Sunset*, gift from Robert Taylor Heape, 1911

Day, H. R. *Amen Corner (A Bit of Old Rochdale, Lancashire)*, unknown acquisition method

De Léon y Escosura, Ignacio 1834–1901, *The Artist's Studio*, gift from Robert Taylor Heape, 1913

Deutsch, Ludwig 1855–1935, *An Arab Schoolmaster*, gift from J. S. Crompton, 1921, photo credit: www.bridgemanart.com

Dickinson, Lowes Cato 1819–1908, *John Bright (1811–1889)*, gift from Colonel T. Thomasson, 1931

Dicksee, Thomas Francis 1819–1895, *Ophelia*, gift from Robert Taylor Heape, 1908

Dierckx, Pierre Jacques 1855–1947, *The Knitting Lesson*, gift from Robert Taylor Heape, 1913, © DACS 2011

Dollman, John Charles 1851–1934, *'Marquis', a Gordon Setter*, gift from Robert Taylor Heape, 1903

Dugdale, Thomas Cantrell 1880–1952, *The Bathing Cove*, gift from an anonymous donor, 1904, © Joanna Dunham

Dunlop, Ronald Ossory 1894–1973, *Memory of Honfleur, France*, purchased from the artist, 1961, © Touchstones Rochdale

Dunlop, Ronald Ossory 1894–1973, *Southwold, Suffolk*, purchased from R. H. Spurr, 1939

Dunstan, Bernard b.1920, *The Zip Fastener*, purchased from the artist, 1961, © Touchstones Rochdale

Earl, George 1824–1908, *Excelsior*, purchased from F. M. Evans, 1936

Eastman, Frank S. 1878–1964, *A Little Sleep*, gift from the executors of the estate of Walter Scott, 1929

Ellis, Edwin (attributed to) 1841–1895, *Picking Berries*, presented by James Hunt, 1937

Elmore, Alfred 1815–1881, *Charles V at the Monastery of Yuste*, gift from Robert Taylor Heape, 1911

Etchells, Jessie 1892–1933, *Flowers*, gift from the Contemporary Art Society, 1924

Eurich, Richard Ernst 1903–1992, *Mousehole, Cornwall*, purchased from R. H. Spurr, 1939, © the artist's estate/Bridgeman Art Library

Faed, Thomas 1826–1900, *Highland Lassie*, bequeathed by J. S. Littlewood, 1919, photo credit: www.bridgemanart.com

Fagnani, Giuseppe 1819–1873, *Richard Cobden (1804–1865)*, gift from the former General Purchasing Committee

Fagnani, Giuseppe 1819–1873, *John Bright (1811–1889), and Richard Cobden (1804–1865)*, gift from the former General Purchasing Committee, 1972

Falk, Alan b.1945, *Bedroom Piece*, gift from the artist, 1981, © the artist

Farquharson, David 1839–1907, *Early Morning on Beer Common, South Devon*, gift from Robert Taylor Heape, 1911

Farquharson, Joseph 1846–1935, *Through the Crisp Air*, purchased from F. M. Evans, 1931

Federov, A. A. *Russia* (copy of Ivan Shishkin), bequeathed by A. W. Kay-Menzies, 1945

Feyen, Jacques Eugène 1815–1908, *Oyster Fishers (Cleaning the Oysters after the Catch)*, gift from J. S. Crompton, 1921

Fidler, Harry 1856–1935, *Energy*, purchased from the executors of the artist's estate, 1935

Fildes, Luke 1843–1927, *Lady Royds (1846–1925)*, gift, 1925

Fisher, Horace 1861–1934, *Autumn, Capri, Italy*, gift from the executors of the estate of Walter Scott, 1929

Fisher, Mark 1841–1923, *Sheep Shearing*, gift from W. H. Wood, 1924

Fisher, Mark 1841–1923, *Farm Work*, purchased from the Spring Exhibition, 1904

Fishwick, Janet active 1909–1913, *Amen Corner, Rochdale, Lancashire*, purchased from the artist, 1909

Fishwick, Janet active 1909–1913, *Belfield Hall, Rochdale, Lancashire*, purchased from the artist, 1913

Flemish (Antwerp) School *The Adoration of the Magi*, acquired via the Thomas Kay Bequest, 1912; transferred from Heywood, 1974

Flemish School 17th C, *Portrait of a Monk*, acquired via the Thomas Kay Bequest, 1912; transferred from Heywood, 1974

Flint, William Russell 1880–1969, *Maruja the Strong*, purchased from the artist, 1935, © Touchstones Rochdale

Francis, Eva 1887–1924, *Snowdrops and Violets*, purchased from the Spring Exhibition, 1904

French School *Philippe le Bon (1396–1467), Duc de Bourgogne*, acquired via the Thomas Kay Bequest, 1912; transferred from Heywood, 1974, photo credit: www.bridgemanart.com

French School *Philip II (1527–1598), King of Spain*, acquired via the Thomas Kay

Bequest, 1912; transferred from Heywood, 1974

Freud, Lucian b.1922, *Woman's Head with a Yellow Background*, purchased from the Mayor Gallery, 1983, © Lucian Freud

Frost, William Edward 1810–1877, *Aurora and Zephyr*, gift from Robert Taylor Heape, 1911

Fry, Roger Eliot 1866–1934, *Studland Bay, Dorset*, gift from the Contemporary Art Society, 1924, photo credit: www.bridgemanart.com

Gabain, Ethel Leontine 1883–1950, *The Dancer and the Canary*, gift from John Coply, 1950, © the artist's estate

Gauld, John Richardson 1885–1961, *The Students*, purchased from the artist, 1950

Gertler, Mark 1891–1939, *The Bokhara Coat*, purchased from the Crane Kalman Gallery, 1959, photo credit: www.bridgemanart.com

Giovanni di Paolo 1403–1482, *The Crucifixion*, acquired via the Thomas Kay Bequest, 1912; transferred from Heywood, 1974

Glasson, Lancelot Myles 1894–1959, *The Young Rower*, gift from Councillor A. W. Kay-Menzies, 1933, photo credit: www.bridgemanart.com

Gledhill, David b.1959, *Unidentified Street, Rochdale, Lancashire*, gift from the artist, 2006, © the artist

Glehn, Wilfrid Gabriel de 1870–1951, *Shadows on the Wall, Cannes, France*, purchased from the artist, 1935, © Touchstones Rochdale

Goodall, Frederick 1822–1904, *Rebekah*, gift from Robert Taylor Heape, 1911

Goodall, Frederick 1822–1904, *The Marriage Procession*, gift from Robert Taylor Heape, 1903

Goodall, Frederick 1822–1904, *Shepherdess and Her Flock at a Pool Left by the Subsiding of the Overflow of the Nile*, gift from Robert Taylor Heape, 1903

Gorbatov, Konstantin Ivanovich 1876–1945, *A Sunny Terrace*, purchased from the Cooling Galleries Ltd, 1937, © Touchstones Rochdale

Gotch, Thomas Cooper 1854–1931, *Mother Goose*, purchased from the artist, 1908, photo credit: www.bridgemanart.com

Graham, Peter 1836–1921, *Highland Mists*, gift from Abraham Haigh Crowther, 1913

Graham, Peter 1836–1921, *Highland Landscape*, gift from Abraham Haigh Crowther, 1913

Grant, Duncan 1885–1978, *Fort St Louis, Toulon, France*, purchased from the artist, 1940, © Touchstones Rochdale

Grant, Keith b.1930, *Snow Drift, Clear Sky* (polyptych, panel 1 of 4), purchased from the artist, 1976, ©

the artist

Grant, Keith b.1930, *Snow Drift, Clear Sky* (polyptych, panel 2 of 4), purchased from the artist, 1976, © the artist

Grant, Keith b.1930, *Snow Drift, Clear Sky* (polyptych, panel 3 of 4), purchased from the artist, 1976, © the artist

Grant, Keith b.1930, *Snow Drift, Clear Sky* (polyptych, panel 4 of 4), purchased from the artist, 1976, © the artist

Green, Anthony b.1939, *Our Tent, the Fourteenth Wedding Anniversary*, purchased from the Rowan Gallery with the assistance of the Victoria and Albert Museum Purchase Grant Fund, 1976, © Anthony Green RA

Greenwood, E. *W. Atkinson*

Gregory, Edward John 1850–1909, *A Study of Boulter's Lock, Maidenhead, Berkshire*, gift from Robert Taylor Heape, 1910

Grundy, Cuthbert Cartwright 1846–1946, *Fresh and Breezy*, gift from the artist, 1912

Gunn, Herbert James 1893–1964, *Pauline (d.1950), Wife of the Artist*, purchased from the Beaux Arts Gallery, 1932, © estate of the artist

Gunn, Herbert James 1893–1964, *Gracie Fields (1898–1979)*, gift from the sitter, 1938, © estate of the artist

Hacker, Arthur 1858–1919, *By the Waters of Babylon*, gift from Robert Taylor Heape, 1911

Hackert, Jacob Philipp 1737–1807, *Landscape*, gift from Mrs M. Heath, 1956

Hackert, Jacob Philipp 1737–1807, *Landscape*, gift from Mrs M. Heath, 1956

Hague, Joshua Anderson 1850–1916, *Summer Flowers*, purchased from the artist, 1913

Haite, George Charles 1855–1924, *A Venetian Fruit Stall*, gift from Robert Taylor Heape, 1913

Halswelle, Keeley 1832–1891, *On the Thames*, gift from Mrs Bright, 1925

Harding, James Duffield 1798–1863, *An Italian Coast Scene*, gift from Robert Taylor Heape, 1903

Hardy, Frederick Daniel 1827–1911, *The Solo*, gift from Robert Taylor Heape, 1913, photo credit: www.bridgemanart.com

Hardy, Frederick Daniel 1827–1911, *Waiting for Mother*, gift from Robert Taylor Heape, 1911

Hardy, Heywood 1842–1933, *Hunting Scene*, gift from Robert Taylor Heape, 1913

Harmar, Fairlie 1876–1945, *Cheyne Walk, Chelsea, London*, purchased, 1950, © Touchstones Rochdale

Haughton, Benjamin 1865–1924, *Church Hill Wood*, gift from Mrs Haughton, 1937

Havers, Alice 1850–1890, *End of Her Journey*, gift from Robert Taylor Heape, 1901

Hayes, Edwin 1819–1904, *Falmouth Harbour, Cornwall*, gift from Robert Taylor Heape, 1911

Hayllar, Jessica 1858–1940, *The Robin*, gift from Alderman Wilson Dumming, 1912, © the artist's estate/Bridgeman Art Library, photo credit: www.bridgemanart.com

Haynes-Williams, John 1836–1908, *A Spanish Warrior*, gift from Robert Taylor Heape, 1902

Haynes-Williams, John 1836–1908, *A Spanish Matador*, gift from Robert Taylor Heape, 1908

Heath, Frank Gascoigne 1873–1936, *The Gentleness of Heaven Is on the Sea*, purchased from the artist, 1913

Heffner, Karl 1849–1925, *The Aqueduct of Claudius, Rome*, bequeathed by Mrs Helen Crowther, 1910

Heineman, T. *Preparing the Meal*, purchased from R. Bateman, 1928

Heineman, T. *The Quayside*, purchased from R. Bateman, 1928

Hemingway, Harold 1908–1976, *Rochdale, Lancashire, 1856*, purchased by the General Purchasing Committee, 1956; transferred to the permanent collection, 1961

Hemingway, Harold 1908–1976, *Rochdale, Lancashire, 1956*, purchased by the General Purchasing Committee, 1956; transferred to the permanent collection, 1961

Hemy, Charles Napier 1841–1917, *The Armed Merchant Man*, purchased from Thomas Agnew & Sons, 1926

Henry, James Levin 1855–1929, *In Winter Quarters (Hayle Harbour, Cornwall)*, purchased from the Spring Exhibition, 1906

Henshaw, Frederick Henry 1807–1891, *A Forest Glade*, gift from W. H. Lawton, 1929

Hepple, Norman 1908–1994, *Early Morning, Lake Garda, Italy*, purchased from the artist at the Royal Academy Summer Exhibition, 1961, © Touchstones Rochdale

Hepple, Norman 1908–1994, *Spring Flowers*, purchased from the artist at the Royal Academy Summer Exhibition, 1957, © Touchstones Rochdale

Herkomer, Hubert von 1849–1914, *Clement Royds (1842–1916), CB*, gift from the Royds Bequest, 1925

Herman, Josef 1911–2000, *Miners against a Mountain*, purchased from Mr A. Freet, 1984, © estate of Josef Herman. All rights reserved, DACS 2011

Herring, John Frederick II 1815–1907, *Farmyard Scene*, bequeathed by J. S. Littlewood, 1919

Hewit, Forrest 1870–1956, *Mount Orgueil, Jersey*, purchased from the artist, 1940, © Touchstones

Rochdale

Hill, Robert W. 1932–1990, *The Wave*, purchased from the artist at the Royal Academy Summer Exhibition, 1968, © Touchstones Rochdale

Hiller, Susan b.1940, *Gulf 1*, gift from the Contemporary Art Society, 1996

Hiller, Susan b.1940, *Gulf 2*, gift from the Contemporary Art Society, 1996

Hillier, Tristram Paul 1905–1983, *Las lavanderas*, purchased from the artist, 1966, © Touchstones Rochdale

Hitchens, Ivon 1893–1979, *Sussex, Spring*, purchased from Alan Freer, 1981, © Ivon Hitchens' estate/ Jonathan Clark & Co.

Hitchens, Ivon 1893–1979, *Open Terrace*, purchased from the Tib Lane Gallery, 1959, © Touchstones Rochdale

Hoggatt, William 1879–1961, *Top of the 'Howe Glen'*, gift from Miss E. Wisken, 1964

Holl, Frank 1845–1888, *Newgate, Committed for Trial*, gift from Robert Taylor Heape, 1910

Hollinrake, J. *Hare Hill Road Corner, Littleborough, Lancashire*, gift from Littleborough Council Chamber

Holmberg, August Johann 1851–1911, *The Connoisseur*, gift from Samuel Tweedale Santridge, 1913

Holt, Charlie b.1947, *Sacred Books*, purchased from the artist, 1998, © the artist

Horley, S. *Capri, Italy*, purchased from Ian Peace & Co., 1999

Hornel, Edward Atkinson 1864–1933, *Among the Lilies*, purchased from the Spring Exhibition, 1906, photo credit: www.bridgemanart.com

Horsley, John Callcott 1817–1903, *St Valentine's Morn*, gift from Robert Taylor Heape, 1902, photo credit: www.bridgemanart.com

Horsley, John Callcott 1817–1903, *Going to a Party*, gift from Robert Taylor Heape, 1911

Hughes, Arthur 1832–1915, *The Sluggard, Market Women, Brittany, France*, gift from an unknown donor, 1948

Hughes, Edward 1829–1908, *The Alarm*, gift from Robert Taylor Heape, 1902

Hughes, Talbot 1869–1942, *A Court Belle, 1770*, gift from Robert Taylor Heape, 1911, photo credit: www.bridgemanart.com

Hughes, Talbot 1869–1942, *The Morning of the Duel*, gift from Robert Taylor Heape, 1911

Hulme, Frederick William 1816–1884, *Bolton Abbey, North Yorkshire*, gift from Robert Taylor Heape, 1911

Hunter, Alexis b.1948, *Passionate Instincts No.13*, gift from the Contemporary Art Society, 1990, © Alexis Hunter. All rights reserved, DACS 2011

Hutchinson, Betty active 1964–1965, *View from Okenrod School, Rochdale, Lancashire*, purchased from the artist, 1965

Inskip, John Henry 1864–1947, *Walmer, Kent*, purchased from the Spring Exhibition, 1905

Inskip, John Henry 1864–1947, *Whitstable, Kent*, purchased from the Spring Exhibition, 1905

Irmer, Carl 1834–1900, *The Edge of a Bavarian Forest, Germany*, gift from Robert Taylor Heape, 1902

Italian School 17th C, *St Ignatius of Loyola (1491–1556)*, acquired via the Thomas Kay Bequest, 1912; transferred from Heywood, 1974

Italian School 19th C, *Madonna and Child*, acquired via the Thomas Kay Bequest, 1912; transferred from Heywood, 1974

Jackson, Frederick William 1859–1918, *A Welcome Visitor*, gift from Mr W. H. Wood, 1923, photo credit: www.bridgemanart.com

Jackson, Frederick William 1859–1918, *Sunday Morning*, transferred from Middleton Library, 1974

Jackson, Frederick William 1859–1918, *Rushbearing at Middleton, Rochdale, Lancashire*, presented to Middleton Corporation, 1918; transferred from Middleton Library, 1974

Jackson, Frederick William 1859–1918, *At Venice*, purchased from the Spring Exhibition, 1905

Jackson, Frederick William 1859–1918, *A. G. C. Hanley, President of the Liberal Association*, transferred from Middleton Library, 1978

Jackson, Frederick William 1859–1918, *Cattle in a Meadow*, transferred from Middleton Library, 1978

Jackson, Frederick William 1859–1918, *Farm Scene*, transferred from Middleton Library, 1978

Jackson, Frederick William 1859–1918, *Landscape, Farm Scene*, gift from the artist's Memorial Fund from subscribers, 1921

Jackson, Frederick William 1859–1918, *Middleton Wakes, Rochdale, Lancashire*, gift from Mrs John Ashworth; transferred from Middleton Library, 1974

Jackson, Frederick William 1859–1918, *The High Tide, Runswick Bay, North Yorkshire*, transferred from Middleton Library, 1978

Jackson, Frederick William 1859–1918, *The Last of the Hand Loom Weavers*, transferred from Middleton Library, 1978, photo credit: www.bridgemanart.com

Jackson, Frederick William 1859–1918, *The Old Weaver*, gift from Mrs W. Taylor; transferred from Middleton Library, 1974

Janssens van Ceulen, Cornelis (follower of) 1593–1661, *Portrait of a Young Nobleman*, acquired via the Thomas Kay Bequest, 1912; transferred from Heywood, 1974

Jaray, Tess b.1937, *Remain*, gift from the Contemporary Art Society, 1986, © the artist

Jervas, Charles (circle of) c.1675–1739, *James Thomson (1700–1748)*, gift from Mr Chalkley, 1880

Jiménez Aranda, José 1837–1903, *El santo óleo*, gift from Robert Taylor Heape, 1910

John, Augustus Edwin 1878–1961, *Eve Kirk (1900–1969)*, purchased from J. W. Freshfield, 1946, © the artist's estate/Bridgeman Art Library, photo credit: www.bridgemanart.com

Johnson, Andrew *Flowers*, purchased from the artist at the Royal Academy Summer Exhibition, 1961, © Touchstones Rochdale

Johnson, Charles Edward 1832–1913, *Cub Hunting in the Midlands*, gift from Robert Taylor Heape, 1910

Jones-Hughes, Michelle b.1944, *Migration*, purchased from the artist, 1976, © the artist

Jones-Hughes, Selwyn b.1943, *Upright Edges Leading to the Sea*, purchased from the artist, 1976, © the artist

Kay, Phil *'Mr Manchester', Tony Wilson (1950–2007)*, gift from Councillor Robin Parker, Mayor of Rochdale, 2008

Kelly, Gerald Festus 1879–1972, *Saw Ohn Nyun IV*, purchased from the artist, 1944, © Touchstones Rochdale

Kemp-Welch, Lucy 1869–1958, *Hill Folk*, purchased from the artist, 1926, © David Messum

Kennedy, Cecil 1905–1997, *June Arrangement*, purchased from the Fine Art Society, 1962, © Touchstones Rochdale

Kern, Hermann 1839–1912, *Old Man Shelling Peas*, bequeathed by J. S. Littlewood, 1919

Kershaw, Walter b.1940, *Rochdale Arts Festival, 1971*, gift from the Amateur Societies to celebrate Rochdale's first Arts Festival week, 1972, © the artist

King, Henry John Yeend 1855–1924, *River Banks and River Blossoms*, unknown acquisition method

Kingsley, Harry 1914–1998, *The Cooling Tower, Stockport, Cheshire*, gift from the artist, 1968, © Touchstones Rochdale

Kingsley, Harry 1914–1998, *New Street*, gift from the artist, 1968, © Touchstones Rochdale

Kingsley, Harry 1914–1998, *Embryo, Moss Side, Manchester*, gift from the artist, 1980

Kingsley, Harry 1914–1998, *Cambridge Street, Hulme, Manchester, 1946*, gift from the artist, 1980

Knight, George active 1872–1892, *Seascape*, gift from Mrs M. Heath, 1956

Knight, George active 1872–1892, *Seascape*, gift from Mrs M. Heath, 1956

Knight, Harold 1874–1961, *The Young Seamstress*, purchased from the artist, 1908, © reproduced with permission of the estate of Dame Laura Knight, DBE, RA, 2011. All rights reserved

Knight, Laura 1877–1970, *The Elder Sister*, purchased from the artist, 1907, © reproduced with permission of the estate of Dame Laura Knight, DBE, RA, 2011. All rights reserved

Knight, Laura 1877–1970, *The Trick Act*, purchased from R. Howarth, 1938, © reproduced with permission of the estate of Dame Laura Knight, DBE, RA, 2011. All rights reserved

La Thangue, Henry Herbert 1859–1929, *Packing Cherries in Provence, France*, purchased from the artist, 1924

La Thangue, Henry Herbert 1859–1929, *The Festa*, gift from the artist's widow, 1942

Ladell, Edward 1821–1886, *Still Life with Fruit*, gift from J. S. Crompton, 1921

Lamb, Henry 1883–1960, *Late News*, purchased from the artist, 1953, © Touchstones Rochdale

Lance, George 1802–1864, *Still Life*, gift from Mrs M. Heath, 1956

Landini, Andrea 1847–1912, *A Distinguished Guest*, gift from F. M. and A. Riley, 1993

Landini, Andrea 1847–1912, *Contentment*, gift from F. M. and A. Riley, 1993

Landini, Andrea 1847–1912, *Une bonne bouteille*, gift from F. M. and A. Riley, 1993

Lavery, John 1856–1941, *Schooling the Pony*, purchased from the artist, 1935, © Touchstones Rochdale, photo credit: www.bridgemanart.com

Le Bas, Edward 1904–1966, *The Misericordia, Venice*, purchased from the artist, 1949, © Touchstones Rochdale

Leader, Benjamin Williams 1831–1923, *Ben Vorlich*, gift from Bertram Porrill, 1931

Leader, Benjamin Williams 1831–1923, *Scene on the Llugwy with Moel Siabod in the Distance*, bequeathed by J. S. Littlewood, 1919

Leader, Benjamin Williams 1831–1923, *The Stream through the Birch Woods*, gift from A. W. Kay-Menzies, 1945

Leader, Benjamin Williams 1831–1923, *Glyder Fawr, Snowdon Range*, bequeathed by Mrs Helen Crowther, 1910

Leader, Benjamin Williams 1831–1923, *Haymaking*, gift from Robert Taylor Heape, 1913

Learoyd, Barbara *Conflict*, purchased from the artist, 1965, © Touchstones Rochdale

Lee, Sydney 1866–1949, *The Norman Column*, gift from Councillor Wilson Dumming, 1906

Leighton, Edmund Blair 1852–1922, *Hales Old Hall, Hales Green, near Norwich, Norfolk*, gift from John Stothert Littlewood, 1919

Leslie, George Dunlop 1835–1921, *The Gardener's Daughter*, gift from Robert Taylor Heape, 1910, photo credit: www.bridgemanart.com

Lessore, Thérèse 1884–1945, *Hop Gardens, Kent*, gift from the Sickert Trust, 1947, © Henry & John Lessore

Levene, Ben 1938–2010, *Green Still Life*, acquired from the Royal Academy Summer Exhibition, 1977, © the artist's estate

Lhermitte, Léon-Augustin 1844–1925, *Rue, Mont-Saint-Père, France*, gift from J. S. Crompton, 1923

Linnell, James Thomas 1826–1905, *Redstone Wood, Spring*, gift from Robert Taylor Heape, 1911

Linnell, William 1826–1906, *O'er the Muir among the Heather*, gift, 1919

Lloyd, Walker Stuart 1875–1929, *A Mile from the Sea, Newton Ferrers, River Lynter, South Devon*, gift from Alderman J. E. Jones

Lord, W. *St Chad's, Rochdale, Lancashire*, presented by Jack Salkeld

Lorimer, John Henry 1856–1936, *Hush*, gift from Mr Walter Scott, 1907

Lowry, Laurence Stephen 1887–1976, *Our Town*, purchased from the artist, 1944, © courtesy of the estate of L. S. Lowry

Lucas, John 1807–1874, *'Love', Portrait of a Lady ('Grace was in all her steps. Heaven in her eye, in every gesture dignity and love')* (from John Milton's 'Paradise Lost'), gift from C. M. Royds, 1903

Lyons, John C. M. b.1933, *Performance*, commissioned through the Handley Bequest, 2000, © the artist

MacWhirter, John 1839–1911, *The Fisherman's Haven, St Monans, Fifeshire*, gift from Robert Taylor Heape, 1911

MacWhirter, John 1839–1911, *Over the Border*, gift from Robert Taylor Heape, 1908

MacWhirter, John 1839–1911, *The Lake*, gift from Joseph Crowther, 1940

Magarshack, Stella active 1964–1968, *Interior, Night*, purchased from the Royal Academy Summer Exhibition, 1964

Magarshack, Stella active 1964–1968, *Portrait of the Artist*, purchased from the artist, 1968

Mann, Cathleen 1896–1959, *Flowers in a Vase and a Statuette*, purchased from the Leger Galleries, 1958, © Touchstones Rochdale

Mason, Bateson 1910–1977, *Châteauneuf, France*, gift from the Contemporary Art Society, 1946

Mason, Bateson 1910–1977,

Venice, purchased from the artist, 1968, © Touchstones Rochdale

McEvoy, Ambrose 1878–1927, *Mrs Julian Lousada*, gift from Anthony Lousada, 1956

McEvoy, Ambrose 1878–1927, *Daphne (The Honourable Daphne Baring, 1904–1986, Wife of the Sculptor)*, purchased from M. A. Bazell, 1948

McGlynn, Terry 1903–1973, *Italian Beach*, purchased from the artist, 1958

Meade, Arthur 1863–1948, *The Wreck (After the Storm)*, gift from Sam Turner, 1929, © the artist's estate

Methuen, Paul Ayshford 1886–1974, *Neuville-les-Avignon and Mont Ventoux, France*, purchased from the artist, 1957, © Touchstones Rochdale

Mignard, Pierre I (circle of) 1612–1695, *Cardinal Richelieu (1585–1642)*, acquired via the Thomas Kay Bequest, 1912; transferred from Heywood, 1974

Miller, Roy b.1938, *The Field from Above*, purchased from the artist, 1961, © Touchstones Rochdale

Montezin, Pierre Eugène 1874–1946, *Soleil d'automne*, purchased from the artist, 1938, © Touchstones Rochdale

Morales, Luis de (follower of) c.1509–c.1586, *Ecce Homo*, acquired via the Thomas Kay Bequest, 1912; transferred from Heywood, 1974

Morland, George (studio of) 1763–1804, *Interior with Sheep*, acquired via the Thomas Kay Bequest, 1912; transferred from Heywood, 1974

Morreau, Jacqueline b.1929, *Sisyphus*, purchased from the artist, 1999, © the artist

Morris, Philip Richard 1836–1902, *The End of the Journey*, gift from Robert Taylor Heape, 1911

Morris, William Bright 1844–1912, *John Bright (1811–1889)*, gift from Mrs Bright, 1925

Mostyn, Thomas Edwin 1864–1930, *The Tryst*, purchased from the Spring Exhibition, 1904, photo credit: www.bridgemanart.com

Mostyn, Thomas Edwin 1864–1930, *Lieutenant Colonel Henry Fishwick (1835–1914), FSA*, presented to the town on behalf of subscribers by Alderman Miles Ashworth at the opening of the Jubilee Portrait Exhibition, 1907

Mostyn, Thomas Edwin 1864–1930, *The Sanctuary*, gift from Philip Bright, 1929

Mostyn, Thomas Edwin 1864–1930, *The Valley of Sunshine*, gift from an anonymous donor

Müller, Leopold Carl 1834–1892, *Tric-Trac Players*, gift from Abraham Haigh Crowther, 1913

Murillo, Bartolomè Esteban (follower of) 1618–1682, *The Crucifixion*, acquired via the

Thomas Kay Bequest, 1912; transferred from Heywood, 1974

Murray, David 1849–1933, *Loch Linnhe at Port Appin, Argyllshire*, gift from Robert Taylor Heape, 1911

Nardi, Angelo (attributed to) 1584–1665, *The Martyrdom of St Bartholomew*, acquired via the Thomas Kay Bequest, 1912; transferred from Heywood, 1974

Neep, Victor 1921–1979, *Winter Sea*, purchased from the artist, 1967, © Touchstones Rochdale

Nevinson, Christopher 1889–1946, *After the Recapture of Bapaume, France*, gift from Mr Lye, 1928, © the artist's estate/Bridgeman Art Library, photo credit: www.bridgemanart.com

Nevinson, Christopher 1889–1946, *The Old Harbour*, purchased from the Leger Galleries, 1958, © the artist's estate/Bridgeman Art Library, photo credit: www.bridgemanart.com

Newton, Algernon Cecil 1880–1968, *Port*, gift from the Contemporary Art Society, 1959

Nicholls, Bertram 1883–1974, *Easby Abbey, Richmond, North Yorkshire*, purchased from the artist, 1940, © Touchstones Rochdale

Noble, John Sargeant 1848–1896, *Out in the Cold*, gift from Robert Taylor Heape, 1911, photo credit: www.bridgemanart.com

Norbury, Frank *Carpet-Making Factory*, gift from L. P. Brown, 1987

North, John William 1842–1924, *Over Hedges and Ditches*, gift from Robert Taylor Heape, 1908

Nurse, C. W. *Old Farmhouse, Syke, Rochdale, Lancashire*, gift from Mrs A. Hartley, 1979

Nuvolone, Carlo Francesco (attributed to) 1608–1665, *Hagar in the Wilderness*, acquired via the Thomas Kay Bequest, 1912; transferred from Heywood, 1974

Oakes, John Wright 1820–1887, *Mountain Stream, Glen Derry, Aberdeenshire, 'Like time the restless waters rush along'*, gift from Robert Taylor Heape, 1908

Ogden, Charles *'Swinger'*

Olsson, Albert Julius 1864–1942, *Off The Needles, Isle of Wight*, purchased from the Spring Exhibition, 1905

Olsson, Albert Julius 1864–1942, *Sunset at Land's End, Cornwall*, gift from William Lloyd, 1921

Parrott, William 1813–after 1891, *The Fountain, Port of Genoa, Italy*, gift from Robert Taylor Heape, 1913

Partington, John Herbert Evelyn 1843–1899, *Old Salts, Whitby, North Yorkshire*, gift from Robert Taylor Heape, 1902

Passini, Alberto 1826–1899, *A Moorish Market Place*, gift from J. S. Crompton, 1913

Payne, Steve b.1949, *Landscape*,

purchased from S. Payne, 1985, © the artist

Pearson, Christine *'Tate' Shapes, Night*, purchased at auction, 2008

Percy, William 1820–1893, *Edwin Waugh (1817–1890)*, gift from Robert Taylor Heape, 1908

Petker, J. (attributed to) *Landscape*, gift from Mrs M. Heath, 1956

Pettie, John 1839–1893, *Distressed Cavaliers Turned Highwaymen*, gift from Robert Taylor Heape, 1911

Phillip, John 1817–1867, *The Convent Dole*, gift from Robert Taylor Heape, 1908

Phillip, John 1817–1867, *The Spanish Widow*, gift from Mrs M. Heath, 1956

Pickering, James Langsdale 1845–1912, *From English Seas (White Nose Cliff, the Highest in Dorset)*, purchased from the Spring Exhibition, 1910

Pickersgill, Frederick Richard 1820–1900, *Ferdinand and Miranda* (from William Shakespeare's 'The Tempest'), gift from Robert Taylor Heape, 1902

Piper, John 1903–1992, *Rievaulx Abbey, North Yorkshire*, purchased from Ernest Brown & Phillips Ltd, 1951, © the artist's estate

Pissarro, Lucien 1863–1944, *A Muddy Lane, Hewood, Dorset*, purchased from the artist, 1942, © Touchstones Rochdale, photo credit: www.bridgemanart.com

Potter, Charles 1832–1907, *Samuel Bamford (1788–1872), 'The Radical', Silk Weaver of Middleton*, gift from Robert Taylor Heape, 1908

Priestman, Arnold 1854–1925, *The Windmill*, purchased from the artist, 1913

Priestman, Bertram 1868–1951, *A Cotswold Village*, purchased from the artist, 1945, © Touchstones Rochdale

Pyne, James Baker 1800–1870, *Norwegian Scene*, gift from Mrs A. Donegani, 1950

Radford, Gordon b.1936, *Untitled*, gift from the Friends of Rochdale Art Gallery, 1990, © the artist

Rankle, Alan b.1952, *Untitled Painting I (Calder Heights)*, presented by the Tramman Trust through the Art Fund, © the artist

Reckelbus, Louis Joseph 1864–1958, *Canal near Bruges, Belgium, Autumn*, gift from William Lloyd, 1921

Reid, Flora Macdonald 1860–c.1940, *French Politicians, Royalist and Republican*, gift from R. N. D. Holt, 1903

Reynolds, Hettie Tangye active 1914–1934, *Roses*, gift from Mrs S. Turner, 1935, © Touchstones Rochdale

Richter, Herbert Davis 1874–1955, *Reflections in a Silver Ball*, purchased from the artist, 1932, © Touchstones Rochdale

Roberts, David 1796–1864, *Ruins of the Temple, Kom Ombos, Upper*

Nile, Egypt, gift from Robert Taylor Heape, 1903

Roberts, David 1796–1864, *Milan Cathedral, Italy*, gift from Robert Taylor Heape, 1908

Rose, Gerard de 1918–1987, *Wrestlers*, purchased from the artist, 1957, © Touchstones Rochdale

Rötig, Georges Frédéric 1873–1961, *Sangliers allant boire*, gift from Harold Barker

Royds, John J. *The Critics*, gift, 1914

Rutherford, Harry 1903–1985, *Rochdale, Lancashire*, purchased from the Tib Lane Gallery, 2006, © the artist's estate

Sadler, Walter Dendy 1854–1923, *Experientia docet*, gift from Robert Taylor Heape, 1913

Sadler, Walter Dendy 1854–1923, *Played Out*, gift from Lady Duckworth in memory of Sir James Duckworth, JP, 1919

Sant, James 1820–1916, *The First Sense of Sorrow*, gift from Robert Taylor Heape, 1903

Schedoni, Bartolomeo 1578–1615, *La carità*, gift from Mrs Lydia Kemp, 1905

Schlesinger, Henry Guillaume 1814–1893, *Peine perdue*, gift from Robert Taylor Heape, 1908

Schmaltz, Herbert Gustave 1856–1935, *Queen of the May*, gift from Robert Taylor Heape, 1911, photo credit: www.bridgemanart.com

Schofield, G. P. S. *Hill Top Farm*, purchased from the artist, 1953

Schofield, John 1853–1928, *In a Little Difficulty*, gift from Alderman William Cunliffe, 1907

Schofield, John 1853–1928, *Blackstone Edge, Hollingworth Lake in the Distance, Rochdale, Lancashire*, gift from Littleborough Council Chamber

Schofield, John 1853–1928, *Lydgate, Rochdale, Lancashire*, purchased from the artist, 1926

Schofield, John 1853–1928, *Going to the Meet*

Scognamiglio, Antonio (attributed to) active 1879–1900s, *Vesuvius in Eruption, 7 April 1906*, acquired via the Thomas Kay Bequest, 1912; transferred from Heywood, 1974

Seemann, Enoch the younger (attributed to) 1694–1744, *Bridget Domville (d.1750), Daughter of Sir Thomas Domville*, acquired via the Thomas Kay Bequest, 1912; transferred from Heywood, 1974

Segal, Arthur 1875–1944, *Aluminium Pans and Oranges*, gift from Miss Marianne Segal, 1955, © the artist's estate

Sephton, George Harcourt 1860–1923, *Ducklings*, transferred from Heywood Library, 1974

Shackleton, William 1872–1933, *Christ at Jerusalem*, purchased with the assistance of the Ogden Bequest Fund

Shackleton, William 1872–1933,

Phryne at Eleusis, bequeathed by the artist, 1933

Sharp, Dorothea 1874–1955, *Low Tide*, purchased from the Southport Corporation Art Gallery, 1931, © Touchstones Rochdale

Shayer, William 1788–1879, *A Group of Gypsies*, gift from C. H. Stott, 1921

Sickert, Walter Richard 1860–1942, *The Fair, Dieppe, France*, purchased from Mrs Oswald Sickert, 1942, © Touchstones Rochdale, photo credit: www.bridgemanart.com

Simcock, Jack b.1929, *Rockside, Mow Cop, Staffordshire*, purchased from the artist, 1971, © the artist

Simpson, Kate A. *Sister of Kate Simpson, Eyla Laurence*, unknown acquisition method

Skeaping, Kenneth Mathieson 1857–1946, *Richard Heape*, presented by artist's family, 1928

Skeaping, Kenneth Mathieson 1857–1946, *Robert Taylor Heape (1848–1917)*, gift from Richard Taylor Heape, 1917

Skeaping, Kenneth Mathieson 1857–1946, *Lord Byron (George Gordon Byron, 6th Baron Byron of Rochdale, 1788–1826)*, gift from Robert Taylor Heape, 1908

Smith, George 1829–1901, *Obliging the Company*, gift from Robert Taylor Heape, 1910

Smith, George 1829–1901, *An Interior*, gift from Robert Taylor Heape, 1902

Smith, Matthew Arnold Bracey 1879–1959, *Blue Vase with Fruit*, purchased from the Tib Lane Gallery, 1959, © Touchstones Rochdale

Somerset, Richard Gay 1848–1928, *Mountain Pasture, Snowdonia*, purchased from the artist, 1908

Sosnica, Jerzy active 1963–1965, *Rochdale, Lancashire, Fording the Roche* (copy of an earlier painting), purchased from the artist, 1965

Southern German School *The Crucifixion*, acquired via the Thomas Kay Bequest, 1912; transferred from Heywood, 1974

Spencer, Gilbert 1892–1979, *Sheep in a Field*, gift from the Contemporary Art Society, 1928, © the artist's estate/Bridgeman Art Library

Spencer, Stanley 1891–1959, *Bellrope Meadow, Cookham, Berkshire*, purchased from Arthur Tooth & Sons Ltd, 1941, © Touchstones Rochdale, photo credit: www.bridgemanart.com

Spenlove-Spenlove, Frank 1866–1933, *The Light at the Door, a January Night in Flanders (No.96)*, purchased from the artist, 1909

Steer, Philip Wilson 1860–1942, *Richmond Castle through the Trees, North Yorkshire*, purchased from J. Lockett Thompson, 1944, © Tate, London 2011

Steinthal, Emeline Petrie 1855–1921, *John Petrie, Engineer*,

gift from Mrs George Petrie

Stephen, Dan b.1921, *The Painter's Studio*, purchased from the artist, 1961, © Touchstones Rochdale

Stevens, Norman 1937–1988, *Castle Garden*, purchased from The Redfern Gallery with the assistance of the Victoria and Albert Museum Purchase Grant Fund, 1980, © the artist's estate

Stott, Edward William 1859–1918, *Ploughing, Early Spring*, purchased from the Fine Art Society, 1969

Stott, Edward William 1859–1918, *The Horse Pond*, purchased from Mr Lockett Thompson, 1937, photo credit: www.bridgemanart.com

Stott, Edward William 1859–1918, *Sunrise in Winter*, purchased from Lockett Thompson, 1948

Stott, Edward William 1859–1918, *The Fold*, purchased from the Fine Art Society, 1969, photo credit: www.bridgemanart.com

Stott, Edward William 1859–1918, *There Was No Room in the Inn*, purchased from the artist at the Spring Exhibition, 1911

Stott, Edward William 1859–1918, *Approaching Night*, purchased from the Fine Art Society, 1969

Stott, Edward William 1859–1918, *Self Portrait*, gift from Mrs Victor H. Stott, 1937

Stott, William 1857–1900, *The Two Sisters*, gift from Robert Taylor Heape, 1903, photo credit: www.bridgemanart.com

Stroudley, James 1906–1985, *First-Floor Front*, purchased from the artist, 1959, © Touchstones Rochdale

Stroudley, James 1906–1985, *The Sun from the West, Saltdean, East Sussex*, purchased from the artist, 1968, © Touchstones Rochdale

Taylor, Arnold 1892–1951, *Wellfield Old Mill, Rochdale, Lancashire*, purchased from the artist, 1937

Taylor, Arnold 1892–1951, *Brierley's Mill, Rochdale, Lancashire*, purchased from the artist, 1951

Taylor, Arnold 1892–1951, *Miller Bridge, Kendal, Cumbria*, purchased from the artist, 1934

Taylor, Charles Donald 1922–2005, *Hey Head*, purchased from the artist, 1955

Taylor, Charles Donald 1922–2005, *The Construction of College Bank Flats, Rochdale, Lancashire*, purchased from Mrs Constance McGarry, 2006

Taylor, Leonard Campbell 1874–1969, *Still Life*, purchased from the artist, 1932, © Touchstones Rochdale

Taylor, Walter active 1952–1955, *Mill Lodge*, purchased from the artist, 1953

Taylor, Walter active 1952–1955, *Salmon Nets at Cocker Sands, Lancashire*, purchased from the artist, 1955

Ten Kate, Herman Frederik Carel

1822–1891, *A Royal Musical Party*, gift from Robert Taylor Heape, 1911

Teniers, David II (follower of) 1610–1690, *The Alchemist*, acquired via the Thomas Kay Bequest, 1912; transferred from Heywood, 1974

The Master of the Countess of Warwick (attributed to) active c.1560–c.1570, *Margaret of Austria (1522–1586), Duchess of Parma*, acquired via the Thomas Kay Bequest, 1912; transferred from Heywood, 1974

Thornton, R. *Welding*, gift from Mike Hill, 2005

Tibble, Geoffrey Arthur 1909–1952, *Graham Bell (1910–1943)*, gift from the Contemporary Art Society, 1939

Topham, Frank William Warwick 1838–1924, *The Story of Ruth and Boaz*, gift from Robert Taylor Heape, 1902, photo credit: www.bridgemanart.com

Turley, Keith John b.1950, *Gracie Fields (1898–1979)*, © the artist

unknown artist 17th C, *Travellers Leaving a Hostelry, Dawn*, acquired via the Thomas Kay Bequest, 1912; transferred from Heywood, 1974

unknown artist *Portrait of a Woman*

unknown artist *Alderman Fred Lord Kay, Mayor of Middleton Borough (1935–1936)*, gift from Mr John F. Kay

unknown artist *Alderman William Cuncliffe, JP, OBE, Mayor of Rochdale (1911–1913)*, presented, c.1923

unknown artist *Benjamin Heape, Son of Robert Heape*, unknown acquisition method

unknown artist *Benjamin Heape, Son of Robert Heape*, unknown acquisition method

unknown artist *Capri, Italy*

unknown artist *Interior of the Town Hall, Rochdale, Lancashire*, unknown acquisition method

unknown artist *James Wild, 'Jem Jarvis', Fought at the Battle of Waterloo, Drummer in the 2nd Life Guards*, gift from Mrs Proctor, 1907

unknown artist *John Ashworth*, gift from the Trustees of the Baillie Street United Methodist Free Church, 1876

unknown artist *Joseph Henry, MD*

unknown artist *Landscape*

unknown artist *Mill in a Valley*, unknown acquisition method

unknown artist *Old Rochdale, Lancashire*, gift from Mr D. Mortimer Maddow

unknown artist *Portrait of a Man*, unknown acquisition method

unknown artist *Portrait of an Unknown Lady*

unknown artist *Portrait of an Unknown Man*

unknown artist *Portrait of an Unknown Man*

unknown artist *Portrait of an Unknown Man*

unknown artist *Portrait of an Unknown Man*

unknown artist *Portrait of an Unknown Man*

unknown artist *Portrait of an Unknown Mayor*

unknown artist *Portrait of an Unknown Woman*

unknown artist *Seascape*

unknown artist *Seascape*

unknown artist *Still Life with Fruit*

unknown artist *Textile Industry*

unknown artist *The Reverend William Seaton*

unknown artist *'Tim Bobbin', John Collier (1708–1786)*, gift from R. P. Close, 1922

Vanni, Francesco (attributed to) 1563–1610, *Saint Catherine of Siena Receiving the Stigmata*, acquired via the Thomas Kay Bequest, 1912; transferred from Heywood, 1974

Vause, William Allan 1903–1987, *Gracie Fields (1898–1979)*, gift from the artist, 1985

Vergé-Sarratt, Henri 1880–1966, *Île d'Yeu, France*, gift from the Contemporary Art Society, 1952

Vespignani, Renzo 1924–2001, *Paesaggio urbano*, gift from the Contemporary Art Society, 1962, © DACS 2011

Von Ambros, Raphael 1855–1895, *An Eastern Doorway; At the Moslem Chief's Door*, gift from Lady E. A. Nicholls, 1938, photo credit: www.bridgemanart.com

A. V. W. *Belfield Bridge, Rochdale, Lancashire*, gift from Mrs Crossley, 1958

A. V. W. *Idlers' Corner*

G. H. W. *Landscape with Sheep*, gift

Waldron West, Ernest 1904–1994, *Cyril Smith (1928–2010), MP*, gift from the artist, 1975

Walters, George Stanfield 1838–1924, *Fishing Boats off Gorleston, Norfolk*, bequeathed by Miss Emma Taylor, 1944

Walton, Allan 1891–1948, *Landscape*, gift from the Contemporary Art Society, 1931

Wane, Richard 1852–1904, *Ebb Tide*, gift from Mrs Bright, 1925

Wane, Richard 1852–1904, *Tywyn near Conway*, gift from Mrs Bright, 1925

Ward, Henrietta Mary Ada 1832–1924, *The Princes in the Tower*, gift from Robert Taylor Heape, 1902

Waterhouse, John William 1849–1917, *In the Peristyle*, gift from Robert Taylor Heape, 1908, photo credit: www.bridgemanart.com

Waterlow, Ernest Albert 1850–1919, *Mending the Nets, Newlyn, Cornwall*, gift from Robert Taylor Heape, 1911, photo credit: www.bridgemanart.com

Watson, Derek 1934–1992, *A Well-Earned Rest*, gift from Maud Sulter, 1992

Watson, George Spencer 1869–1934, *Three Wise Kings*, gift from A. J. Law, 1920, photo credit:

www.bridgemanart.com

Weatherby, William *Edgar Brierley*

Webb, James 1825–1895, *Namur, Belgium*, gift from Robert Taylor Heape, 1911

Webb, James 1825–1895, *Evening Scene*, gift from H. B. Brierley, 1949

Weight, Carel Victor Morlais 1908–1997, *The Library*, purchased from the artist, 1971, © the artist's estate/Bridgeman Art Library

Weisbrod, Richard 1906–1991, *Winter, near Clitheroe, Lancashire*, purchased from the artist, 1958

West, George *River Roch at Midge Hall, Lancashire*, purchased from H. R. Kershaw, 1971

Whaite, Henry Clarence 1828–1912, *Mountains in Wales*, gift from Councillor J. E. Jones

White, Noreen b.1948, *Akhtar and a Kameez*, gift from the artist, 2003, © the artist

Whittle, Thomas c.1842–after 1900, *The Next Field*, gift from Mrs M. Heath, 1956

Whittle, Thomas c.1842–after 1900, *Arundel Castle, Sussex*, gift from Mrs M. Heath, 1956

Wilkinson, Norman 1878–1972, *Below Tilbury, Essex*, purchased from the Royal Academy Summer Exhibition, 1964, © the Norman Wilkinson estate

Williams, Terrick John 1860–1936, *Low Tide, St Ives, Cornwall*, purchased from the artist, 1934

Williams, Terrick John 1860–1936, *A Silvery Sky*, gift from Lady E. A. Nicholls, 1938

Willis, William 1841–1923, *Pilchard Fishers*, gift from William Wiles, 1903

Wilson, Richard 1714–1787, *Landscape*, gift from Mrs M. Heath

Wilson, Susan b.1951, *Self Portrait with a Clematis Wreath*, purchased from the artist, 1997, © the artist

Winstanley, Hamlet 1694–1756, *Sir Darcy Lever (1703–1742)*, gift from the Middleton Corporation, 1974

Winstanley, Hamlet 1694–1756, *Frances Lever*, gift from the Middleton Corporation, 1974

Winstanley, Hamlet 1694–1756, *John Lever of Alkrington*, gift from the Middleton Corporation, 1974

Winstanley, Hamlet (attributed to) 1694–1756, *John Lever*, gift from William Logan Home to the Middleton Corporation

Winstanley, Hamlet (attributed to) 1694–1756, *Dame Dorothy Lever with Her Daughter, Martha*, gift from William Logan Home to Middleton Corporation

Wonnacott, John b.1940, *Crescent Road II (The Artist and His Grandfather)*, purchased from the artist, 1978, © the artist

Wood, Edgar Thomas 1860–1935, *San Remo, Italy*, purchased from the Morris Fine Art Gallery, 1980

Wood, Edgar Thomas 1860–1935,

View from Campo dei Fiori, Varese, Italy, presented to Middleton Corporation by the Committee of the Unitarian Chapel; transferred from Middleton Library

Wood, Edgar Thomas 1860–1935, *Italian Landscape*, transferred from Middleton Library, 1984

Wood, Edgar Thomas 1860–1935, *The Artist's Father*

Woods, Brian b.1938, *The Rainbow*, purchased from the artist, 2000, © the artist

Wright, John Michael 1617–1694, *Miss Butterworth of Belfield Hall*, bequeathed by Colonel T. R. Philippi, 1913

Wright, John Michael 1617–1694, *Miss Butterworth of Belfield Hall*, bequeathed by Colonel T. R. Philippi, 1913

Wyndham, Richard 1896–1948, *Head of a Boy*, gift from the Contemporary Art Society, 1927, © the artist's estate, photo credit: www.bridgemanart.com

Yadegar, Manijeh b.1951, *C6-04*, gift from the Contemporary Art Society, 2007, © the artist

Ziem, Félix François Georges Philibert 1821–1911, *Venice in Flood*, gift from J. S. Crompton, 1921

Rochdale Town Hall

Percy, William 1820–1893, *Jacob Bright (1821–1899)*, acquired, before 1871

unknown artist *Alderman Edward Taylor (1813–1895)*, gift, 1893

Westcott, Philip 1815–1878, *C. L. Ashworth (1823–1873)*, gift, 1871

Saddleworth Museum and Art Gallery

Bowie, Janis b.1956, *Mule Spinning Frame*, purchased, 2009, © the artist

Bradley, Helen 1900–1979, *Market Place behind Stockport Road*, gift, 1993

Carse, John (attributed to) b.1821 (?), *Frenches Mill, Greenfield, Saddleworth, Yorkshire*, gift, 2010

Holland, John c.1805–1880, *Rushcart Festival at Saddleworth Church, Yorkshire*, purchased, 2001

Mansel, Lowell Dobbs *Sunday Wedding at Heights Chapel, Delph, Saddleworth, Greater Manchester*, gift, 2009, © Saddleworth Museum and Art Gallery

McCombs, John b.1943, *Saddleworth Viaduct, Uppermill, Greater Manchester*, gift, 1993, © the artist

McCombs, John b.1943, *Afternoon Sunlight, Summer, Delph, Saddleworth, Greater Manchester*, gift, 2002, © the artist

McCombs, John b.1943, *Saddleworth Parish Church, Greater Manchester, Summer*, gift, 2002, © the artist

McCombs, John b.1943, *Fletcher's Mill from Tanner's Dam, Greenfield, Saddleworth, Greater Manchester*, gift, 2002, © the artist

McCombs, John b.1943, *The Square, Dobcross, Saddleworth, Greater Manchester*, gift, 2002, © the artist

McCombs, John b.1943, *Wade Lock, Uppermill, Saddleworth, Greater Manchester*, gift, 2002, © the artist

McCombs, John b.1943, *Winter, Denshaw Church, Saddleworth, Greater Manchester*, gift, 2002, © the artist

McCombs, John b.1943, *Morning Sunlight, Austerlands, Saddleworth, Greater Manchester*, gift, 2002, © the artist

McCombs, John b.1943, *Morning Sunlight, Clough Lane, Grasscroft, Saddleworth, Greater Manchester*, gift, 2002, © the artist

McCombs, John b.1943, *The Manns, Friezland, Saddleworth, Greater Manchester*, gift, 2002, © the artist

McCombs, John b.1943, *Winter Sunlight, Diggle, Saddleworth, Greater Manchester*, gift, 2002, © the artist

unknown artist *Saddleworth, Yorkshire*, gift, 2001

unknown artist *John Andrew (d.1856), Huntsman*, gift, 2001

Stockport Heritage Services

Allori, Cristofano (copy of) 1577–1621, *Judith Holding the Head of Holofernes*, unknown acquisition method

Amorosi, Antonio 1660–1738, *Two Men Playing Cards Outdoors, Watched by a Youth*, acquired via the John Benjamin Smith Bequest, 1879

Amorosi, Antonio 1660–1738, *Two Youths Gambling Outdoors, Watched by a Third*, acquired via the John Benjamin Smith Bequest, 1879

Austin, Alfred R. active 1873–1899, *The Farmer's Supper*, gift, 1933

Austin, Alfred R. active 1873–1899, *Game of Crib (Oliver Goldsmith, Dr Samuel Johnson and David Garrick)*, gift, 1945

Barabino, Simone c.1585–c.1620, *Christ in the Carpenter's Shop*, acquired via the John Benjamin Smith Bequest, 1879

Barber, Alfred R. 1841–1925, *Four Rabbits*, unknown acquisition method

Bates, Frederick Davenport 1867–1930, *Portrait of a Gentleman*, unknown acquisition method

Bates, Frederick Davenport 1867–1930, *Alderman William Lees*, unknown acquisition method

Bates, Frederick Davenport 1867–1930, *Frank Brown*, gift, 2006

Batoni, Pompeo (circle of) 1708–1787, *The Penitent Magdalen*, acquired via the John Benjamin Smith Bequest, 1879

Belgian School 19th C, *The Cock Fight*, gift, 1945

Bell, W. H. *Portrait of a Gentleman*, unknown acquisition method

Bell, W. H. *Portrait of a Lady*, unknown acquisition method

Boar, J. active 1903–1904, *The Bridge*, unknown acquisition method

Boar, J. active 1903–1904, *Rural Cottage*, unknown acquisition method

Browning, Amy Katherine 1881–1978, *Block Makers*, purchased, 1977, © Joanna Dunham

Browning, Amy Katherine 1881–1978, *Shaping the Hats*, purchased, 1977, © Joanna Dunham

Browning, Amy Katherine 1881–1978, *At the Sewing Machines*, purchased, 1977, © Joanna Dunham

Browning, Amy Katherine 1881–1978, *Hatting Factory Workers*, purchased, 1977, © Joanna Dunham

Browning, Amy Katherine 1881–1978, *Packing the Hats*, purchased, © Joanna Dunham

Brueghel, Abraham c.1631–1690, *Flowers in a Pewter Vase, Grapes and Peaches*, acquired via the John Benjamin Smith Bequest, 1879

Burgess, M. *Steelworks*, unknown acquisition method

Bygate, Joseph E. active c.1890, *Durham City*, gift from Sir Thomas Rowbotham

Cairo, Francesco del 1607–1665, *The Salutation (The Visitation)*, acquired via the John Benjamin Smith Bequest, 1879

Callcott, Augustus Wall 1779–1844, *Coastal Scene*, gift, 1940

Carlieri, Alberto (attributed to) 1672–after 1720, *Architectural Capricci with Tobias and the Angel*, acquired via the John Benjamin Smith Bequest, 1879

Carlieri, Alberto (attributed to) 1672–after 1720, *Tobias Curing Tobit's Blindness*, acquired via the John Benjamin Smith Bequest, 1879

Carmichael, John Wilson (attributed to) 1800–1868, *Seascape*, unknown acquisition method

Carrington, James Yates 1857–1892, *Dog Playing the Piano*, unknown acquisition method

Castiglione, Giovanni Benedetto (follower of) 1609–1664, *Saint Jerome*, acquired via the John Benjamin Smith Bequest, 1879

Castiglione, Giovanni Benedetto (follower of) 1609–1664, *Saint Onuphrius*, acquired via the John Benjamin Smith Bequest, 1879

Chettle, James Patchell 1871–1944, *Old Swanage, Dorset*, purchased, 1937

Chettle, James Patchell

Chaliava, Luigi 1842–1914, *Summer Time*, unknown acquisition method

Chirnside, J. *Self Portrait*, gift, 1979

Christie, James Elder (attributed to) 1847–1914, *Old Man with Gold Coins*, unknown acquisition method

Clark *The Farmyard*, gift, 1933

Clarke, J. (attributed to) *English Landscape*, unknown acquisition method

Clater, Thomas 1789–1867, *The Proposal*, gift, 1927

Clegg, H. active 1888–1889, *Arden Hall, Bredbury, Cheshire*, unknown acquisition method

Clegg, H. active 1888–1889, *St Paul's Church, Portwood, Stockport, Cheshire*, on loan from a private individual

Cobbett, Edward John 1815–1899, *Science*, gift, 1951

Cole, John *The Wallace Monument, Stirling*, purchased, 1936

Collier, John 1708–1786, *Portrait of a Jovial Young Man*, gift, 1955

Colombo, Giovanni Battista Innocenzo (attributed to) 1717–1793, *Travellers Ambushed in a Wood*, acquired via the John Benjamin Smith Bequest, 1879

Cooper, Thomas Sidney 1803–1902, *Landscape with Sheep*, unknown acquisition method

Corbishley, M. M. *Bridge in the Park*, unknown acquisition method

Cotman, John Sell 1782–1842, *The Mill (copy of Rembrandt van Rijn)*, gift

Cottrell, Mary *VE Street Party, 1945*, unknown acquisition method

Cowley, Mollie *Old and New, Lancashire Hill*, purchased, 1970

Cresti, Domenico (circle of) 1559–1638, *The Visitation*, acquired via the John Benjamin Smith Bequest, 1879

Davies, James Hey 1844–1930, *The Stackyard*, gift

De Luna, Charles b.c.1812, *À Mlle Floranet*, gift, 1976

Desubleo, Michele (circle of) c.1601–1676, *The Madonna Adoring the Sleeping Child*, acquired via the John Benjamin Smith Bequest, 1879

Detti, Cesare Augusto 1847–1914, *A Garden Party*, unknown acquisition method

Domenichino (style of) 1581–1641, *Virgin and Child with Saint John*, unknown acquisition method

Dunstan, Bernard b.1920, *Girl Holding a Blue Nightdress*, purchased, 1972, © the artist/ Bridgeman Art Library

Eastlake, Charles Lock 1793–1865, *Held for Ransom*, gift, 1950 (?)

Eisler, Georg 1928–1998, *Stockport, Cheshire*, gift, 1992

Eley, William b.1938, *Fall*,

purchased, © the artist

Ellis, Edwin 1841–1895, *The Harbour*, gift, 1940

Eyre, C. *Henry Walker, Mayor*, gift, 1994

Fidanza, Francesco (follower of) 1747–1819, *A Galley in a Mediterranean Harbour*, acquired via the John Benjamin Smith Bequest, 1879

Fidanza, Francesco (follower of) 1747–1819, *A Mediterranean Harbour*, acquired via the John Benjamin Smith Bequest, 1879

Fidanza, Francesco (style of) 1747–1819, *A Mediterranean Inlet at Sunrise*, acquired via the John Benjamin Smith Bequest, 1879

Fox, Allan H. b.1859, *Henry Bell*, unknown acquisition method

Fox, Allan H. b.1859, *Portrait of an Unknown Lady*, unknown acquisition method

Fox, Allan H. b.1859, *John Andrew*, gift, 1961

Fox, Allan H. b.1859, *Portrait of an Unknown Lady*, unknown acquisition method

Frost, Terry 1915–2003, *Black and White*, gift, 1986, © estate of Terry Frost. All rights reserved, DACS 2011

Gagliardi, Filippo d.1659, *Architectural Capricci*, acquired via the John Benjamin Smith Bequest, 1879

Gagliardi, Filippo d.1659, *Architectural Capricci*, acquired via the John Benjamin Smith Bequest, 1879

Garbutt, S. *'The Crown' Inn*, unknown acquisition method

Gessard, V. *Lady at a Window*, gift, 1940

Goodall, Frederick 1822–1904, *Ready for the Journey*, gift, 1945

Gough, Thomas b.1858, *Prestbury Church, Cheshire*, gift, 1939

Grant, Ian 1904–1993, *Margaret Reading*, purchased, 1964

Green, Ewart *From a Stockport Window*, unknown acquisition method

Gregory, Jessica *Dawn*, purchased, 1974

Grimbleby, David *Chaos Ground*, gift, 2004

Grozier, R. *Girl and a Baby*, unknown acquisition method

Guercino (follower of) 1591–1666, *A Sibyl*, acquired via the John Benjamin Smith Bequest, 1879

Hague, Joshua Anderson 1850–1916, *Burdock*, gift, 1935

Hague, Joshua Anderson 1850–1916, *Coast near Deganwy, Conwy*, gift, 1932

Hague, Joshua Anderson 1850–1916, *In the Mold Valley, Flintshire*, gift, 1944

Hague, Joshua Anderson 1850–1916, *Late Autumn*, gift, c.1925

Hague, Joshua Anderson 1850–1916, *The Mill Stream*, gift, c.1925

Harding, Philip b.1962, *Flower Study 8*, unknown acquisition

method, © the artist

Harding, Philip b.1962, *Flower Study 14*, unknown acquisition method, © the artist

Hardy, James II 1832–1889, *Gaming Birds*, unknown acquisition method

Harvey, Douglas c.1821–after 1900, *Nymphs, Cherubs and Swans*, unknown acquisition method

Haughton, Benjamin 1865–1924, *Winter Wonderland*, gift, 1937

Haworth, Mike *Oswaldtwistle Landscape, Lancashire*, purchased, 1974

Hemy, Charles Napier 1841–1917, *Seascape*, gift, 1940

Henzell, Isaac 1815–1876, *Village Gossip*, unknown acquisition method

Heusch, Jacob de (after) 1657–1701, *An Italianate Landscape with Three Banditti and a Dog*, acquired via the John Benjamin Smith Bequest, 1879

Heusch, Jacob de (circle of) 1657–1701, *A Rocky Mediterranean Coast with Peasants and a Galley*, acquired via the John Benjamin Smith Bequest, 1879

Hirst, John *Root III*, purchased, 1973

Holder, Edward Henry 1847–1922, *Pastoral Scene*, unknown acquisition method

Horlor, George William active 1849–1891, *Calves and Lambs*, gift, 1940

Houlston, Helen C. b.1927, *1st Age, the Infant*, gift, 1991, © the artist

Houlston, Helen C. b.1927, *2nd Age*, gift, 1991, © the artist

Houlston, Helen C. b.1927, *3rd Age*, gift, 1991, © the artist

Houlston, Helen C. b.1927, *4th Age*, gift, 1991, © the artist

Houlston, Helen C. b.1927, *5th Age, Justice*, gift, 1991, © the artist

Houlston, Helen C. b.1927, *6th Age, Pantaloon*, gift, © the artist

Houlston, Helen C. b.1927, *7th Age, Sans Everything*, gift, © the artist

Hughes-Stanton, Herbert Edwin Pelham 1870–1937, *On the French Coast*, gift, 1940

Hunt, Charles 1829–1900, *The School Room*, unknown acquisition method

Hyde-Pinion, A. b.1878, *James Watts*, unknown acquisition method

Isherwood, James Lawrence 1917–1989, *Old Spanish Lady*, gift, 1986

Isherwood, James Lawrence 1917–1989, *Mijas, Spain*, gift, 1986

Italian (Roman) School 18th C, *The Penitent Magdalen*, acquired via the John Benjamin Smith Bequest, 1879

Italian (Roman) School (attributed to) *Pope Urban VIII (1568–1644), with His Nephews Cardinal Francesco Baberini (1597–1679), and Cardinal Antonio Barberini (1607–1671)*, acquired

via the John Benjamin Smith Bequest, 1879

Italian (Tuscan) School (attributed to) 17th C, *Saint Francis of Paola Saving a Lime Kiln near Paterno Calabro, Italy*, acquired via the John Benjamin Smith Bequest, 1879

Italian School 17th C, *Saint Ursula Arriving on a Rocky Coast*, acquired via the John Benjamin Smith Bequest, 1879

Italian School (attributed to) 17th C, *The Adoration of the Magi (after Peter Paul Rubens)*, acquired via the John Benjamin Smith Bequest, 1879

Jackson, Frederick William 1859–1918, *Returning with the Catch*, gift, 1932

Jennings, Derrick *Reflections*, purchased, 1980

Jervas, Charles (follower of) c.1675–1739, *Anne Masters (1673–1763), 4th Countess of Coventry*, unknown acquisition method; on long-term loan to Lynne Hall, National Trust

Johnson, Charles Edward 1832–1913, *The Horse Pond*, gift

Johnson, Helen *Mountain Scene (A Highland Spate)*, gift, 1959

Joli, Antonio (circle of) c.1700–1777, *The Campo Vaccino, Rome*, acquired via the John Benjamin Smith Bequest, 1879

Keil, Bernhard 1624–1687, *A Scene of Sacrifice at an Altar*, acquired via the John Benjamin Smith Bequest, 1879

Keil, Bernhard 1624–1687, *The Supper at Emmaus*, acquired via the John Benjamin Smith Bequest, 1879

Kershaw, Joseph Franklin 1885–1917, *Renaissance of Spring*, gift, 1929

King, Henry John Yeend 1855–1924, *A Cottage Garden, Braemar, Aberdeenshire*, gift, 1940

Kingsley, Harry 1914–1998, *The Cooling Tower, Portwood, Stockport, Cheshire*, unknown acquisition method

Kingsley, Harry 1914–1998, *Newbridge Lane, Stockport, Cheshire*, gift, 1969

Kingsley, Harry 1914–1998, *Storm in a Teacup*, gift

Kingsley, Harry 1914–1998, *Alpine Road, Stockport, Cheshire*, gift, 1979

Kingsley, Harry 1914–1998, *The Old Chimney, Stockport, Cheshire*, gift, 1980

Kingsley, Harry 1914–1998, *Early Morning, Stockport, Cheshire*, gift, 1979

Kingsley, Harry 1914–1998, *The Roundhouse, Ancoats, Manchester*, purchased (?)

Kingsley, Harry 1914–1998, *The Cooling Tower, Stockport, Cheshire*, gift, 1982

Kitchen, Edna *The Cat's Park, Hillgate, Stockport*, purchased

Kneller, Godfrey 1646–1723, *Sir John Egerton of Wrinehill*

(1658–1729), unknown acquisition method

Knight, John William Buxton 1843–1908, *Harvest, Eventide*, gift, 1940

Knighton-Hammond, Arthur Henry 1875–1970, *The Crook of Lune*, gift

Leader, Benjamin Williams 1831–1923, *Harvest Landscape*, gift, 1958

Leader, Benjamin Williams 1831–1923, *Mountain Solitude*, gift, 1959

Lee, Moses 1950–1995, *Round Flight*, purchased, 1991

Lee, Moses (attributed to) 1950–1995, *Abstract*, unknown acquisition method

Lees, E. H. *Little Underbank, Stockport, Cheshire*, unknown acquisition method

Lees, E. H. *St Mary's, Stockport, Cheshire*, unknown acquisition method

Lees, Fred *Market Place, Stockport, Cheshire*, gift, 1940

Lees, Fred *Waiting for the Boats, North Devon*, gift, 1940

Levy, Emmanuel 1900–1986, *Maria*, gift, 1964

Liverseege, Henry (circle of) 1803–1832, *Thomas Whalley, Esq.*, bequeathed, 1994

Llatka, Eut L. *Coastal Scene*, unknown acquisition method

Lowe, Doreen *Tenements with Figures*, purchased, 1973

Lowe, George *Bredbury Old Hall, Stockport, Cheshire*, purchased, 1971

Lowe, George *Stockport Market Place, Cheshire, 1809*, unknown acquisition method

Lowndes, Alan 1921–1978, *Gasworks*, gift, 1979, © the artist's estate

Lowndes, Alan 1921–1978, *Stockport Street Scene, Cheshire*, on loan from a private individual, since 1989, © the artist's estate

Lowndes, Alan 1921–1978, *In the Park*, unknown acquisition method, © the artist's estate

Lowndes, Alan 1921–1978, *Love Lane Corner*, on loan from a private individual, since 1985, © the artist's estate

Lowry, Laurence Stephen 1887–1976, *Crowther Street, Stockport, Cheshire*, purchased, 1935, © courtesy of the estate of L. S. Lowry

Lucchesi, Raffaello *La Madonna della sedia* (after Raphael), gift

Ludlow, Henry Stephen 1859–c.1934, *The Gamekeeper's Daughter*, gift, 1933

Luti, Benedetto 1666–1724, *A Penitent Magdalen Fainting before a Vision of an Angel*, acquired via the John Benjamin Smith Bequest, 1879

March y Marco, Vicente 1859–1927, *Reading the Will*, gift, 1940

Marchis, Alessio de (follower of) 1684–1752, *A Fortified Bridge over a River*, acquired via the John Benjamin Smith Bequest, 1879

Matania, Eduardo 1847–1929, *Mother and Child*, gift, 1940

Mawson, Elizabeth Cameron 1849–1939, *Tintern Abbey, Monmouthshire*, gift, 1957

Mayer-Marton, George 1897–1960, *Wet Lane*, gift, 1975, © estate of George Mayer-Marton. All rights reserved, DACS 2011

Mayer-Marton, George 1897–1960, *Sea Wall, Blue Anchor, West Somerset*, gift, 1975, © estate of George Mayer-Marton. All rights reserved, DACS 2011

Megget *Portrait of a Lady*, unknown acquisition method

Miller, Alva *Watts of Abney*, unknown acquisition method

Mola, Pier Francesco (circle of) 1612–1666, *Figures near Classical Ruins*, acquired via the John Benjamin Smith Bequest, 1879

Mola, Pier Francesco (circle of) 1612–1666, *Figures near Classical Ruins*, acquired via the John Benjamin Smith Bequest, 1879

Mola, Pier Francesco (circle of) 1612–1666, *Saint Francis*, acquired via the John Benjamin Smith Bequest, 1879

Morris, C. *Landscape with a Windmill*, unknown acquisition method

Morris, Philip Richard 1836–1902, *Home, Sweet Home*, gift, 1933

Morris, Philip Richard 1836–1902, *Lady and a Dog*, gift, 1940

Mort, Marjorie 1906–1989, *Factories*, purchased, 1935

Mostyn, Thomas Edwin 1864–1930, *The Jewel Box*, unknown acquisition method

Mostyn, Thomas Edwin 1864–1930, *River Scene*, gift, 1932

Newenham, Frederick 1807–1859, *Cromwell Dictating to Milton*, purchased, 1958

Niemann, Edmund John 1813–1876, *River Scene with an Angler*, gift

Niemann, Edmund John 1813–1876, *Landscape*, gift, 1959

Nithsdale, John Maxwell *Councillor Headridge, Mayor of Stockport (1983)*, gift, 1992

Nithsdale, John Maxwell *Day at the Museum*, unknown acquisition method

Nithsdale, John Maxwell *Lancaster Bombers*, unknown acquisition method

Nithsdale, John Maxwell *Selecting the 'Champion of Champions'*, purchased (?)

Nithsdale, John Maxwell *State Occasion*, gift, 1992

Nithsdale, John Maxwell *The Blackpool Excursion Train*, unknown acquisition method

Nithsdale, John Maxwell *The Red Arrows*, unknown acquisition method

Noble, John Sargeant 1848–1896, *'None but the brave deserve the fare'*, gift, 1933

Nomé, François de c.1593–after 1644, *Aeneas and Anchises Fleeing the Burning of Troy*, acquired via the John Benjamin Smith Bequest, 1879

Nowell, Arthur Trevethin 1862–1940, *Dr Murray (d.1931)*, commissioned, 1932, © the artist's estate

O'Brien, Ivor 1918–2003, *St Petersgate, Stockport, Cheshire*, unknown acquisition method

Oliver, William 1823–1901, *Portrait of a Lady*, gift, 1940

Osborn, Emily Mary 1828–1925, *Sailing Barges*, unknown acquisition method

Owen, Joseph *A Woodland Clearing*, gift, 1928

Partington, John Herbert Evelyn 1843–1899, *Girl on a Beach*, unknown acquisition method

Partington, John Herbert Evelyn 1843–1899, *Edward Walmsley (b.1815)*, unknown acquisition method

Partington, John Herbert Evelyn 1843–1899, *William Rayner, MD*, unknown acquisition method

Partington, John Herbert Evelyn 1843–1899, *George Cooper*, unknown acquisition method

Patton, Ernest *River Scene*, unknown acquisition method

Payne, David c.1844–1891, *A Scene on the Wye, near Haddon Hall, Derbyshire*, gift, 1976

Peel, James 1811–1906, *Near Capel Curig, Conwy*, gift, 1932

Penney, David *Culture Cul-de-Sac*, purchased, 1976

Phillip, John 1817–1867, *The Castanet Player*, gift, 1927

Phillips, Brian b.1939, *A Sluggish Sort of Day near Stockport, Cheshire*, gift, © the artist

Phillips, Brian b.1939, *'Urry Up You, We've Got to Be at Mi Mother's in 'Alf an Hour*, unknown acquisition method, © the artist

Poole, Paul Falconer 1807–1879, *Summer*, gift, 1927

Priestman, Arnold 1854–1925, *A Norfolk Broad*, gift, 1940

Przepiora, David Stefan b.1944, *People*, purchased, 1974, © the artist

Ramsay, George S. *Landscape*, gift, 2000

Redfern, Richard *Still Life with Fruit*, unknown acquisition method

Reynolds, Joshua (attributed to) 1723–1792, *A Young Bacchus*, unknown acquisition method

Richardson, Edward Harrison 1881–1952, *A Corner of My Studio*, gift

Riding, Harold active from c.1925, *The River at Llanyblodwel, Shropshire*, gift, 1946

Rivers, Leopold 1852–1905, *Evening at Beccles, Suffolk*, gift, 1932

Robert, Hubert (attributed to) 1733–1808, *Capricci of Classical Ruins*, acquired via the John Benjamin Smith Bequest, 1879

Robert, Hubert (attributed to) 1733–1808, *Capricci of Classical Ruins*, acquired via the John Benjamin Smith Bequest, 1879

Romeyn, Willem (circle of) c.1624–1694, *Italianate Landscape with Drovers*, acquired via the John Benjamin Smith Bequest, 1879

Romeyn, Willem (circle of) c.1624–1694, *Italianate Landscape with Drovers*, acquired via the John Benjamin Smith Bequest, 1879

Romney, George (attributed to) 1734–1802, *Captain John Joseph Vernon, 3rd Dragoon Guards*, gift, 1994

Roos, Philipp Peter 1657–1706, *Farm Animals in a Landscape with an Old Man Drinking*, acquired via the John Benjamin Smith Bequest, 1879

Rosa, Salvator 1615–1673, *Landscape with Brigands*, acquired via the John Benjamin Smith Bequest, 1879

Rosa, Salvator (follower of) 1615–1673, *Landscape with Brigands*, acquired via the John Benjamin Smith Bequest, 1879

Roscoe, F. *Portrait of an Unknown Gentleman*, unknown acquisition method

Rossi, Pasquale de' 1641–1725, *A Jesuit Instructing the Populace*, acquired via the John Benjamin Smith Bequest, 1879

Rossi, Pasquale de' 1641–1725, *A Jesuit Instructing Youths*, acquired via the John Benjamin Smith Bequest, 1879

Rothmer, Dorothy b.1926, *Cheshire in Autumn*, purchased, 1975, © the artist

Rutherford, Harry 1903–1985, *September, Mottram, Cheshire*, purchased, 1937, © the artist's estate

Saker, John *Landscape with Sheep*, unknown acquisition method

Salucci, Alessandro (attributed to) 1590–c.1655, *A Capriccio of Classical Buildings in a Port*, acquired via the John Benjamin Smith Bequest, 1879

Schmalz, Herbert Gustave 1856–1935, *The Temple of Eros*, unknown acquisition method

Schmalz, Herbert Gustave 1856–1935, *Where Is the Lord, My King?*, gift, 1938

Schmalz, Herbert Gustave 1856–1935, *Beth-El*, unknown acquisition method

Schmalz, Herbert Gustave 1856–1935, *Shiloh*, unknown acquisition method

Schmalz, Herbert Gustave 1856–1935, *Captain T. N. C. Nevill*, unknown acquisition method

Schmalz, Herbert Gustave 1856–1935, *Rabboni*, gift, 1971

Seiter, Daniel 1649–1705, *The Dead Christ, with the Madonna and Saint John the Evangelist*, acquired via the John Benjamin Smith Bequest, 1879

Selous, Arthur *Coastal Scene, Guernsey*, gift, c.1946

Shaw, David Carson b.1942, *Mountain at the Sound*, gift, © the artist

Shaw, Peter 1926–1982, *Stockport from Pendlebury Hill, Cheshire*, purchased, 1968

Shaw, Peter 1926–1982, *Stockport Market, Cheshire*, gift, 2003

Shaw, Peter 1926–1982, *Matley Moor, Rowarth, Derbyshire*, purchased

Short, Frederick Golden 1863–1936, *Autumn*, unknown acquisition method

Shuttleworth, William b.1785, *Church of St Mary, Stockport, Cheshire*, gift

Shuttleworth, William b.1785, *Stockport Market Place, Cheshire*, gift, 1888

Shuttleworth, William b.1785, *View of a Town*, gift, 1938

Shuttleworth, William b.1785, *Hope Hill Mill, Stockport, Cheshire*, unknown acquisition method

Shuttleworth, William b.1785, *Hope Hill Mill, Stockport, Cheshire*, unknown acquisition method

Smart, Rowley 1887–1934, *Chrysanthemums*, gift, 2005

Smith, E. E. *Stockport from Brinksway, Cheshire*, unknown acquisition method

Snyders, Frans (follower of) 1579–1657, *A Wild Boar Hunt*, unknown acquisition method; on long-term loan to Lynne Hall, National Trust

Somerset, Richard Gay 1848–1928, *On the Conway*, gift, c.1925

Somerset, Richard Gay 1848–1928, *Venice*, gift, c.1925

Somerset, Richard Gay 1848–1928, *Waterfall*, gift, c.1925

Spadino, Giovanni Paolo 1659–c.1730, *A Melon and Other Fruit*, acquired via the John Benjamin Smith Bequest, 1879

Spadino, Giovanni Paolo 1659–c.1730, *Fruit and Tendrils*, acquired via the John Benjamin Smith Bequest, 1879

Spadino, Giovanni Paolo 1659–c.1730, *Fruit on Stone Steps*, acquired via the John Benjamin Smith Bequest, 1879

Spenlove-Spenlove, Frank 1866–1933, *The End of a Weary Day*, gift from the artist, 1928

Stark, James 1794–1859, *Landscape with Sheep*, gift, 1932

Sumner, Roger *Skipping in Bourne Street*, purchased, 1976

Swift, Reginald *The Cathedral*, unknown acquisition method

Tassi, Agostino c.1579–1644, *Mediterranean Coast with Shipping*, acquired via the John Benjamin Smith Bequest, 1879

Tassi, Agostino (follower of) c.1579–1644, *Mediterranean Coast with Shipping*, acquired via the John Benjamin Smith Bequest, 1879

Ten Kate, Herman Frederik Carel 1822–1891, *Cavaliers*, unknown acquisition method

Thompson, Alan J. b.1940, *Moston Evening Landscape, Cheshire*, purchased, 1973

Trowski, Laura *Saint Andrew*, purchased, 1977

Trust, Peter 1936–2008, *Eye Condemn*, purchased, 1979, © the artist's estate

Turchi, Alessandro (circle of) 1578–1649, *The Pietà*, acquired via the John Benjamin Smith Bequest, 1879

Turner, William McAllister 1901–1976, *Street in Crémieu, France*, purchased, 1973

unknown artist *Portrait of an Unknown Gentleman* (said to be Judge John Bradshaw, 1602–1659), acquired from the Marple Hall Collection; gift, 1996

unknown artist *Portrait of an Unknown Man*, acquired from the Marple Hall Collection; gift, 1996

unknown artist *Portrait of an Unknown Woman*, acquired from the Marple Hall Collection; gift, 1996

unknown artist *Portrait of an Unknown Woman in a Red Dress*, unknown acquisition method

unknown artist *Stockport Market and Traders, Cheshire*, unknown acquisition method

unknown artist *Peter Marsland (b.1770)*, unknown acquisition method

unknown artist *Portrait of an Unknown Man*, acquired from the Marple Hall Collection; gift, 1996

unknown artist *Portrait of an Unknown Man*, acquired from the Marple Hall Collection; gift, 1996

unknown artist *Portrait of an Unknown Woman*, acquired from the Marple Hall Collection; gift, 1996

unknown artist *Mary Ann Howard*, acquired via the Rostron Bequest, 1994

unknown artist *George Cooper Bellman*, unknown acquisition method

unknown artist *Seascape*, unknown acquisition method

unknown artist *The Race Meeting*, unknown acquisition method

unknown artist *Thomas Kay (1841–1914), Mayor of Stockport*, unknown acquisition method

unknown artist *Chrysanthemums*, unknown acquisition method

unknown artist *George Edward Rostron*, acquired via the Rostron Bequest, 1994

unknown artist *A Group Portrait*, unknown acquisition method

unknown artist *A Venetian Scene*, unknown acquisition method

unknown artist *Augustus Henry Venables-Vernon (1829–1883), 6th Baron Vernon*, unknown acquisition method

unknown artist *Boating Scene*, unknown acquisition method

unknown artist *Bolton Abbey, North Yorkshire*, unknown acquisition method

unknown artist *Bolton Abbey, North Yorkshire, Side Keep*, unknown acquisition method

unknown artist *Boy Overlooking the Sea*, unknown acquisition method

unknown artist *Bramall Hall, Stockport, Cheshire*, purchased

unknown artist *Bramall Hall, Stockport, Cheshire*, unknown acquisition method

unknown artist *Captain Salusbury Pryce Humphreys (d.1845)*, gift, 1945

unknown artist *Cows in a Field*, unknown acquisition method

unknown artist *Dr Calveley Legh (1682–1727)*, unknown acquisition method; on long-term loan to Lynne Hall, National Trust

unknown artist *East Front of Bramall Hall, Stockport, Cheshire*, unknown acquisition method

unknown artist *Edward Carrington Howard*, unknown acquisition method

unknown artist *Edwin Rayner, Governor (1880–1921)*, unknown acquisition method

unknown artist *Emma Magnus of Fallowfield*, unknown acquisition method

unknown artist *Figure of a Woman*, unknown acquisition method

unknown artist *Girl in the Wood*, unknown acquisition method

unknown artist *Italian Pastoral Landscape*, unknown acquisition method

unknown artist *James Leech*, acquired via the Rostron Bequest, 1994

unknown artist *John Roberts*, unknown acquisition method

unknown artist *Lady with a Child on Her Knee*, unknown acquisition method

unknown artist *Landscape with a Tree*, unknown acquisition method

unknown artist *Man Sitting on a Rock*, unknown acquisition method

unknown artist *Martha Brownell*, unknown acquisition method

unknown artist *Miss Lowe*, unknown acquisition method

unknown artist *Mother and Child*, unknown acquisition method

unknown artist *Mrs Howard*, acquired via the Rostron Bequest, 1994

unknown artist *Old Stockport, Cheshire*, gift, 1948

unknown artist *Old Stockport, Cheshire*, gift, 1948

unknown artist *Pitt Outwitted*, unknown acquisition method

unknown artist *Portrait of a Bearded Man*, unknown acquisition method

unknown artist *Portrait of a Lady*, unknown acquisition method

unknown artist *Portrait of a Man in a Ruff*, on loan from a private individual

unknown artist *Portrait of a Young Lady*, unknown acquisition method

unknown artist *Portrait of an Unknown Gentleman*, unknown

acquisition method

unknown artist *Portrait of an Unknown Man*, acquired from the Marple Hall Collection; gift, 1996

unknown artist *Portrait of an Unknown Woman*, purchased, 1994

unknown artist *Samuel Oldknow (1756–1828)*, gift, 2001

unknown artist *Scene with a Swan*, unknown acquisition method

unknown artist *Scene with Putti*, unknown acquisition method

unknown artist *Sir Ralph Pendlebury (1790–1861), JP*, unknown acquisition method

unknown artist *The Ten Commandments I–IV*, unknown acquisition method

unknown artist *The Ten Commandments V–X*, unknown acquisition method

unknown artist *Thomas Lees (1826–1897), JP*, unknown acquisition method

unknown artist *Thomas Pendlebury (1758–1840)*, unknown acquisition method

unknown artist *William Davenport VIII*, on loan from Mr Davenport of Clipsham Hall

unknown artist *William Williamson, Trustee (1861–1879)*, unknown acquisition method

unknown artist *William Wilson Prescott (d.1878)*, gift

unknown artist *Young Musicians*, unknown acquisition method

Valette, Adolphe 1876–1942, *Still Life, Fruit*, gift, 1948

Vauchelet, Théophile Auguste 1802–1873, *The Birth of Cain*, purchased, 1958

Vermiglio, Giuseppe (circle of) c.1585–after 1668, *Saint Apollonia*, acquired via the John Benjamin Smith Bequest, 1879

Vermiglio, Giuseppe (circle of) c.1585–after 1668, *Saint Ursula*, acquired via the John Benjamin Smith Bequest, 1879

Waite, Edward Wilkins 1854–1924, *Calm Decay*, unknown acquisition method

Walker, Peter John active 1974–1978, *Winter Landscape, Evening*, purchased, 1974

Walker, Peter John active 1974–1978, *Rock Formation No.II*, purchased, 1978

Wane, Richard 1852–1904, *Sea View, Conway*, gift, 1951

Wane, Richard 1852–1904, *The Orchard*, gift, 1951

Waterhouse, B. *Boat Pond, Edgeley, Stockport, Cheshire*, gift, 1950

Waterhouse, B. *Boat Pond, Edgeley, Stockport, Cheshire*, gift

Waterlow, Ernest Albert 1850–1919, *A Country Scene*, gift, 1940

Watson, William II d.1921, *Crossing the Moor*, gift, 1951

Webb, James 1825–1895, *Snape, Suffolk*, gift, 1932

Webb, James 1825–1895, *A Sussex Common*, gift, 1932

Whistler, James Abbott McNeill (style of) 1834–1903, *The Thames, Evening*, gift, 1940

Wilkinson, Derek 1929–2001, *Church*, unknown acquisition method

Williams, H. C. *A Sunset*, gift, 1940

Williams, Matti *Harbour Scene*, purchased, 1973

Williamson, George *William Crossley*, gift, 2007

Wimperis, Edmund Morison 1835–1900, *Landscape with Sheep*, unknown acquisition method

Wynne, Anthony *Stockport '67 Triptych* (left wing), gift, 2008

Wynne, Anthony *Stockport '67 Triptych* (centre panel), gift, 2008

Wynne, Anthony *Stockport '67 Triptych* (right wing), gift, 2008

Zoffany, Johann (circle of) 1733–1810, *Cupid*, acquired via the John Benjamin Smith Bequest, 1879

Tameside Museums and Galleries Service: The Astley Cheetham Collection

Allori, Alessandro (circle of) 1535–1607, *Portrait of a Gentleman*, bequeathed

Andrew, A. *Golden Lake Scene*, unknown acquisition method; accessioned, 1992

Astley, John 1724–1787, *Portrait of a Lady*, bequeathed

Barrow, Leslie *Rainy Day, Uppermill, Yorkshire*, purchased from the artist, 1959

Bigg, William Redmore 1755–1828, *Charity*, bequeathed

Bissill, George William 1896–1973, *Kirkhallen Farm*, gift from the Contemporary Art Society via the Dr Harold Widdup Collection, 1965

Bone, Stephen 1904–1958, *Gibraltar from Gaucin*, gift from the Contemporary Art Society, 1965, © the artist's estate

Bonington, Richard Parkes 1802–1828, *Near Rouen, France*, bequeathed, 1932

Bradshaw, Arthur (attributed to) *First Town Council, Borough of Dukinfield*, unknown acquisition method

Breakspeare, William Arthur 1855–1914, *The Maidservant*, gift, 1951

Bridge, Anthony active 1925–1939, *Self Portrait*, unknown acquisition method; accessioned, 1992

Burne-Jones, Edward 1833–1898, *Saint Nicholas*, bequeathed, 1932

Chuhan, J. b.1955, *Dipak Chauhan (1934–2006)*, purchased from the artist, 2004, © J. Chuhan

Churchill, Gwendeline 1885–1941, *Landscape*, gift from the Contemporary Art Society via the Sir Edward Marsh Collection, 1963, © the artist's estate

Cleve, Joos van c.1464–c.1540, *Portrait of a Gentleman in a Landscape*, bequeathed, 1932

Collier, John 1850–1934, *Francis Dukinfield Astley (b.1853?)*, gift, 1979

Collier, John 1850–1934, *William Nicholson*, gift, 1979

Collins, William 1788–1847, *Boys Fishing*, bequeathed

Collins, William 1788–1847, *Rustic Shed*, bequeathed, 1932

Connolly, Leo *The Glade*, purchased from the artist, 1959

Cox, David the elder 1783–1859, *A Road by a Common, Windy Day*, bequeathed, 1932

Danby, James Francis 1816–1875, *Ship on Fire*, gift, 1935

Danby, James Francis 1816–1875, *Isle of Arran*, bequeathed, 1932

Danby, James Francis 1816–1875, *Lake Scene*, bequeathed, 1932

Danby, Thomas c.1818–1886, *Lake Scene with a Fishing Boat*, unknown acquisition method; accessioned, 1992

Deane, Frederick b.1924, *Harry Rutherford (1903–1985)*, gift, 1985, © the artist

Delaney, Barbara b.1941, *Acrylic/Paper January III 76*, gift from the Contemporary Art Society, 1986, © the artist

Della Monica, Gennaro 1836–1917, *Incident in the Life of Garibaldi*, purchased, 1979

Flemish School *Portrait of a Man*, bequeathed, 1932

Garside, Ben *Joseph Rayner Stephens (1805–1879)*, gift, 1992

Geeraerts, Marcus the elder (attributed to) c.1520–before 1604, *Portrait of a Lady*, bequeathed, 1932

Gertler, Mark 1891–1939, *Daffodils*, gift from the Contemporary Art Society, 1954

Giulio Romano 1499–1546, *The Holy Family with Saint Anne and Saint John* (copy of Raphael), bequeathed, 1932

Grant, Duncan 1885–1978, *The Harbour, King's Lynn, Norfolk*, gift from the Contemporary Art Society, 1938, © 1978 estate of Duncan Grant

Halsband, Gertrude 1917–1981, *Breakfast at Seaview*, unknown acquisition method

Hattemore, Archibald 1890–1949, *Interior, the Mantelpiece*, gift from the Duveen Paintings Fund, 1962

Hattemore, Archibald 1890–1949, *The Dead Flamingo, Interior of Bethnal Green Museum*, gift from the Duveen Paintings Fund, 1962

Hewit, Forrest 1870–1956, *Portrait of a Woman*, unknown acquisition method; accessioned, 1992

Hewit, Forrest 1870–1956, *Portrait of an Italian Gentleman*, unknown acquisition method; accessioned, 1992

Hewit, Forrest 1870–1956, *Malay Boy*, unknown acquisition method

Hines, Theodore c.1860–1889, *A Distant View of Balmoral Castle, Aberdeenshire*, gift, 1939

Hines, Theodore c.1860–1889, *Luss, Loch Lomond*, gift, 1939

Hines, Theodore c.1860–1889, *Stirling Castle*, gift, 1939

Hines, Theodore c.1860–1889, *The Boat Pier, Loch Katrine, Stirling*, gift, 1939

Hodgkinson, George 1914–1997, *The Immigrant*, gift, before 1992

Hodgkinson, George 1914–1997, *The Old Farm, Lancashire*, gift; accessioned, 1992

Hodgkinson, George 1914–1997, *Winter, Stalybridge, Cheshire*, purchased from the artist, 1985

Hodgkinson, George 1914–1997, *Self Portrait*, gift, 2000

Holder, Edward Henry 1847–1922, *Rephidim, Desert of Sinai*, bequeathed, 1932

Italian (Florentine) School *Virgin and Child with Saints* (triptych), bequeathed, 1932

Italian School *Madonna and Child with Saints*, bequeathed, 1932

Jacopo di Cione c.1320–1400, *Madonna and Child with Angels*, bequeathed, 1932

Key, Geoffrey b.1941, *Hillside Woods*, purchased from the artist, 1987, © the artist

Kingsley, Harry 1914–1998, *Werneth Low War Memorial, Cheshire*, unknown acquisition method; accessioned, 1992

Kingsley, Harry 1914–1998, *Broadbottom, Cheshire*, gift from the artist, 1983

Kingsley, Harry 1914–1998, *Blue Jeans, Moss Side, Manchester*, gift from the artist, 1992

Kingsley, Harry 1914–1998, *The Gateway, Moss Side, Manchester*, gift from the artist, 1992

Kingsley, Harry 1914–1998, *The Playground, Dukinfield, Cheshire*, gift from the artist, 1980

Knight, Joseph 1837–1909, *The Corn Field*, bequeathed, 1932

Lawson, Cecil Gordon 1851–1882, *Landscape*, bequeathed, 1932

Lees, John *St George's Church, Stalybridge, Cheshire*, unknown acquisition method; accessioned, before 1985

Linnell, John 1792–1882, *Sheep at Rest, Minding the Flock*, bequeathed, 1932

Liverseege, Henry 1803–1832, *Enjoying a Pipe*, gift, 1935

Liverseege, Henry 1803–1832, *The Betrothed*, gift, 1936

Luini, Bernardino (after) c.1480–c.1532, *Saint Catherine of Alexandria*, bequeathed, 1932

MacDiarmid, John 1865–1942, *River Scene*, transferred from Hyde Library, 1986, © the artist's estate

Maclaurin, Robert b.1961, *Mountain Journey*, gift from the Contemporary Art Society, before 1992, © the artist

Marinari, Onorio (attributed to) 1627–1715, *Eleanor of Toledo (1522–1562)*, bequeathed, 1932

Master of the Straus Madonna c.1385–1415, *Virgin and Child with Angels and Saints*, bequeathed, 1932

Morris, Cedric Lockwood 1889–1982, *Llangennith Church, Swansea*, gift, 1935, © trustees of the Cedric Lockwood Morris Estate/Foundation

Morris, Cedric Lockwood 1889–1982, *Heron*, gift from the Contemporary Art Society, 1946, © trustees of the Cedric Lockwood Morris Estate/Foundation

Mura, Frank b.1863, *White Roses*, gift, 1935

Newton, Marie *Dutch Triumph*, purchased from the artist, 1959

Nicholls, Bertram 1883–1974, *San Andrea, Volterra, Italy*, gift from Mrs Lucy Wertheim, 1935

Ousey, Buckley 1850–1889, *A Welsh Cottage*, gift

Ousey, Buckley 1850–1889, *Cronies*, purchased, 1964

Padwick, Philip Hugh 1876–1958, *Littlehampton Front, West Sussex*, gift, 1935

Palmer, Martin b.1958, *Hartshead Pike, Cheshire*, purchased, 2007

Peppercorn, Arthur Douglas 1847–1926, *The Estuary*, gift from the Museums Association, 1962

Pier Francesco Fiorentino 1444–1445–after 1497, *Madonna Adoring the Christ Child, with Saint John the Baptist and Angels*, bequeathed, 1932

Radford, Gordon b.1936, *Passing Storm*, purchased from the artist, 1978, © the artist

Raphael, Wendy active 1988–2011, *Clown*, gift, 1996, © the artist

Raphael, Wendy active 1988–2011, *Cossack Rider*, gift, 1996, © the artist

Ratcliff, Sonia active 1976–1978 *Oldham Market, Lancashire*, purchased from the artist, 1978

Ray-Jones, Raymond 1886–1942, *Lorna Beadle*, gift, 1996, © the artist's estate

Ray-Jones, Raymond 1886–1942, *The Artist's Wife, Effie Irene Ray-Jones (1899–1996)*, gift, 1996, © the artist's estate

Rigby, J. *Landscape with a Lake, Mountains and a Sailing Boat*, unknown acquisition method; accessioned, 1992

Royle, Herbert F. 1870–1958, *Ashurst Lane*, gift, 1955, © the artist's estate

Royle, Herbert F. 1870–1958, *Castle Berg Scar, Nessfield-in-Wharfedale*, gift, 1955, © the artist's estate

Royle, Herbert F. 1870–1958, *Hay Harvesting*, gift, 1955, © the artist's estate

Royle, Herbert F. 1870–1958, *Haytime, Halsall Moss, Lancashire*, gift, 1955, © the artist's estate

Royle, Stanley 1888–1961, *Wintertime*, bequeathed, 1940, © the artist's estate/Bridgeman Art Library

Royle, Stanley 1888–1961, *Fishing Gear, Brittany, France*, purchased, 1963, © the artist's estate/Bridgeman Art Library

Rutherford, Harry 1903–1985, *S. Ashworth*, transferred from Hyde

Library, 1985, © the artist's estate

Rutherford, Harry 1903–1985, *The Hollander*, purchased from the artist, 1985, © the artist's estate

Rutherford, Harry 1903–1985, *Flight Sergeant Donald S. Mitchell (1922–1945)*, bequeathed, 1976, © the artist's estate

Rutherford, Harry 1903–1985, *Marion Rutherford (1899–1976)* (recto), donated, 2005, © the artist's estate

Rutherford, Harry 1903–1985, *House on Fire* (verso), donated, 2005, © the artist's estate

Rutherford, Harry 1903–1985, *Rue des Arquebusiers, Paris*, gift from the artist, 1960, © the artist's estate

Rutherford, Harry 1903–1985, *Ashton Market, Tameside*, purchased from the artist, 1985, © the artist's estate

Rutherford, Harry 1903–1985, *Paris Street Scene*, purchased from the estate of John Goddard, 2003, © the artist's estate

Rutherford, Harry 1903–1985, *Sheila Mumford*, purchased from the artist, 1985, © the artist's estate

Rutherford, Harry 1903–1985, *Vigo, Spain*, purchased from the estate of John Goddard, 2003, © the artist's estate

Rutherford, Harry 1903–1985, *Yorkshire Street, Oldham, Lancashire*, gift from the Contemporary Art Society, 1976, © the artist's estate

Rutherford, Harry 1903–1985, *The Square, Hyde, Lancashire*, on loan from a private collection, © the artist's estate

Rutherford, Harry 1903–1985, *Tap Room, Hyde, Lancashire*, purchased from the artist, 1978, © the artist's estate

T. S. *Early Summer, River Scene with a Farmhouse*, acquired, before 1992

Sabela, H. J. active 1905–1907, *Still Life with Fruit*, acquired, 1986

Sánchez Coello, Alonso (circle of) c.1531–1588, *Portrait of a Lady*, bequeathed, 1932

Scott, David Montagu 1945–2001, *Avenue, Broughton*, gift from the Contemporary Art Society, 1975

Sellaio, Jacopo del c.1441–1493, *Virgin and Child in a Landscape*, bequeathed, 1932

Shackleton, William 1872–1933, *Leda and the Swan*, gift, 1951

Sicciolante da Sermonta, Girolamo (attributed to) 1521–c.1580, *Virgin and Child before a Green Curtain*, bequeathed, 1932

Sidley, Samuel 1829–1896, *Mrs Gillingham Smith*, unknown acquisition method; accessioned, 1992

Sidley, Samuel 1829–1896, *Family Group*, transferred from Hyde Library, before 1986

Slack, H. N. *Stalybridge Market Place, Greater Manchester*, purchased, 1974

Soyer, Paul Constant 1823–1903, *The Mother*, gift, 1935

Stokes, Adrian Durham 1902–1972, *Olive Terraces*, gift from the Contemporary Art Society, 1972, © the artist's estate

Stokes, Adrian Durham 1902–1972, *Olive Trees, Torre del Benaco, Italy*, gift from the Contemporary Art Society, 1968, © the artist's estate

Swinnerton, B. R. *Goldfish and Horse*, gift from the Duveen Paintings Fund, 1962

Taylor-Heap, Frank active 1950–1959, *On Dartmoor, Devon*, gift from the artist, 1959

Thompson, Alan J. b.1940, *Bushes on a Hillside*, purchased from the artist, 1979

Thompson, Alan J. b.1940, *Mushrooms*, purchased from the artist

Thornley, B. R. *Fishing Boats in a Harbour*, acquired, before 1992

Topolski, Feliks 1907–1989, *The City (Married Life)*, gift from the Contemporary Art Society, 1965, © the trustees of the estate of Feliks Topolski

Townsend, Ernest 1885–1944, *George Henry Kenyon (1840–1917)*, on loan from a private collection

unknown artist *Edward Hyde (c.1650–1712), Governor of North Carolina (1710–1712)*, purchased, 1936

unknown artist *Italian Landscape* (detail), unknown acquisition method; accessioned, 1992

unknown artist *Francis Dukinfield Astley in Procession as High Sheriff*, gift, 1979

unknown artist *Portrait of a Gentleman*, transferred from Hyde Library, 1986

unknown artist *Landscape with a River and Cliffs*, acquired, before 1992

unknown artist *Scottish Woman and Child in a Landscape*, unknown acquisition method; accessioned, 1992

unknown artist *Joseph Hall, Master of the Staley Hunt*, gift, 1956

unknown artist *Figures Outside a Cottage Dated 1720*, unknown acquisition method; accessioned, 1992

unknown artist *Landscape with a River and a Fisherman*, unknown acquisition method; accessioned, 1992

unknown artist *W. G. Bayley (1802–1891), Charter Mayor of Stalybridge (1857–1860?)*, gift, 1988

unknown artist *Besom Jack*, acquired, 1986

unknown artist *Chapel Street Sunday School, Stalybridge, Cheshire*, unknown acquisition method; accessioned, 1992

unknown artist *Portrait of a Woman with a Cameo*, unknown acquisition method; accessioned, 1992

unknown artist *Two Sheep and a Ram in a Barn*, unknown

acquisition method; accessioned, 1992

unknown artist *Four Sheep and Two Lambs in a Barn*, unknown acquisition method; accessioned, 1992

unknown artist *Bamburgh Castle, Northumberland*, unknown acquisition method; accessioned, 1992

unknown artist *First Town Council, Borough of Dukinfield*, gift, before 1992

A. W. *St Lawrence's Church, Denton, Lancashire*, unknown acquisition method; accessioned, 1992

Walker, Edward Bent 1860–1917, *The Musician*, bequeathed, 1941

Watts, George Frederick 1817–1904, *Sir Perceval*, bequeathed, 1932

Webb, James 1825–1895, *View on the South Coast*, gift, 1936

Webb, William J. c.1830–c.1904, *The Lost Sheep*, bequeathed, 1932

Webbe, Jenny active 1983–1990, *Model in a Yellow Gown*, purchased from the artist, 1985

Webbe, Jenny active 1983–1990, *Paula Sitting on the Radiator*, purchased from the artist, 1990

Wells, Henry Tanworth 1828–1903, *J. F. Cheetham (1835–1916)*, bequeathed, 1932

Whitehead, F. (Mrs) *Dukinfield Old Hall Congregational Chapel, Cheshire*, gift from the artist, 1980

Wilde, Fred active 1961–1981, *Wet Whit Walk*, purchased from the artist, 1981

Wilde, Fred active 1961–1981, *'An dese teef ah ma own teef'*, purchased from the artist, 1981

Wilde, Fred active 1961–1981, *'T'bull's getten loose'*, purchased from the artist, 1981

Wilson, Richard (follower of) 1714–1787, *A Classical Landscape*, bequeathed, 1932

Wolfe, Edward 1897–1982, *Hassan*, gift from the Contemporary Art Society, 1946, © the estate of Edward Wolfe

The Rutherford Gallery

Rutherford, Harry 1903–1985, *The Model, Sickert's Class*, on loan from a private collection, © the artist's estate

Rutherford, Harry 1903–1985, *The Comedians (Hyde Theatre)*, purchased from the artist, 1985, © the artist's estate

Rutherford, Harry 1903–1985, *Theatre Royal, Hyde, Tameside*, purchased from the artist, 1985, © the artist's estate

Rutherford, Harry 1903–1985, *Comedian's Corner*, on loan from a private collection, © the artist's estate

Rutherford, Harry 1903–1985, *Great Yarmouth, Norfolk*, on loan from a private collection, © the artist's estate

Rutherford, Harry 1903–1985, *Sir John Barbirolli Conducting the Hallé Orchestra*, gift from the artist, 1985, © the artist's estate

Rutherford, Harry 1903–1985, *The Custodian*, purchased, 1985, © the artist's estate

Rutherford, Harry 1903–1985, *Mill Girls, Ashton, Lancashire*, purchased, 1985, © the artist's estate

Rutherford, Harry 1903–1985, *Northern Saturday*, purchased from the artist, 1948, © the artist's estate

Rutherford, Harry 1903–1985, *Blackpool Sands, Lancashire* (study), purchased from the artist, 1985, © the artist's estate

Rutherford, Harry 1903–1985, *View from the Studio Window, Hyde, Lancashire*, purchased from the artist, 1985, © the artist's estate

Rutherford, Harry 1903–1985, *The Red Caravan*, purchased from the artist, 1985, © the artist's estate

Rutherford, Harry 1903–1985, *Borneo Landscape, Indonesia*, on loan from a private collection, © the artist's estate

Rutherford, Harry 1903–1985, *Bar Parlour*, purchased from the artist, 1985, © the artist's estate

Rutherford, Harry 1903–1985, *Joan Hughes*, gift from the artist, 1985, © the artist's estate

Rutherford, Harry 1903–1985, *Near Bredon Hill, Worcestershire*, acquired from the estate of John Goddard, 2003, © the artist's estate

Rutherford, Harry 1903–1985, *The Domino Players* (recto), on loan from a private collection, © the artist's estate

Rutherford, Harry 1903–1985, *Street Scene* (verso), on loan from a private collection, © the artist's estate

Rutherford, Harry 1903–1985, *Clarendon Hotel, Interior*, purchased from the artist, 1985, © the artist's estate

Rutherford, Harry 1903–1985, *Conversation Piece, Rochdale, Lancashire*, gift from the artist, 1985, © the artist's estate

Rutherford, Harry 1903–1985, *The Green Door*, purchased from the artist, 1978, © the artist's estate

Rutherford, Harry 1903–1985, *The Opening of the Chartists' Meeting House, Hyde, Lancashire*, gift, 1989, © the artist's estate

Collection Addresses

Oldham

Gallery Oldham:

Gallery Oldham
Greaves Street, Oldham OL1 1AL
Telephone 0161 770 4653

Oldham Civic Centre
West Street, Oldham OL1 1UT
Telephone 0161 770 3000

Pennine Acute Hospitals NHS Trust:

Rochdale Road, Oldham,
Greater Manchester OL1 2JH
Telephone 0161 6240420

North Manchester General Hospital
Delaunays Road, Crumpsall,
Greater Manchester M8 5RB
Telephone 0161 6240420

The Royal Oldham Hospital
Rochdale Road, Oldham,
Greater Manchester OL1 2JH
Telephone 0161 6240420

Rochdale

Greater Manchester Fire Service Museum
Maclure Road, Wilmslow Road, Rochdale,
Greater Manchester OL11 1DN
Telephone 01706 901227

Rochdale Arts & Heritage Service:

Rochdale Arts & Heritage Service
c/o Touchstones Rochdale
The Esplanade, Rochdale OL16 1AQ
Telephone 01706 924492

Heywood Library
Church Street, Heywood OL10 1LL
Telephone 08452 729260

Middleton Arena
Corporation Street, Middleton M24 1AG
Telephone 0161 662 4000

Middleton Library
Long Street, Middleton M24 6DU
Telephone 0161 643 5228

Portico Library
57 Mosley Street, Manchester M2 3FF
Telephone 0161 236 6785

Rochdale Town Hall
The Esplanade, Rochdale OL16 1AB
Telephone 01706 647473

Springhill Hospice
c/o Touchstones Rochdale
The Esplanade, Rochdale OL16 1AQ
Telephone 01706 924492

Touchstones Rochdale
The Esplanade, Rochdale OL16 1AQ
Telephone 01706 924492

Rochdale Town Hall
The Esplanade, Rochdale OL16 1AB
Telephone 01706 647473

Saddleworth

Saddleworth Museum and Art Gallery
High Street, Uppermill, Saddleworth OL3 6HS
Telephone 01457 874093

Stockport

Stockport Heritage Services:

Stockport Heritage Services
Unit 14, Brookfield Business Park
The Paddock, off Brookfield Road
Cheadle, Stockport SK8 2PN
Telephone 0161 218 1347

Abney Hall
Manchester Road, Cheadle, Stockport SK8 2PD
Telephone 0161 218 1347

Bramall Hall
Bramall Park, Bramhall, Stockport SK7 3NX
Telephone 0161 485 3708

Lyme Park
Disley, Stockport SK12 2NR
Telephone 01663 762023

Staircase House
30/31 Market Place, Stockport SK1 1ES
Telephone 0161 480 1460

Stockport Art Gallery
Wellington Road South, Stockport SK3 8AB
Telephone 0161 474 4453

Stockport Story
30/31 Market Place, Stockport SK1 1ES
Telephone 0161 480 1460

Vernon Park Museum
Vernon Park, Turncroft Lane, Offerton
Stockport SK1 4AR
Telephone 0161 474 4460

Tameside

Tameside Museums and Galleries Service: The Astley Cheetham Art Collection:

Tameside Museums and Galleries Service
Portland Basin Museum, Heritage Wharf
Ashton-under-Lyne OL7 0QA
Telephone 0161 343 2878

Ashton Town Hall
Market Place, Ashton-under-Lyne OL6 6DL
Telephone 0161 342 3094

Astley Cheetham Art Gallery
Trinity Street, Stalybridge SK15 2BN
Telephone 0161 338 6767

Central Art Gallery
Old Street, Ashton-under-Lyne OL6 7SG
Telephone 0161 342 2650

Dukinfield Town Hall
King Street, Dukinfield SK16 4LA
Telephone 0161 342 3391

Hegginbotton Mill
Old Street, Ashton-under-Lyne OL6 7SF
Telephone 0161 342 4093

The Rutherford Gallery
Union Street, Hyde SK14 1NF
Telephone 0161 343 2878

The Rutherford Gallery
c/o Tameside Museums and Galleries Service
Portland Basin Museum, Heritage Wharf
Ashton-under-Lyne OL7 0QA
Telephone 0161 343 2878

The Rutherford Gallery
Union Street, Hyde SK14 1NF
Telephone 0161 343 2878

Index of Artists

In this catalogue, artists' names and the spelling of their names follow the preferred presentation of the name in the Getty Union List of Artist Names (ULAN) as of February 2004, if the artist is listed in ULAN.

The page numbers next to each artist's name below direct readers to paintings that are by the artist; are attributed to the artist; or, in a few cases, are more loosely related to the artist being, for example, 'after', 'the circle of' or copies of a painting by the artist. The precise relationship between the artist and the painting is listed in the catalogue.

The Public Catalogue Foundation

The Public Catalogue Foundation is a registered charity. It was launched in 2003 to create a photographic record of the entire national collection of oil, tempera and acrylic paintings in public ownership in the United Kingdom.

Whilst our public galleries and civic buildings hold arguably the greatest collection of oil paintings in the world, over 80 per cent of these are not on view. Few collections have a complete photographic record of their paintings let alone a comprehensive illustrated catalogue. What is publicly owned is not publicly accessible.

The Foundation is publishing a series of fully illustrated, county-by-county catalogues that will cover, eventually, the entire national UK collection. To date, it has published over 30 volumes, presenting over 72,000 paintings.

In partnership with the BBC, the Foundation will make its database of the entire UK collection of 200,000 oil paintings available online through a new website called *Your Paintings*. The website will be launched in the summer of 2011 and it is expected that the entire collection will be on bbc.co.uk by mid-2012.

Your Paintings will offer a variety of ways of searching for paintings as well as further information about the paintings and artists, including links to the participating collections' websites. For those interested in paintings and the subjects they portray *Your Paintings* will be an unparalleled learning resource.

Collections benefit substantially from the work of the Foundation, not least from the digital images that are given to them for free following photography, and from the increased recognition that the project brings. These substantial benefits come at no financial cost to the collections.

The Foundation is funded by a combination of support from individuals, charitable trusts, companies and the public sector although the latter provides less than 20 per cent of the Foundation's financial support.

Supporters

Master Patrons

The Public Catalogue Foundation is greatly indebted to the following Master Patrons who have helped it in the past or are currently working with it to raise funds for the publication of their county catalogues. All of them have given freely of their time and have made an enormous contribution to the work of the Foundation.

Peter Andreae (*Hampshire*)
Sir Henry Aubrey-Fletcher, Bt, Lord Lieutenant of Buckinghamshire (*Buckinghamshire*)
Sir Nicholas Bacon, DL, High Sheriff of Norfolk (*Norfolk*)
Sir John Bather, Lord Lieutenant of Derbyshire (*Derbyshire*)
The Hon. Mrs Bayliss, JP, Lord Lieutenant of Berkshire (*Berkshire*)

Ian Bonas (*County Durham*)
Peter Bretherton (*West Yorkshire: Leeds*)
Michael Brinton, Lord Lieutenant of Worcestershire (*Worcestershire*)
Sir Hugo Brunner, KCVO, JP (*Oxfordshire*)
Mr John Bush, OBE, Lord-Lieutenant of Wiltshire (*Wiltshire*)
Lady Butler (*Warwickshire*)

Financial support

The Public Catalogue Foundation is particularly grateful to the following organisations and individuals who have given it generous financial support since the project started in 2003.

National Sponsor

Christie's

Benefactors (£10,000–£50,000)

The 29th May 1961 Charitable Trust
The Barbour Trust
City of Bradford Metropolitan District Council
Deborah Loeb Brice Foundation
The Bulldog Trust
A. & S. Burton 1960 Charitable Trust
Christie's
City of London Corporation
The John S. Cohen Foundation
Covent Garden London
Department for Culture, Media and Sport
Sir Harry Djanogly, CBE

Mr Lloyd Dorfman
The Elmley Foundation
Fenwick Ltd
Fidelity Foundation
Marc Fitch Fund
The Foyle Foundation
J. Paul Getty Jr Trust
Hampshire County Council
The Charles Hayward Foundation
Peter Harrison Foundation
Mr Robert Hiscox
Hiscox plc
David Hockney, CH, RA
ICAP plc

First published in 2013 by The Public Catalogue
Foundation, Printed Catalogue Division,
8 Frederick's Place, London, EC2R 8AB

© 2013 The Public Catalogue Foundation,
registered charity number 1096185. Company
limited by guarantee incorporated in England and
Wales with number 4573564. VAT registration
number 833 0131 76. Registered office: The
Courtyard, Shoreham Road, Upper Beeding,
Steyning, West Sussex, BN44 3TN.

We wish to thank the individual artists and all the
copyright holders for their permission to reproduce
the works of art. Exhaustive efforts have been
made to locate the copyright owners of all the
images included within this catalogue and to meet
their requirements. Any omissions or mistakes
brought to our attention will be duly attended to
and corrected in future publications. Owners of
copyright in the paintings illustrated who have
been traced are listed in the Further Information
section.

Photographs of paintings are © the collections that
own them, except where otherwise acknowledged.

Forewords to each collection are © the respective
authors.

The responsibility for the accuracy of the
information presented in this catalogue lies solely
with the holding collections. Suggestions that
might improve the accuracy of the information
contained in this catalogue should be sent to the
relevant collection and emailed to
info@thepcf.org.uk.

ISBN 978-1-909475-23-6

Designed by Sally Jeffery

FSC
www.fsc.org
MIX
Paper from
responsible sources
FSC® C114687

Printed in the UK by Gomer Press Ltd on paper
sourced from sustainable forests

Acknowledgements

The Public Catalogue Foundation would like to thank
the individual artists and copyright holders for their
permission to reproduce for free the paintings in this
catalogue. Exhaustive efforts have been made to locate
the copyright owners of all the images included within
this catalogue and to meet their requirements. Copyright
credit lines for copyright owners who have been traced are
listed in the Further Information section.

The Public Catalogue Foundation would like to express its
great appreciation to the following organisations for their
kind assistance in the preparation of this catalogue:

Bridgeman Art Library
Flowers East
Marlborough Fine Art
National Association of Decorative & Fine Arts Societies
(NADFAS)
National Gallery, London
National Portrait Gallery, London
Royal Academy of Arts, London
Tate